Command Line for MacOS Terminal

An Introduction to Understanding and Using
Command Line For MacOS Terminal

James Little

Table of Contents

Introduction

Thank you for taking the time to download this book: Command Line For MacOS Terminal.

This book covers the topic of the command line for MacOS and how you can learn how to use it. At the completion of this book, you will have a good understanding of the terminal and the command line for your Mac computer, and you will be able to complete some of your own commands through this system in no time.

While most people are used to working with the graphical user interface (the kind where they just click on the icons to tell the computer how to behave, working with the terminal can be so much better. This is going to help you to command the computer how to behave much easier, can help you complete more complex tasks, and can even make it easier to troubleshoot what is going on with your computer.

Working with the terminal and the command line can take some time to get used to, but it is one of the best options out there. And this guidebook will help you to get it all set up and ready to go. After practicing some of the different commands that you can use, you will find that it is actually easier to work with the command line than it is to work without it. This guidebook will provide you with all the tools and the practice commands that you need to get the hang of it and start using it for your own needs.

When you are ready to start understanding your computer in a way that you never imagined before, and you want to be able to see the inner workings of it while still being in control, make sure to check out this guidebook to learn how to get started with the command line on the Mac operating system.

Once again, thanks for downloading this book, I hope you find it to be helpful!

Chapter 1
The Basics of the MacOS Command Line

Working with the command line can be a bit scary when you are first getting started. It does look different than what you may be used to with the Linux system and with the Windows operating system. You may be starting out with the MacOS and have no idea how to work with the command line to start with. It doesn' help when you open up the instructions that tell you how to get started, and you see a long list of phrases and words that make no sense.

The good news is that the MacOS command line is really not as difficult to use as it may appear in the beginning. Whether you are a beginner or you have been working with programming for a long time, you will be able to work with the MacOS command line and get things done in no time. Let's get started with some of the basics that come with the MacOS command line to help you to get started.

Opening up the command line

The first thing that we need to learn how to do is open up the command line. You will need to find the command line so that you can use it in the ways that you would like. This is a simple process. You will just need to open up the terminal. Go ahead and turn on your Mac computer. When it is ready, you can open up the Applications folder followed by the Utilities folder Inside the Utilities folder, you should see the Terminal application.

At this point, you may want to consider adding the Terminal application to your dock so that it is easier to find and you will not have to spend so much time searching for it. Another way that you can do this to save time is to launch your terminal by doing the Spotlight search and then looking for "terminal". Any of these methods will open up the terminal for you so that you can start working.

The parts of the console

Before you can get a lot of work done on your console, there are a few parts that need to come together. Some of the terms that you should know to help all of this make sense include:

- Console: The console is the system as a whole. The console is going to include the command line, as well as any output that shows up from the previous commands.

- Command line: When you are looking at the command line, you are looking at the actual line inside of the console where you will type in the commands.

- Prompt: The prompt is going to be the beginning of your command line. It is often going to hold onto some contextual information. This may include information like where you are and who you are. This prompt is going to end with a $. Once the prompt is done, you will start typing in your commands.

- Terminal: The terminal is going to be the interface of the console. It is the program that you will use to interact with the console. When you are working with what is known as the terminal emulator, you will get the experience of typing inside an old terminal while still working in the modern graphical operating system.

Running a command

When you are on the console, you will want to learn how to run a command. Most of the commands that you will do on the MacOS will have three main parts. These three parts include the program, the options, and the arguments.

The program is going to be like the verb of your command. The program will be in charge of telling the program what you want it to do. There are a lot of different programs that you can use based on what you would like your console to do.

Next are the options and you can think about them like the adverb of your command. They are the modifiers of the program and can make changes in how it runs. These options are completely optional, so you can run a program without one of them. Each command will have its own options though so you will have to be careful about adding these in. Most often the order of your options is not going to matter that much, but there are times when they will, and we can discuss those later.

And finally, the arguments are whatever is left. They are considered the objects of the sentence, and they will tell the command what to act on. Each program will have a different argument, and it is going to matter the order of the arguments or the command can get confused.

When you are looking to create a new program, or you are working on controlling how your computer works, you need to make sure that you can bring out the command line and make it work the way that you want. The MacOS command line is going to be a little bit different than some of the other command lines that you may have used in the past, but it can be really powerful and can help you to write out some unique codes that are easy and fun to work with.

Chapter 2
The Different Parts to Know

Getting started with programming can be a lot of fun. There are a lot of different commands that you can give to your computer, whether you are looking to open up and move files around, or you are looking to write one of your own codes. Before you get started with working with the command line, it is important to know some of the important parts that come with the command line on the MacOS.

What is a command line?

The first thing that we are going to take a look at is the command line. This is the seat of power when it comes to running your computer. When you use the command line, you can tell the computer exactly what you want it to do. Whether you want to get it to open up a file, to create a new program, or do something else, the command line is going to help you to get it done. However, while you can get a lot of power from the command line, these can actually complex and will take some time to learn how to do.

To keep things simple, the command line is just going to be the place where you will type in the commands that you want to give to the computer. As long as you write out a command that the computer can understand, it will execute that command.

One thing to note is that the computer is not going to speak English or any other language that humans know, even though there are some elements that are recognizable. This means that you will need to learn a new language, the language of the computer, before you can give these commands.

Most people do not use this command line very often. They just click on the little icons to do the work for them. They also don't have many opportunities to write a new program or any chance to tell the computer a specific command so they may not know how to find the command line.

This command line is going to be present in different locations based on the operating system that is found on your computer. When it comes to the Mac command line, you will use a program that is known as Terminal. It is found under the /Applications/Utilities.

What is a shell?

The next part that you are going to work with when programming is the shell. The shell is the user interface that allows you to access the services of an operating system. The shell is either going to be a graphical user interface or the command line interface, depending on the role of the computer.

When we are talking about the graphical user interface, this is what most people use when they are on their computers. If you are on the desktop and there are a lot of icons there for you to click on, then you are working with a graphical user interface. This is easier to use for most people and if you don't want to create your own programs or do anything more technical with your computer, then working with this interface is fine.

However, if you are looking to write out your own codes and to make sure that your computer does exactly what you want you would use with the command line interface. In this case, the shell is going to be the screen where you can write out the codes that you want to work with.

What is the terminal?

The terminal is the interface where you can type out your codes and then get the computer to execute the commands that you want to be done. When you open up the command line, you will receive a little black box that should be empty when it is first opened. You will then be able to type inside of it to tell the computer how to behave. The place where you are typing these commands will be the terminal.

How are Ubuntu and MacOS similar and different?

If you have done some programming in the past, it is likely that you have worked with Ubuntu, or Linux, in the past. This is one of the most popular command lines to use because it can work on almost any kind of computer. There are some issues with using MacOS and Windows OS for programming; often when you make a program on one of those systems, they will have trouble working on the others in some cases.

However, when you work on the Linux system, this command line can work on programs that can work on all the other major systems as well. This makes it one of the most popular systems to use to make a program that you want.

You will see that the MacOS is actually pretty similar to working with the Ubuntu system. The MacOS is similar in simplicity, and the window dialogs tend to be really similar as well. When it comes to usability, both of these operating systems are going to be pretty similar.

You will find that Mac OS is like a special kernel of Ubuntu, and most of the differences between the two come up because Apple wants to make sure that none of the programming or software is considered open source. Linux is considered an open-sourced platform, which means that anyone can use it for free, to make changes, and to improve upon the software whenever they want, without having to get some special licenses or pay extra money. With Mac OS, you will find that it is closed source, so you are not able to make these changes.

Overall, these two systems are going to be very similar, and they are very compatible. You could technically take a Linux packaging system into the MacOS, and it will work just fine.

While there are some differences that come with Ubuntu and the MacOS, they do work together very well. The main difference is that you will not be able to get the MacOS for free and you will not be able to make changes to the source code like you can with Linux. Otherwise, they are compatible with each other and if you have worked with Linux, or you would like to bring your Linux program into the MacOS terminal, this is easy to do as the two are very similar.

Chapter 3
The Basics of the MacOS Terminal

If you are looking for a way to work directly with the system on your computer, rather than having to deal with the clunky graphical user interfaces, then you will want to work with the command line. This may seem a little bit complicated when you first get started, but in reality, it can really make life simpler. You will be able to type in the exact thing that you want to get done, and you will not need to worry about searching through the computer to find what you want.

Looking at the command line is not something that most people are used to doing, but starting out with the basics will make it a little bit easier. Once you get going, you will see that the command line is not all that different from the graphical world that you may use on your computer in most cases. In addition, learning how the terminal works will help to give you a better understanding of how the Mac works behind the scenes and makes it easier for you to troubleshoot any issues that come up. Let's take a look at some of the basics of the MacOS terminal to help you get used to working with it.

What is the Mac terminal?

There are very few things that are as misunderstood as the Mac terminal. Most people will work with the graphical user interface so that they can just click on the icons on their desktop and get things done. But working with the terminal to create specific commands will make working with your Mac easier than ever before. If you have a command that would be cumbersome or would need some extra software to complete, or you would like to troubleshoot a problem on your computer, then working with the terminal can make things easier.

First, you must understand that the terminal is simply an application available on your computer. You can launch it just like you do with other applications and once you do, you will see a UNIX command line environment, which is known as a shell. There are a variety of shells that you can work with, but the one that is found on Apple computers is known as Bash.

The top of the terminal window is going to contain the title bar which will display the name of the current user (you), the shell that is being used, and the size of your window in pixels. If you take a look at the command line, you will see that each of them will start with the name of your Mac and this will be followed by your name or the name of the current user.

It is possible to have different shells in the terminal, but you will have to take the time to install those. Commands in UNIX are going to be specific to their shell, so you will want to make sure that you are using the right shell for the commands that you want, or the computer may be confused.

Using a terminal on your Mac

Once you get to using the terminal, you will find that it is pretty easy. You will get to the command line, type out your command and then press Return to get the computer to execute that command. There are a couple of rules that you should remember when you are working with the command line interface. The first one is that all characters, even spaces, will matter. So, if you take a command from a book, website, or another source, you must make sure that it is typed the right way, or it may not work.

It is possible to rerun some of the previous commands that you have without needing to retype them. To do this, you would just need to use the up arrow to find the command and then press on Return. You can also interrupt any of the commands that you are using by pressing Control-C.

Commands

You will find that there are a variety of commands that you can use. To see which commands are available, you will just need to hold down the Escape key and then press Y when the computer asks if you would like to display a specific number of options. Then you will receive a list of commands, along with their meanings right by them. If you press on the spacebar, there will be more commands to load. When you are done looking at the commands, you can just press Q, and it takes you back to the command prompt.

Unix has placed a manual into the system, and you can call it up inside of your terminal if you need some information about a specific command. To use this manual, you would just need to type in "man [command]" The command is going to be the name of the command that you want to learn more about.

Locations

When you type in a new command in your terminal, it will automatically execute in your current location. You can change this, but you must specifically state this in your command to happen. When you start up a new terminal window, that location will be the top level of your Home directory so all commands will be relative to that location.

If you want to change up the location before doing one of your commands, you will use the command "cd" followed by the path of the location you wish to move to. If you would like to end up back at your default location, you would need to type "cd~/" If you would like to see a list of all the folders and files that are in your current location by simply typing in "ls"

Choosing your terminal emulator

Before you can start working on the command line, you need to pick out the terminal emulator that you want to work with.

There are various emulators that you can pick from based on the interfaces and features that you want. You will find that there are limited options when it comes to terminals with OS X but if you want to keep things simple, you can work with the terminal app that comes with your computer. It doesn't have a lot of features on it, but it does offer pane splitting to view a few inputs at the same time, a few color schemes to personalize it and some tabs.

There are some users who would like to have a bit more power when it comes to their terminal. A good one to work with is the iTerm2. It is free so you won't have to worry about having to pay a lot of extra money, and it has a lot of options. In addition to the features that you can find with the default terminal above you will also be able to get customizable profiles, enhanced pane splitting, and more.

Working with your terminal can be an exciting way to interact with your computer. While there are many users, who like to work with the graphical interface because then they don't need to worry about learning commands, the command line, and the terminal, make it easier to control what is going on in your computer. You can take on more complex things on your computer, and even deal with troubleshooting better when you work with a command line terminal.

Chapter 4
Why Would I Want to Use the Command Line and the Terminal

It is common for most people to get on their computers and never use the command line at all. This is true whether they are using a Windows computer, a Linux computer, or a Mac computer. They see the command line as something that only computer programmers and those who really know how to work on a computer would use. They don't think that it is worth their time to know how to make this command line work and they miss out on a lot of the power that they could yield to their computers. Instead, they focus on using the graphical user interface.

This may make life easier since you just need to click on the icon rather than learning any commands along the way, but there is just so much that you can do with a command line that it is definitely worth your time to learn. Let's take a look at some of the different reasons why you would want to consider learning how to use the command line, and how to write commands in the terminal, rather than sticking with the graphical user interface that you currently use.

Adds more power

When you start using your command line, you will be surprised by how much power is behind it. This command line is going to make it easier for you to do tasks that may have seemed impossible before. While some commands may have taken a lot of searching and button clicking before, the command line will allow you to get it done with a few keystrokes.

You do not need to worry about the command line being too difficult. It does take a little bit of time to learn how the commands work, but whether you are a beginner or someone who has been working with command lines and programming in the past, you will find that it is really easy to learn. Once you learn a few commands (and we will discuss a few of these commands throughout this book), you will be able to hold all the power of the command line in your hands.

Helps you to troubleshoot your computer

One reason that a lot of people will learn how to use the command line is that it can make it easier to troubleshoot any issues that come up on the computer. Whether your computer is brand new or you have owned it for some time, there are likely problems that can come up with it that will slow down the system, make it not work properly, or something else.

Trying to troubleshoot your computer with the graphical user interface can make it really hard for you to troubleshoot what is going on in the system. You can give it a try, but it is likely that you will just end up frustrated in the long run. If you have ever taken your computer in to a professional to fix an issue, you will notice that they will bring up this command line to help them fix it for you.

Once you learn how to work with the command line, you will be able to do your own troubleshooting, even if you do not have a lot of experience working with computers. This command line will let you look behind the scenes of your computer and see things that were not possible before. You may still need the help of a professional if you have a major issue on the computer, but with some of the little ones, you may be able to do some of the work on your own.

Easier to do complex tasks and commands

You will find that it is actually easier to complete some of the tasks that you want on your computer when you can work with the command line. You may be used to working with the graphical interface and just click on the icon that you want to ise. For some of the tasks that you want to complete, you will find that this is much easier. But there are a lot of tasks that should be pretty easy, but if you don't use the command line, you will find that they are really difficult.

When you are working with the command line, you can just tell the computer exactly what you would like it to do. There isn't any searching around to find what you want or any guessing about whether you are doing it the right way or not. You just have to learn a few simple commands, and it will all be taken care of for you.

Working with the command line may not be something that you are used to working with, but it is actually pretty simple. It will allow you to tell the computer exactly what you would like it to do and can just make things so much easier once you learn how to make it work.

Chapter 5
How to Navigate the Mac's File System

Navigating inside of your terminal is pretty simple. You will b able to do a few different commands, and then all the world o your computer will be at your fingertips. Whether you are tryin; to list out all of the folders that are on your system or you wan to be able to navigate around the terminal, the commands in this chapter will help you to get it done.

Navigating the system

It is important to have an idea of how to navigate you filesystem. You will find that there are two commands that ar used quite a bit. These include ls (lst) and cd (change directory) These commands are going to be used to list the contents of directory as well as moving one directory to another.

When you open up your terminal, no matter which one yo want to use, you will be placed in the home directory. This wil usually be under your name. To understand how this works an relates to the GUI equivalent, you can open up a new Finde window and then select your name on the column on the left You should then see a few different folders such a "Documents," "Desktop," and "Applications."

Looking at this same column, you can select the hard drive o the computer in "Devices." This is going to be considered th lowest level that you can get in the filesystem, and it is calle the root. You will showcase this in command line terms with th "/" symbol. The root directory is going to contain all of the file that are needed to get the operating system to work, so unles you really know what you are doing, do not spend time messin; around here or your computer will not work properly.

Listing the directories

Now that the terminal window is open, you can type in "ls" to list the files that are present in your home directory. You should be able to see all of the directories that are there by default on the OS X system such as "Music," "Movies," "Documents," and Downloads". If you type in the command "ls -a", it is going to activate what is known as the "all" flag that lists everything, including all of the folders and files that are hidden from view.

Moving around the terminal

There are some times when you will want to move around the directories using your terminal. Perhaps you want to go from the root section to one of the other directories that you have. To jump to one of the directories that we talked about above, you would just need to type in the command "cd ./Foldername". The cd command is going to let the computer know that you want to move forward relative to your current location.

An alternative that you can use would include specifying the directory with the help of an absolute path. What this means is that the path is going to stay the same regardless of whether you need to go forward or backward to get to the file. To do this, you would just need to type the full directory path, starting from the root and then going all the way to the directory that you would want to be in. An example of this would be /Users/Name/Documents/".

This step is going to be really useful to you as a beginner. The first thing that you will want to do when you are in a new directory is to take some time to look around. You can type "ls" to list out all the contents that are inside of that new directory. And if you would like to go back to the directory that was above it, you can just type in "cd" to get it done.

Take some time to move to the different directories, using the commands that we have listed out above, so that you can become familiar with it. These commands can be used many times, and they are pretty simple to work with. Just remember that you need to outline exactly what you would like to do to ensure

Chapter 6
Customizing Your Mac with the Terminal

Working with the terminal on your Mac computer will help you to get so much done. It is really simple to use, once you get used to the whole process, and you can gain a lot more power than you would be able to do with your graphical user interface. To see some of the things that you can do with this terminal, we are going to use it to help you customize your Mac computer.

Step 1: Open the terminal

The first thing that you will need to do is open up the terminal. Look at your desktop and search for the spotlight. This should be on the top right hand of the screen at the top of your menu bar. When you click on this, it is going to open up a search bar that shows up in the middle of your screen.

From here, you will need to type in "terminal" and then press on Return. This is going to open up a new terminal window for you to use. If you are not able to find the search icon, you can open up your terminal by using the Finder. To do this, click on Finder, then Applications, Utilities, and then double-click on the Terminal.

Step 2: Use the terminal commands

Now that your terminal window is open, it is time to make some changes. There are a lot of ways that you can customize your Mac computer, as long as you have the right commands to make it work.

The first thing that we are going to do is add a new message to the login screen. All that you will need to do for this one is to type in the following command:

sudo defaults write
/Library/Preferences/com.apple.loginwindow

LoginwindowText "If this laptop is lost, please call 555-555-5555. Cash reward"

When you have this typed in, press the Return button. You can always change out the message that is inside of the quotes to be whatever you would like it to be on your welcome screen. Then the next time that you get to your login screen, you will see this message show up.

You can also decide to add some blank spaces to your doc. To do this is to write out the following command:

defaults write com.apple.dock persistent-apps -array-add '{"tile-type "="spacer-tile";}' killall Dock

Then press Return. This is going to make sure that there is a blank space to your dock each time that this command is entered. You will be able to click and drag the space and move it around in the dock, allowing a divider in for organization. If you are then prompted for your password, you just need to type it in and press Return. If you would like to delete the blank space from your dock, you just need to drag the space out of the dog until it shows "Remove" and then let it go.

There are times when your computer will go to sleep if you are not using it for a certain amount of time. This can be a hassle if you are worried about the computer not staying on long enough to complete the task that you would like. If you want to make sure that the computer will not go to sleep, you just need to type the following command:

Caffeinate

And then press Return. This is going to make sure that the Mac will not fall asleep or log you out just because the computer is not being actively used. If you would then like to allow the Mac to go to sleep again at a later time, like when you are done with he task at hand, you just need to press Control+C, and the terminal will end the caffeinate task.

Next, you can choose to hide a folder. If you made a new folder and called it "HiddenFolder" and you wanted to make sure that no one else can see it, there is a command to help you do this. Let's say that your name is Steve. Use the following command to make it happen:

chflags hidden "/Users/Steve/Desktop/HiddenFolder"

And then press Return. You would, of course, replace the "Steve" with your actual username and then replace "HiddenFolder" with the name of the folder that you would like to hide.

If you would like to make this command a little bit easier, you can also just open up the terminal window and type in "chflags hidden" before dragging and dropping the folder right into the Terminal window before pressing return.

Next, you can change the location of some of your screenshots. The Mac computer is going to save your screenshots on the desktop by default, but you can easily change this if you would like these screenshots to be located in a different folder. We are going to save these on the Desktop in a folder called "Screenshots." Use the following command to make this happen:

defaults write com.apple.screencapture location "/Users/Steve/Desktop /Screenshots" killall SystemUIServer

And then press Return. You can change the name of the user as well as the name of the folder to work with what you created. For this to work, you must have the folder already created. Otherwise, the screenshots will continue to go to the default of the desktop.

And finally, you can disable your Dashboard completely if you would like. This is something that you would do if you don't use your dashboard at all or if you do not want it to be able to use up the resources on your computer. To disable your dashboard make sure to use the following command:

defaults write com.apple.dashboard mcx-disabled -boolean yes; killall Dock

And then press Return. If you just want to disable the Dashboard for a little bit, you can always re-enable it at a later time. You will use the exact same command that we have above but replace the "yes" to "no" and the Dashboard will come back.

These are just a few of the things that you can do with the terminal to personalize the way that your Mac computer works. They may not be the most complicated things that you can do with the command line, but they help to show you what all the terminal can do and can give you some good practice using the terminal. Take some time to practice some of these commands so that you can become more familiar with the terminal and how these commands will work.

Chapter 7
Basic File Management

Now that you have spent some time looking at the MacOS terminal, it is time to learn some of the basic ways to manage files through that terminal. By this, we mean that we are going to learn how to do a few basic file operations such as copying, moving, and opening up the files. If you are interested in giving a few of these a try, it is a good idea to create your own test file. Then if you do something wrong, you will not lose out on important information.

To get started with this, you need to open up TextEdit and then create a new file. We are going to call it "TestFile.txt" to keep things easier, and the folder that you are creating inside of it will be known as "Test". So, let's take a look at some of the different things that you can do when managing your files on the MacOS command line.

Copying

The first thing that we are going to do is learn how to copy a directory or a file. To do this, you will need to use the cp command. This is easier than you would think. Simply open up the command line terminal that you are going to use and then type in the command "cp TestFile.txt TestFile-Copy.txt". This is going to duplicate the file.

What this is going to do is help you to create a new copy of your file inside of the same directory. So, you will end up having two of the same files in the same place if you use the command above. If you want to create a copy of that same file but it needs to be placed in a different directory you would use the command "cp TestFile.txt /Some/Folder/".

Moving

The next thing that you can work on is the moving command. This helps you to take your file and move it over to another directory. This is helpful if you placed the file in the wrong place or you want to share it with others in a new file. The command that you will use for this one is the "mv" command. It will be used the same way that you did with copying. You can also use the mv command to rename your file. The command that you would do to rename your file would be "mv TestFile.txt TestFile-Renamed.txt".

Deleting

You can also use the command line to delete one of the files that you have on your computer. If you accidentally made the file or you are done with it and want to clear up some space on your computer, you would use the delete command to help this happen. The "rm" command will delete your directories and your files. While there are a lot of commands that you can use with this command line, the rm is going to be the most ruthless, and it is really hard to get the file back if you do this command. Make sure that you are using it only on files that you want to permanently get rid of.

Also, if someone has told you to run the command "rm -rf/", do not do this. This is going to delete your files forcefully, and then the file is deleted without asking you for confirmation. We are going to give it a try since we are just working with a test file, but make sure that you really want to get rid of the file ahead of time. To delete a file forcefully, you would type in the command "rm -rf Test".

Chapter 8
What a Profile is and How to Customize It

If you are working on a Mac computer that is all your own, then you do not need to worry about creating a profile as much. But if you share a computer, then it is important to set up profiles for each person who will be on that computer. These profiles can be really nice. They allow you to save your personal information on the computer, and even to personalize or change things on your profile without making these changes to the other profiles. For example, if there is a special program that you only want to have available on your profile, you can do that without affecting the other profiles.

When you share your Mac computer, it is going to be helpful to create a new profile, or account, for each user who is on that computer. Having these separate accounts will allow the individuals to change up the wallpaper and other settings on their account, add in some programs that they use frequently, and to set up the desktop to their own preferences. In addition, you will be able to choose between Standard and Administrator accounts, and there are even some special purpose accounts, like Managed Accounts that will make it easier for you to add in Parental Controls and other special features.

If you need to set up these accounts, you will find that the steps to get it done can be pretty simple. Some of the steps that you need to take include:

- Turn on the computer and get it all set up. When the computer is on, click on the Apple menu and then choose System Preferences. If this does not work, you can also click on your Applications folder on your Dock and then scroll down to System Preferences before selecting the icon.

- From here, you can click on the Users and Groups or the Accounts. Look for which one is present because it will depend on the OS version you are using. Once you click on that, you can click on the Lock icon, located in the lower left of your Accounts window. Then enter you password before clicking OK.

- Now you will need to click the "+" sign under you Account list. This is going to allow you to set up a new account. You can pick which kind of account you would like to select from the "New Account" drop-down menu

- At this point, you will need to type in the name of the new user under the "Full Name' text box. You can also type in the account name, which is going to be the new login name for the user. Type this login name into the Account Name text box.

- Here you will need to type in a new password to help keep the new profile safe and secure. You can choose which password you would like to use, or you can click on the Password Assistant. This icon is going to help you out because it will create a random password of the type and length that you ask for. You can type in the password to the Verify box. Make sure that you enter a good hint into the Password Hint box before clicking to Create Account.

- If you are someone who gets onto your profile without using a password, then take a moment to click "Turn Off Automatic Login"> If you forget to do this, the computer is automatically going to open up your account regardless of who is on the computer. That user would be able to get ahold of all your information as they would need to log out of your profile before they could log in to theirs. Make sure to click the Lock icon.

- Take some time to check whether the new account is working the proper way. You can click on your Apple icon and log out of the account. From here, you will log in with the new username and password that you created. When you can confirm that this new account is working properly, you can begin to work on it, give it to the person who will use that account, or log out and go back to your original account.

And that is all that you need to know to get started with creating new profiles on your Mac computer. This can be helpful if you plan to have more than one user on the same computer and you want to make sure that you keep your information separate from each other. It really only takes a few minutes to get the new profile set up and tested, and you can create as many of these profiles as you would like.

Personalizing your profile

Now that you have your own profile on the Mac computer, it is time to start adding some personalization. You can have a little fun with this and change up as many things as you would like inside of it. This can also be a good way to distinguish your account from one of the other accounts to make it easier to know whether you are in the right place or not. Some of the ways that you can personalize your profile includes:

New wallpaper

You can choose which wallpaper you would like to use. This can be something that is nice and simple to look at, or you can pick out a picture that you would like to add in there. To set up the right wallpaper, you will just need to visit General, then Desktop and Screen Saver, and then Desktop before picking out the option that you would like to have on your computer.

Custom color scheme

When you are picking out a color scheme, you will find that th Apple program is only going to provide you with one other colo besides the default one. It is known as Graphite, and you ca find it under System Preferences, General, and Appearance The best way for you to get a different color scheme is to activat an app-specific theme. For example, if you are using Alfred t help control your Mac and you have already activate Powerpack, you can use a custom theme to change the way tha Alfred looks.

If you would like to add a sleeker look to the menu bar, you wil be able to set it so that it appears black. You can do this b clicking on System Preferences and then General befor selecting on Use dark menu bar and Dock to make it happer You can also pick out the color for your highlighted text b selecting (from the same menu) Highlight color and pickin, from the drop-down menu.

Changing the icons

You can scale your icons up and down and even change the wa that they look, and you can do all of this without needing t bring in a third party to help get it done. If you would like t scale your icons up or down, you will need to click on View Show View Options, and Icon Size.

To use one of your custom images as a folder icon, which ca make the folders easier to see and recognize, then you will firs need to copy that image over to the clipboard. Then you can g into Finder to select the folder that will get the new icon. Onc you have found the folder, click on File and then Get Info.

In the box that opens up, you can click on the icon at the to and then click Edit and Paste. At this point, the custom ico should be in place. If you do not like how the icon looks or yo picked out the wrong picture, you can select it and then hit the delete key so that you go back to the default icon.

Better login screen

It is even possible to add some personalization to your login screen when you are using a Mac. You will need to replace your default image and the user picture for your account. It is even possible to add a new message to the lock screen.

If you would like to switch out the login background, you first need to find the picture that you would like to use. It needs to be a .PNG image that also matches the resolution of the Mac display. You can take an existing image and then crop it to fit into the right place, or you can download the image that you like from the web. If you are getting an image from the Web, make sure that there are no copyright restrictions on it. We are going to name that image com.apple.desktop.admin.png.

If you are looking for a picture and you are not sure what the display resolution of your Mac is, you can easily find this. Just open the command line and then look under Apple, About This Mac, and then Displays.

Now you need to navigate to the Caches folder. This is found in the main library of the Mac, so the /Library/Caches. From here you will be able to find the picture file that we saved earlier. Make sure that you back it up somewhere safe and then replace it with the custom image file. If it all goes well, the next time that you restart the Mac, the image that you picked out is going to be in the background for your login screen.

You can also do this with your user picture. To replace the default picture, you will need to click on System Preferences, Users and Groups, and Password. You can click the picture that is already there and then swap it out for any other picture that you would like to use. Make sure to hit Save to make sure that the selected picture is saved on your screen the proper way.

Now, if you would like to set a new message for your lock screen you just need to add a few steps as well. To do this, visit System Preferences, Security and Privacy, and General. You can then select the first box next to Show a message when the screen is locked. If this option is already grayed out, you will need to click on your lock icon (found at the bottom of the pain), so that you can enter the system password and give yourself access to this setting.

Next, you can click on the Set Lock Message and then type in the message that you want your lock screen to say. Hit OK. You will need to restart the Mac, but the next time that you do, this message is going to show up at the bottom of the screen. You will see it right above the power options.

Custom sounds

And finally, we are going to take a look at how you can customize some of the sounds that you can hear on your profile. You are not limited to only changing visualize things when you want to personalize. You can easily add some different audio tweaks as well. To start, we are going to change the system voice from the default. To do this, you can click on System Preferences, Accessibility, Speech, System Voice. From here you will be able to choose a new sound for your alerts by clicking on System Preferences, Sound, Sound Effects.

There are a lot of different things that you can do here. For example, you can even set the Mac so that it announced the time in a voice of your choice each hour. To do this, you would just need to select System Preferences, Date and Time, and Clock. Set it up so that the right voice will alert you of the time at each hour (or every few hours if that works best for your schedule). This is just one of the ways that you can change up some of the audio that you can hear on your computer.

As you can see, there are a lot of different ways that you can personalize your profile and make it look and act the way that you want. And if you are one of many profiles, you will be able to make these changes without having to worry about it making the same changes on another profile. Make sure to try out a few of these personalization's to make your computer as unique as you are.

Chapter 9
How to Troubleshoot Your Mac with the Command Line

There are times when your computer is not going to act the way that you would like. Perhaps some of the programs are not running how you want, or it is going slow, or something else is wrong. Knowing how to troubleshoot your own computer can help to make it last longer and can even save you some money compared to going to a professional. The good news is that using the command line will make it easier for you to troubleshoot your Mac computer, even if you do not have a ton of experience doing this on your own. Let's take a look at some of the ways that you can troubleshoot your Mac computer all on your own.

Ipconfig

The first thing that we need to do is open up the terminal and then take a look at all the interface information that is present on the computer. You can type in ipconfig to see this information. Some of the information that will come up includes the DNS servers and routers, the subnet masks, the LAN IP, and more. You can also use this command to configure the network settings.

If you are the administrator of the computer and you have worked with the Windows ipconfig in the past, the OS X ipconfig is going to be pretty much the same thing. This command is not one that you should use for any other reason besides testing and debugging the system, otherwise, it will start to cause some problems.

If you would like to display the IP address for the wireless network (which will be denoted by en1), you need to enter the following command:

pconfig getifaddr en0

If you would like to display the interface's subnet mask, you will need to enter the following command:

pconfig getoption en1 sunet_mask

If you would like to take a look at the DNS and determine if the interface has been set to leverage, you would need to enter the following command:

pconfig gtoption en1 domain_name_server

To figure out the router and the DHCP information that is supplied to the Mac computer, you would need to enter the following command:

pconfig getpacket en1

Traceroute

Another thing that you can do is the traceroute command. One of the most trying of the network failures to diagnose as well as to repair is a failure to connect to a network outside the organization. To run the traceroute command from the location of our Mac over to the destination resource, you will need to use the following command (making sure to substitute your intended address in place of the google.com):

Traceroute google.com

When you use this one, the command is going to print out all of the results of each step from your computer to the destination address. It will also note the IP addresses that this path crosses along the way and the latency delays that are encountered at each stop. With all of this information at hand, you will be able to see right away where the issue is occurring and you can figure out how to make it better.

These are just two of the ways that you can troubleshoot some of the issues that may come up on your computer. The first one is going to allow you a chance to look at what is going on with your computer so you can see where some of the issues may b coming from. There is a lot of information present here, and that can make it easier for you to know where to start with th troubleshooting.

The second command is going to be useful if you are trying to get onto a website or another place that is outside your network and you want to know what it is running into issues. Th traceroute command will provide you with all of the steps tha your computer has to take to get to the other location, and thi command will list out all of the places where an issue can occur You may find that the issue is somewhere with your system somewhere with the host you are trying to reach, or located i another place.

Of course, before you get started with any kind o troubleshooting, you need to make sure that you do some basi steps first. If the computer is acting funny, running slowly, o something else seems like it is off, you should first try restartin the computer. This often takes care of a lot of the issues tha your computer is having. If you do that and it doesn't work, the move on to some of the troubleshooting that we talked abou before.

Many people are not sure how to fix their computers i something goes wrong. The hope that they can get it to work o that they can find a professional to do the work for them. Bu when you start learning how to use the command line, you ca do some of the troubleshooting on your own.

Conclusion

Thanks again for taking the time to download this book!

You should now have a good understanding of the command line for the Mac operating system and how to make it work for your needs. You may be used to working with the graphical user interface, the one where you simply click on an icon to tell the computer how to behave, but you will quickly find that working with the command line can make life so much easier.

This guidebook provided you with all the information that you needed to start using the command line on your Mac computer. We discussed what the command line was, how to open up the terminal to get started, and some of the commands that you can use inside your terminal to open and close files, to troubleshoot issues on your computer, and even to personalize your computer the way that you would like it to be.

When you are ready to start learning more about the command line and how it can work for your needs, make sure to check out this guidebook to help you get started.

If you enjoyed this book, please take the time to leave me a review on Amazon. I appreciate your honest feedback, and it really helps me to continue producing high-quality books.

CPSIA information can be obtained
at www.ICGtesting.com
Printed in the USA

et in Seattle, *Emerald City* follows Benison Behrenreich, the hearing son of Deaf royalty. His father, CEO of a multimillion-dollar deaf access agency, has bribed Myriadal College officials for Benison's spot on their powerhouse basketball team, where he struggles to prove himself and compensate for his father's sins.

Julia Paolantonio has recently lost her father to a drug relapse. Her mother ships her off to live with her estranged granddad, Johnny Raciti, during the summer before her freshman year at Myriadal. Johnny offers her a deal: bring him Peter Fosch—tormented college dropout and the best drug runner west of the Cascades—and he'll give Julia's freshly widowed mother a board seat on his mobbed-up securities firm.

When Benison's father is arrested for defrauding government subsidies for the deaf, the Behrenreichs are left vulnerable to his company's ruthless backers—namely Johnny Raciti—forcing Julia and Peter to navigate the minefield left in the aftermath.

Praise for Emerald City

"In *Emerald City*, Brian Birnbaum expertly creates a kinetic but pained world. The result is an addictive blend of compelling discovery and desultory recognition. Above all, it's the authenticity of the work that most controls. Birnbaum has a true gift for creating individuated characters and people like Julia jump off the page as not just magnetic emblems but as perfect repositories for the empathic magic of fiction. Then there's the prose. It's subtly sly and inventive throughout but also perfectly pitched to particular story and structural demands—expansive enough to encompass the universal but also honed enough to beautify the granular. This is preternatural assurance. A moving and intelligent work that resonates beyond the final page."

—Sergio De La Pava,
Author of *A Naked Singularity* (University of Chicago Press)
and *Lost Empress* (Pantheon)

"Though this nimble and virtuosic novel tracks everything from the long shadow of addiction to the unique pressures of college athletics, *Emerald City* is, at its heart, an intensely moving story about family. Birnbaum's electric, acutely funny storytelling pulls the wool over your eyes and allows the novel's poignance to sneak up on you, and I finished it beguiled by his trick and thrilled at its execution."

—Gabe Habash,
Author of *Stephen Florida* (Coffee House Press)

"A fiercely smart, intricately structured, riveting debut novel. It's a little unfair that Brian Birnbaum should possess so many gifts. Fortunately, *Emerald City* is our prize, not his."

—David Hollander,
Author of *L.I.E.* (Ballantine Books) and
Anthropica (Forthcoming from Animal Riot Press)

"I want to live in Brian Birnbaum's head for a day to access the dark, loamy place he stores his word magic dust. But only a day. Any longer and I'd be big-pupiled and catatonic, out-cerebrumed and anti-cerebellumed. This novel is a wild ride, and will make you laugh even while you're cold-sweating through his character's choices. You might need a helmet. Or a flask of something. Followed by a shower. Birnbaum is as inventive with language as he is smart with story. He will put you into a world that kind of scares you, a world you don't fully trust not to hurt you, and you'll kind of like it."

—David Olimpio,
author of *This Is Not a Confession* (Awst Press) and
Editor-in-Chief of *Atticus Review*

"Let me say first: I don't like basketball. Or baseball card collections. Maybe you don't either. Do not let this deter you. A sign of a good book is its ability to make us think deeply about the things we would otherwise not care about. Call it empathy, call it precision; either way, I'm thankful. Newly minting the mundane into something thrilling is one rare gift a book can offer us. It's not easy, but *Emerald City* accomplishes this feat thrice over, and more. Not only do I dislike basketball, I'm also bored by securities firms and their boards. Nor am I interested in the ins and outs of government subsidies. Yet, in *Emerald City*, these unlikely elements serve as conduits through which to examine power and access and the systems (and people, families, bodies, feelings) that inevitably braid and fray them. Perhaps every prism is boring on its face (a hunk of featureless glass on a desk), but—like this book—the array of color that emerges through its core captures, enraptures, and transfixes us. Let the light that passes through these pages course into you."

—Dolan Morgan,
author of *That's When the Knives Come Down* (Aforementioned Productions) and *INSIGNIFICANA* (Civil Coping Mechanisms)

"Birnbaum's *Emerald City* is fast-paced and raucous. A contemporary Odysseus-esque journey, where each moment, each conversation, is a fight for one's life. Time feels like a needless and foreign construction because everything that matters is happening in the now. We like to think of people, place and narrative existing within boxes and boundaries, but this is work that is unafraid to veer. One is left feeling like they've been eavesdropping on a conversation they're not supposed to be listening to. The palpable discomfort from this knowing turns physical, quick. Sometimes the passages themselves feel like a low hanging fog. Tangles of sublime language that work to snare and entrap that are as lush as the *Emerald City* herself. Moreover, when the fog dissipates, what one is left with is a landscape fraught with conflict and diversion, and choices that aren't choices at all, a new take on thou mayest, where we keep coming back to the same question: What would you do to survive?"

—Keegan Lester,
author of *this shouldn't be beautiful but it was &*
it's all i had so i drew it (Slope Editions)

"Melding basketball, trust funds, drug mules, and good ol' noirish intrigue, Brian Birnbaum's Dickensian portrayal of a hypercapitalistic Seattle's underbelly (and overbelly) must be read and savored to be believed."

—Leland Cheuk,
author of *The Misadventures of Sulliver Pong* (Chicago Center for Literature and Photography) and *No Good Very Bad Asian* (C&R Press)

"Smart, fascinating, and forceful, Emerald City will leave you stunned. With its intricate prose style, ambitious structure, and a myriad of twists and turns, it never ceases to dazzle and amaze. Birnbaum has a unique perspective and approach, and his is a new voice to celebrate."

—N.J. Campbell,
author of *Found Audio* (Two Dollar Radio)

"Over the last five years, I have read through six iterations of *Emerald City* and watched it progress from a hodge-podge compilation of good writing to the masterful epic that it is today. I can comfortably say that I know of no author as dedicated and passionate for the work than Brian Birnbaum, and no other book deserving of such high praise. *Emerald City* is a wild ride through language and story unlike anything that's out there, and is Birnbaum's gift to his readers. I cannot wait to see what he writes next."

—M.K. Rainey,
author of *Sunny* (Forthcoming from Animal Riot Press)

EMERALD CITY

EMERALD
CITY

A NOVEL

BRIAN BIRNBAUM

Animal Riot Press Fiction
Animal Riot Press
www.animalriotpress.com

ISBN: 978-1-950122-00-4

First Animal Riot Press edition 2019

Designed by Olivia M. Croom
oliviacroomdesign.com

Artwork by Shawn Ferreyra
🐦 @ShawnFerreyra 📷 @mass_hip_steria

Manufactured in the United States of America

Portions of the work were previously published, in different form,
in *Potluck Mag* and *LUMINA Journal*.

To Mom, Dad, and Katie, without whom I'd be merely one of Shakespeare's thousand monkeys banging on a typewriter.

Special thanks to: 25 Stillwell, my EC Crew, the thesis advisor, the mentor, the De La Pava crime family— you all know who you are.

"That's all right, we serve them better than we know, if only we exist for them to reject, for they do not understand as you and I do, doctor, and to be certain of accepting one thing, they must reject another."

—William Gaddis, *The Recognitions*

PART ONE

Slumped in his office chair, Jason Derekson gazed after the sunlight pouring through his picture window. Noon's warm shafts, along with lunch, had him on the nod—numb to his fresh dilemma.

Jason swiveled and faced his locked door, averse to the bright force of joy this day seemed intent on delivering. Feet flung upon his varnished desk, he crossed one argyle sock over the other, bit a thumb's overgrown nail, rerunning his conversation with Rich.

"Let's talk net sports."

And with that, Richard Brelsford, Arkansas's assistant AD, had opened scheduling negotiations for preseason volleyball and non-conference basketball. It was boring but quick work, spanning years within minutes. Just enough time for Jason to destroy six soggy inches of mesquite chicken sub. "How about our boys come up there January five. Still on 2017," Rich added, his bullfrog drawl still raspier over speakerphone.

"Perfect," Jason said, muffled by a mouthful, which he swallowed before adding, "By then we'll have Jalen Taylor at the three."

"The eighth-grader doing windmill dunks from the foul line? You've already bagged him?" Rich scoffed, "You really do take to Tom's tit."

"Please," Jason nickered, picking at a piece of lettuce in his teeth, the last of his sub in the other hand. "The kid was a fixer-upper. New high-rise on the north side, a modest family van. Mr. Lillard doesn't need to hear about a little this and that."

"Right, just plausible deniability." But Rich's chuckle was washed away by the tide of words that followed, "Anyway, you better milk him while he lasts. Before he's put out to pasture, if you catch my drift."

Jason had just stuffed the last of his lunch into his yawning mouth when these ominous rumblings stunned him, leaving that fat lump of sub stuck soaking in his cheek. Had Jason heard him right? Did Rich truly allude to the possibility—or, heaven forbid, the *fact*—that the NCAA's president would soon be forced to abdicate? More than being responsible for Jason's rapid ascension to athletic director here at Myriadal College, President Thomas Lillard III was his mentor, his idol, his godfather emeritus.

"Are you—Mr. Lillard is, is what?" Jason stammered. He'd misplaced his false Ozarks twang among his anxiety's burst of buckshot. "Retiring?"

"I'm just the messenger," Rich deflected. "But you didn't hear it from me."

What Rich meant was that he hadn't heard it from anyone either, which nobody had also heard from no one, each nonperson toeing the line until all that remained was the smoke of corroborative apparitions. Jason could've asked Mr. Lillard himself—they spoke on the phone weekly—but not without revealing his source, which could only be no one.

He didn't lie when excusing himself from the call: indeed, the mesquite sub he'd scarfed for lunch lay in his gut like the sodden dead bird it mostly was. But mainly he was shaken. Put in the parlance of Rich's region, he didn't know whether to shit or wind his watch.

"Well, I'll let you hit the head then," Rich had chuckled before hanging up.

College basketball's was a feudal system. There was the king (President Lillard), his lords (the NCAA Board), and his otherwise noblemen, like Jason—the ADs and coaches and moneymen. And Jason, he was the belle of the balls. He ruled Division I volleyball and wreaked Hun-like havoc over basketball. But he had King Lillard to thank for his seat at court.

So yeah, Rich's allusions worried him. Worse yet, he could only appeal to the gods of the grapevine, seeking Apocrypha's favor.

Then again, to Jason, a pragmatist, one man's word didn't even qualify as rumor. Especially not when that one man had also buried the lede and protected his source. So Jason did what well-adjusted citizens were supposed to do: stuffed his anxiety away with the rest of his indifferences.

The middle of spring trimester meant six months until basketball season—yet only one week from contact period. At the NCAA's signal, it'd be open season on blue chip recruits, whereupon college basketball programs descend on talent like vultures to carrion. Gary Williams would lead his army of lapel-pinned assistant coaches to recruits' homes or have them flown out to Seattle for the full pampering—all while Jason backchanneled through the families' unofficial reps (that college players couldn't sign with agents was both a blessing to Jason's desire to sign talent and a curse to his long-term ambition to reform student-athlete compensation). By signing day in mid-May, the next class of freshmen would have picked up a Rapiers cap, smiled for the flashes, and scribbled bad cursive on dotted lines. Until then, Myriadal's athletic department—including its wunderkind AD, Jason Derekson—was resigned to passing the time between track meets and, of course, begrudging various administrative duties.

Saturday would be a real drooler. Jason would drive an hour south of Seattle just to help hold an outsized cardboard check made payable to the new children's hospital in Tacoma. The rest of the weekend he'd spend genuflecting to Gayle's notes, which would own him to Tuesday, at least. Tonight was supposed to have been about two stiff cocktails, a good whack, and six uninterrupted hours. But with this shit from Rich? Not a chance. He could chuck it atop his Vesuvius of due diligence.

The chicken sub would not budge. He'd have taken a stroll but for his express aversion to areas of student congregation, which was campus during a weekday. Instead, he'd clicked into a deep cut on Reddit—posts on posts of offensive puns—when the phone roused him from droll scrolling. He ran a hand through kempt waves the color of corn burnt by a dry spell and answered.

"Yeah?"

"Hello, this is interpreter eight-four-three-two with Behrenreich Interpreting Services. I'm calling on behalf of a Deaf or Hard-of-Hearing individual for Jason Derekson."

Jason wriggled upright, pushing up the bridge of his glasses. "Excuse me?"

"Hello, Mr. Derekson?"

"Hello?"

Silence for several moments. Jason nearly hung up.

"Yes, hi," the interpreter said. "I'm calling for Jason Derekson."

"This is he," Jason said firmly.

"Hello, Mr. Derekson. How are you?"

"May I ask who's calling?" He grimaced at the phone like it'd said something rude.

"This is Marc Behrenreich—of Behrenreich Interpreting Services. My son Benison plays at Bellevue High. Coach Williams came to see him this summer and said he'd be in touch."

"Mr. Behrenreich. Heard a lot about your son," Jason lied, grinning back in his chair. "Kid's got Jeff Gordon wheels. Gary had good things to say about him."

"My son is excited about the chance to talk to him again."

"Well ah"—clearing his throat—"it's a bit of a waiting game right now."

"Mr. Derekson, I want to work with you to see that my son plays here."

Jason rubbed the bridge of his nose, glasses begrudging him the itching space. "I'm sorry, Mr. Behrenreich, but I can't make any guarantees. We're obviously interested, but I suggest you and your son plan according to the offers that come your way."

"That's what I'm doing now, Mr. Derekson. Planning."

Such a stolid tone, layered over such an implication, unnerved Jason. Such a tone pulled his mind's eye back from what he thought was his wide circumference of certainty.

Jason could make bribes with a hand glued to his foot. Here's what you did: a) You never involved the coaches themselves; b) You never paid off in liquid; c) You had a trusted third party make anonymous purchases of house deeds or vehicle pink slips or whatever appreciable or at least salvageable asset that would suit your recruit's desires; and d) You never, *ever* mentioned to the recruit or their family who that third party was, so help you God.

But *accepting* bribes? He'd failed to imagine, and realizing this now was like catching a glimpse of himself in a lake after years without a mirror. Furthermore, it lent retrospective significance to Gary's comments about the kid and his father.

Benison's three-star recruit status had kept him off Jason's radar—though he did recall a word or two from Gary, who liked him, but had also pointed out the "lack of corporate loopholes built into my basketball program." Translated from Gary-speak, a 'lack of corporate loopholes' meant a few things: that the kid didn't know a day's honest work; that he didn't know thankless work, what it meant to shovel shit into the furnace so the bigwigs could do their jobs; and that a hothouse flower, dependent on his father's cronyism, would inevitably wilt on a court teeming with cutthroat athletes.

Ingenuous as Gary may have been, ever the dogged moralist, the hard-worker—the sucker—he was right about Behrenreich. Both the kid and his father. The prig was a cogent bastard, Oscar Wilde in philistine's clothes. But if Gary had seen this coming, he must've been aware of player assets off the books—and yet if he'd been aware of these activities, then why pretend at ethical dogma? Why waste so much breath on all that edification-of-young-men nonsense? It didn't make any damn sense. Maybe Jason had underestimated him. Maybe he was no sucker at all. Maybe he was the greatest artist of their time. Maybe he was the Keyser Söze of college basketball.

The sun was a flaming lemon sliced by skyscrapers leased to Azalai, the tech company responsible for Seattle's ongoing transformation and, apropos of big business, cause for both controversy and celebration. The spill of light drenched his office's matte blue walls and white molding. Jason made his decision.

"I'm listening," he nearly whispered.

"That's good," the interpreter said. "Do you know how much a Mercedes XLS costs, Mr. Derekson?"

Jason looked up at his door, still closed. "No. But I'm sure it's quite a figure."

"Beats Monroe's," the interpreter lilted. "It's an exquisite vehicle. I think it would suit the youngest board member on record."

"Excuse me?" he said, and heard the interpreter's *whoosh* and salivated *smacks*.

"My company provides transcription services for the NCAA's disability divisions. CART, TypeWell, C-Print—you name it."

"Yes, ADA compliance," said Jason. Speaking of shoveling excrement, much of Jason's first year at Myriadal had involved spearheading every shitmunching initiative known to modern (nominally) liberal man. Though Deaf access services were a diktat handed down by the NCAA's board, it was upon Jason to carry them out via closed captioning clauses included in all media contracts, along with live interpreters for important press conferences.

"Good. It seems we have an understanding, Mr. Derekson. Only this time, you won't have to dry-hump the President to get half of what you really wanted in the first place…Maybe take a few days to remind yourself exactly what it is you want. We'll be in contact soon."

And just before Jason removed the phone from his ear: "This is interpreter eight-four-three-two with Behrenreich Interpreting Services, concluding the call. Have a nice day." Reminding him that another set of eyes and ears had garnered all this. Jason was no fool: he figured interpreters were bound to confidentiality. But that was just the thing: he was no fool. And how in the hell did this Marc Behrenreich know what'd happened with Mr. Lillard in Chicago? Had he just bribed him with an XLS, too?

Cursing all things cryptic, Jason rattled the phone home—then went still. Head canted, drawn back like a curious dog's, he stared at his hand, still on the phone.

The proximity of these past two calls was suspicious. Had this Marc Behrenreich put a little birdie in Rich's ear? Or some other no one's, who'd then told Rich Nobody? In which case Jason's best option would be to hedge. (To paraphrase Jason's professional bible, *Iron Jaw*, it was always best to keep the maximum number of parties happy.) Yes, he'd nudge Gary about the Behrenreich kid, just enough to satisfy the kid's father, but not enough to be *involved*. If it didn't work out, so be it. He'd still have his seat at court, right beside Mr. Lillard.

He dialed Gary's extension to, oh, ask about a few, and was a bit surprised when Myriadal's head basketball coach picked up his office phone midday. After brief overtures, Jason weaseled his way toward the topic of the hour.

"With Jonesy still liable to sign at Maryland—and I'm just planning for the worst here—I guess the Behrenreich kid becomes an option." Jason's thumb slid along the landline's tortile wire. "He's competing in the summer. We're not above a double-double kid in AAU."

"…Well I appreciate your input, Jason."

"…Anyway, I'll be by for a rundown. Got Gayle up my ass about reporting the calls. Wish that woman would stick to volleyball and *assisting* the AD. Kids're gonna play where they wanna play," he chuckled.

"Got to keep the playing field even," Gary said.

The line popped static. Jason flipped off his phone, brought it back to ear, and said, "Right…Well I'll be by in a bit." Hanging up, he fired a finger-gun into his skull.

He'd learned early on that, if you wanted to thrive, you couldn't run from choice simply because making one necessarily contradicted another—you couldn't be afraid of desire, couldn't treat it like a zero-sum game played within the confines of a starvation economy. You could only shrink from choice, recessing into a space so useless, your only contradiction was against life itself. After meeting Mr. Lillard, Jason had instead chosen to survive, necessarily, at cost.

His laptop woke to the Reddit thread—r/offensive_puns—and he read the latest post.

[-]Terror Squad88 [score hidden] ten minutes ago

Anorexia tares lives apart

He let a little air from his mirth valve, laughter like a pneumatic sigh. It was funny because, well, it sorta worked.

Were there rumors about Mr. Lillard or not, it'd taken Behrenreich's call to get him to gauge his stress levels. He sat back, closed his eyes, listened for his breathing, rich and full.

Jason's next moves fell like the flurries before a snowstorm in the snow globe of his mind. First, he'd find out whether his call with daddy Behrenreich could be expunged from record. Then he'd keep nudging about the Behrenreich kid. He'd put little birds in the assistant coaches' ears—the kid's monster stat lines, Bellevue High records, the virtues of plucking local talent—which would then send them buzzing at Gary, but only after Jason continued to sow doubt over Mike Jones's signing. Once the buzz grew to a dull roar, he'd have Gayle schedule a coaches' visit to the Behrenreich household—a harmless trip across the 520.

While working to cover his tracks, his blizzard of manipulation would fuck with Gary's head until the old ball coach wouldn't know whether to shit or shovel the snow. Or whatever it was that Rich would say.

The Myriadal College basketball program gathered for practice twenty minutes south of Seattle proper. There in Tacoma they'd installed the Myriadal College Sports Complex, which everyone called the Balloon. Nothing but a triple-stitched tarp that, laid flat, covered six flush football fields, with convex extensions to spare. Powerfully engineered air units—the pumps, people called them—blew the tarp up taut as a moon bounce. Within this loud and bulbous cyst of a stadium, hardcourts were spread according to sport—several tennis and two basketball—scattered with pullout bleachers and a canteen for water and Gatorade and first aid items.

No one liked the Balloon. The light was caseous yellow. The pumps roared cold air. The mood was grim despite the blinding white. It didn't respect their talent. It was a relic of Myriadal's formative years, beneath their current station. But mostly, no one liked the Balloon because everyone talked about how they didn't like the Balloon, sustaining an open channel for human commiseration.

But today, Gary Williams had moved practice. Coach wanted to let the players—particularly the freshmen—familiarize themselves with their home court. And, with recent practices lacking luster, he thought to source a homeopathic remedy: holding practice on their home floor.

Screech.

"Blue!" Coach boomed from the hashmark, where subs checked in during games. "*Yes*, that means the defense is in Two. Can I get an inference here? Del. TWO. Look, Del." Coach pointed to the dotted lines denoting the restricted area. "There's a drawing for you. See? All you gotta do is sit under the goddamn basket and look scary. Not hard with that deformed mug of yours." Coach backed to the sideline. "Okay, Blue, let's go."

He drew his whistle to mouth and—*screech*—initiated play. He arced north of the scrimmage to keep his vantage without interfering. Mike Jones—referred to endearingly as Jonesy—stepped from the top of the key to set the high screen for Gabe Griffin.

Screech.

"God damn it, Jonesy. This time set a screen, don't just sidle up to Gabe like you wanna tell him about daffodils. Blue."

Screech.

This time Jonesy set the screen with camp, exaggerating your solid screen's rigid posture and crotch protection. It was effective nonetheless, and Benison Behrenreich—referred to tauntingly as Benchin'im—got tangled up top. His exaggerated grunts contained not camp, but an unsavory advertisement of his struggle to fight through Jonesy's screen. He failed. Eddy Dominguez delivered a perfectly vectored bounce-pass to Jonesy, who'd rolled off the screen for a wide-open dunk replete with primal ululation.

Screech.

The squad held fast to their knees, wheezed beyond the repair of oxygen. KeyArena's custodial crew buffed sweat spots as Coach approached.

"Behrenreich. We're in Two. Dominguez is no shooter"—Dominguez *tsking*—"You have help to your middle"—referring to Gabe Griffin, his partner up top of the 2-3 zone—"Who goes over the screen here?"

Benison brooded, arms akimbo.

"No one, is the answer," Coach said, tone devoid of all camp and comedy. "No one goes over the screen."

"Uh, Coach?" Austin Jackson—AJ for short—raised a hand. "Benchin'im just went over the screen though."

Coach spread his glare generously. "Would you guys prefer running suicides over Blue?"

"Nah." "I'm good." "Blue my favorite color."

"I see," Coach said. "Run it again. Blue."

Screech.

Jonesy set the screen with pure utility. Benison again fought—this time to get *under* the screen—and Eddy Dominguez wore a shit-eating grin as he lobbed the ball to Jonesy, who hammered it home with still more authority, sans the primal call.

"What the fuck," whined Gabe Griffin. "You hear me call switch you deaf-ass mothafucka?"

Benison came alive. Starting in his eyes, rippling down his body as if transformed, he started for Gabe Griffin.

"EY-EY-EY." Coach intercepted the altercation before it could start. Gabe Griffin flung a hand and flounced off. "Behrenreich," Coach said, already walking to the sideline. Perched upon the coach's box, he yelled, "Defense in One! Run full."

The team set to scrimmage the length of the court in man-to-man defense. Benison used some jersey to wipe his face. Coach watched the action as he spoke, like a blind man looking off at an angle.

"I heard you moved out of Comp 86."

Benison's anger had already been infected by fear.

"Heard you convinced Jonesy to take a roommate off campus. Hey!" he shouted into the melee.

"Boo be hackin man," AJ whined.

"Bouman! Too old to slide your feet? I know you're hooking over there."

"Why'm I guarding AJ then?" complained fifth-year senior, Andrew Bouman. "He half my dang size."

"You're asking the right questions, Bouman."

Benison breathed shallow. Impressive considering how much energy he'd wasted to win each round of suicides—to win something. Coach's stern practice mien turned soft, maybe even aggrieved, like he'd been duped into recruiting this sorry kid.

"You can play this game. I've *seen* you play this game."

But Benison was all the more abject, for the comparison between now and before—in a world that praised only the before and after. Disgust crinkled Coach's eyes. He strode back out onto the floor, leaving Benison to decide whether to rejoin the fray.

Following the post-practice presser, the team returned courtside, gathering in the first few rows of stands. Assistant coach Brock Wyles bottlenecked the media at the tunnel to the visitors' locker room. Under the stadium lights, famous yellows dim and hot, Coach Williams faced the gleaming court, back to the bantering squad, his Rapiers-blue sport jacket hiked up by hands upon hips.

"Eyo it's the towel boy, y'heard?"

Fault lines cackled out from the joke's epicenter: one Delmar "va Peninsula" James, a behemoth of a freshman out of Alabama. Benison feigned indifference and sat in the front row, next to Jonesy, his back to Delmar.

"Chill, Del," Bouman said from the fringes. He had enough years to trawl for deep laughter.

"Ah I'm just messing with him, Boo. He lookin swole though."

Benison let him reach down and squeeze his biceps, though didn't dignify him a look. Instead he watched the media disappear into the tunnel's abyss, ushered back by Coach Wyles.

"Fellas," Coach began, turning to face them. His jaw was tight. His face shone in a way not dissimilar to the court. His standard '50s haircut showed gray at its fewing roots. "Hope you enjoyed your first press conference. If you thought that was bad, wait'll we play the Bruins. Which is also why you better beat their asses, 'cause if not, y'all are gonna get to answer a lot of stupid questions...I'll make this brief, since you gotta be back here in just about"—checking a watchless wrist—"eighteen hours from now." Contradicting his claim to brevity, Coach paced for a piece, hands clasped behind his back. "You guys've worked hard. You look good, long's you box out for Christ's sake. But it's simple, really. If you for one second think you're entitled to beat Dayton because of some preseason rank that means about as much as my personal happiness, I'll guarantee you right here'n now you'll find yourself on the wrong side of the scoreboard."

Coach stopped pacing and slipped a folded paper from his back pocket.

"Okay, down to business."
He unfolded it. Benison tightened.
"Del, five. Bouman, four. AJ, three. Jonesy, two. Griffin, one."
For a few seconds he gazed at his team. Everyone was still.
"Dismissed."

Head down, features pinched, Benison crawled along the fluo-rescent halls of KeyArena's underbelly. In his ear, JAY-Z flowed over a silky synth arrangement. When alone, he'd sync up to the lyrics, but the locker room's voices still followed him down the hall.

He passed lighted glass displays set with SuperSonics relics—trophies, jerseys, pennants. Between the show windows were large stills of Seattle's hardwood legends. Gary Payton, reaching clean to thief a too-high dribble. Shawn Kemp, rattling the rim, hanging on it and grinning something angry.

Benison expected greatness of himself, and he was blessed with its code. Higher powers had whip-cracked his first step, geared sniper scope to shooting eye, bequeathed him length and energy like light itself. He was built to *play this game.* Impossible to pinpoint what made him this way. His father's height was elastic and unused. His mother's contribution? Elusive, outside her complexion. But there he was, a maudlin boy in a Greek god's body. Surely there was more than element to excellence.

Benison was from the 'burbs, which bred man-children. The type that never wanted, yet were always wanting. The type that sat all sulky in the back of rented cars when forced into a family vacation, headphones strapped tight, slipping into schizoid fan-tasies of fretting a Fender like John Frusciante, or spitting like Eminem, fifty grand a night to kill it for fifty grand in the stands. The type that removed his shirt when running his hilly neighbor-hood, showing off Adonis's abdomen, gleaming and glabrous. Then the shame when the neighbors did look. Just like in high school, when they'd played their rival, Mount Hebron. Each and every time he'd slashed off the dribble, Benison beat the best defender they could put on him, and by the end of the game he couldn't look at the kid's face. He'd felt too sorry for him.

Now that things weren't going his way again—the telegraphed passes, the fighting-over-the-screens—he felt that familiar sorry for himself. Ordain enough in-and-outs and he questioned why why why me. To the bench with you. Then up goes the Gatorade jug, a perfect double-misty off the foldout table, neon-yellow globules spouting out its blowhole. Benison Benchin'im Behrenreich. When things didn't go his way, it didn't matter what the score was, only that he received no standing ovations and therefore couldn't attain the things he *really* wanted from life: surface crust of success and glory; deeper mantle of capability and humility; and a molten core of mineral love.

But this failure problem plagued him—it kept him from drilling past that crust.

When he fucked up, he thought about fucking up, and so fucked up again, precisely because he was fucking up. This feedback loop tortured him. It drew his conscious back into itself. It made him obsess like a man committed, who etches along the borders of his scrap paper an ominous symbol—as this specter of *failure* followed Benison now along KeyArena's mosaic, lost in his loop, when a hand grabbed his shoulder.

Benison regretted his surprised yelp only more for its sole witness.

"Yo chill," Delmar grimaced. "You left something back at 86."

It took a moment for Benison's arterial systems to resume functions, much less remember where he was: leaving KeyArena, or trying to. Then he saw Del was hiding something behind his back.

"Oh word—" he started, trying to reach behind Del's back.

"Ah-ah-ah." Delmar wagged his finger. "First I wanna know why you moved out."

Benison's mouth parted maybe a micron. A sound—a sliver of a stutter.

"Yo. I'm fuckin witchu."

As was Delmar's wont.

AJ, Delmar, Gabe Griffin—they became Myriadal's Big Three after college basketball's crazy uncle, Dick Vitale, used five minutes on *SportsCenter* to proclaim them the best set of diaper dandies since Michigan's Fab Five. Suddenly, basketball heads from Seatown to Spanish Harlem were made aware of Myriadal's *Tres Grandes*. Benison couldn't watch ESPN for ten minutes without a reference to at least one of the Big Three. Just this past week on *E:60*, ESPN's hourlong hand in social consciousness, Jeremy Schaap shadowed AJ as they revisited his house on Hollins Street. They started in a nearby lot, which lay wasting under weeds and works. AJ talked about playing in the lot as a kid, turning up treasures beyond his years—until he grew to better understand them, and therefore his older kin: dope fiends and corner boys; collectors and counters; point women and ladies of the night.

"AJ says his neighbors—medical residents at Johns Hopkins—used to scold his parents for letting their kids loiter around the block late at night," said *E:60*'s Schaap, dubbed over B-roll of Baltimore, steaming manholes and sped-up shots of grim-looking locals, before cutting to AJ and Schaap on his house's stoop.

"All them degrees," AJ responded, "and they think we got a problem with supervision? They had it all messed up."

Delmar James—Myriadal's freshman centerpiece—he was built on Alabama summers. Each Saturday he attended a playground with a clear view of Birmingham's Vulcan statue, whose ass lay veritably bare. There, he threw himself into the court's notoriously rugged games of three-on-three that culminated each year in a tournament sponsored by AND1. Through these half-court rumbles Delmar learned to pound in the post—and ignore the older guys who loitered on the sidelines. Dressed dapper and always affable, these rakish cats had made it their economic policy to trap and rinse the block. But Del, he stonewalled the drug game's headhunters and raked the playground for all its worth, until he was known amongst the known as Delmar "va Peninsula," fleet-footed juggernaut with the size and strength of said topography.

"I'll tell you man, back when I was just a kid, in certain circles of street-ball?" he said to Schaap in front of his mother's clapboard house outside Birmingham. "You take it to the rack, you might get hacked the [censored] up."

Of their physical ilk, Benison should've been able to play alongside the Big Three, come off the bench, make a play here and there to help them carry the load. Hell, he could've done better than that. He could've contributed serious minutes. But he didn't want it like they did—didn't need victory to survive like an indelible amino pattern.

Originally assigned to live with the Big Three on campus, he'd spent his first week bumping hip hop classics with his door ajar, hoping his teammates would sidle up to talk tunes. But they weren't big on '90s rap, so rather than take to his tack, they waited for him to poke out of his room. Bets were made on when this might happen. By the time he wised to this, he was compromised, too conscious of his body separated from theirs by the wall he hid behind. And when he did come out, they sensed the fake shit he laid down, how he mimicked their meme rather than doing him—and he knew it.

Like that one night during the four days off before focus finals, near the end of each trimester, when Myriadal had a sort of Mardi week. On day two, the residents of compartment 86 assembled in the common area for a spot of doomsday drinking. Fluorescent tubes buzzed above beats banging from speakers perched on the windowsill, the TV tuned to an NBA game, Benison secretly annoyed at the competing volumes.

"Now he catchin wreck though," Gabe Griffin said, punctuating some point and pulling at his busy Mark Ecko shirt. The rest, including Benison, rocked Rapiers gear, sweats, shirts, zip-up windbreakers. "You gonna pass that?" he said.

A clipped chuckle from AJ, whose hand appreciated his high-top fade. Looking up with blooded eyes, he drawled, "Nahhh."

But Delmar snatched it up and took a rip. "Ey man you gonna hit this?" he sang, circling the slim cone before Benison's face, the spliff's spirit lifting toward the smoke detector rather than the cracked window. "Ah?"

The mechanism responsible for calibrating Benison's scope of thought was stuck on a 160x lens setting, listening to microbes talk politics. "Ahdunno man. What if we get tested?"

He felt his words grate against the heavy beat from the windowsill. His speech was robbed of colloquial flow, snapping iambics. The second or two before Delmar's response was *long*. He *saw* Del thinking. He *heard* the voices boiling up from street level, frothing over the music and into their compartment. On the pale wood table, his red Solo filled with Gatorade and vodka was disappearing at inch-per-hour increments. Perhaps he needed to increase the rate.

"Please! It's October," Del scowled, ripping another hit.

Gabe Griffin pealed a high laugh, reached to repossess the joint. "Shit's about to be legal in a minute, cuz."

"Also never smoked before," Benison shrugged. His elbows pistoned, his knees joggled. This time, three seconds before any response—then an uproar.

"Hold up," Delmar sprung to his feet. A broad smile formed wormlike. "This gringo *needs to get high*."

"Nah man," Benison laughed and licked his lips. "I'm good."

"Might help your *game* out," AJ said.

Benison was saved by the buzzer: Russell Westbrook tossed an intercontinental alley-oop to Kevin Durant, drawing *oohs* and *ahs* as the first quarter came to a close. Delmar proclaimed he could get up like that. Gabe Griffin concurred but with the caveat that Del couldn't shoot like K-D. So the big man from Bama picked up a balled paper towel and stood, unsteadily, with the intent to prove otherwise.

"Wet," Delmar called as he followed through on his fadeaway, which banked high off the wall and missed the trash can, used paper towel stopping near the can's base.

"Siiiiike," Benison said.

"Sike?" Delmar scowled, looking at the others. "What's that some white boy shit?"

Right there: that had been Benison's chance. A huge one was forming. The punch-line hung by the threads of his tongue. All he needed to do was get up and turn around—"I'll show you some white boy shit"—and let it rip: *pppprrrffff*. Juvenile? Immature? He was a nineteen-year-old kid in serious need of new ways to light his fun-nodes. Alas, his sulfur had slipped silently and, his stretched smile slitting his chapped lip, he said, "Nah…"

"Yo. I'm *playin* with you," Delmar said, nudging his shoulder.

That was when Benison, direct from class or practice, had started routing to his room, the door closed behind him. He came out to the common area like a mouse, only when he thought the coast was clear. Better to be a hermit than inveigled into admitting his most embarrassing sexual experience. Or into dropping the *n-bomb*, whereupon they'd feign outrage before revealing him for the credulous fuck that he was being. They called him Stinky-TO because he always Turned the ball Over, and toes smell bad. Gabe Griffin talked shit while on him at practice—"He don't want it"—or while watching him cook ramen. Benison grew afraid of Delmar's volume, in all senses of the word. He resented how the Rapiers' five-man would guard his eyes against Benison's blinding white aura. By then, Benison lost the ability to decipher when and whether the big man from Bama was messing with him.

His compmates turned him into someone he hated whenever he was around them. He played different, anxious and tentative. He walked different, as if on stilts. He talked different, no music or cadence. He lost himself in fantasies of decking Delmar then hovering over him to urge, "What up now, *bitch?*" But that wouldn't win back the alpha throne he'd so meticulously carved out of milieus past. The truth was, he was the only one with a problem—and the problem begot the problem:

It starts with playing like shit. Then he plays like shit *because* he's been playing like shit—a self-generating shit-mechanism, being shat on by his opponents, stinking up and down the floor and throwing the shit he's covered in, petulantly flinging it everywhere, on everyone. And now the negative capability required of him as an athlete—of forgetting himself—is exposed to assumptions that he will fail. Now he considers his moves on the hardcourt in the way that thinking about thinking can paralyze genius. Then he hesitates. It turns his fluid jump shot into a stilted aim at the basket. His basketball IQ is double-thoughted and therefore dumbed. Failure to *play* extrapolates unto a more insidious failure to *perform* in general, worsening his failure to play, a closed loop of provenance of a piece with the cosmos and all things fated. And up goes the Gatorade jug, or the video game console…

"Ey man, you there?"

Benison's scope throttled back to things tangible and present: Delmar's outstretched arm offering a static composition book labeled "Barz."

"Didn't read it," Del said. "Swear to God, man." He crossed himself then went woozy-eyed.

Benison could think of few scenarios more awkward than standing in quiet spaces with Delmar. He took the notebook, which was filled with metered verses and rhyming doodles, and thanked Del, loathing his autonomic deference.

"Game day tomorrow!" Delmar hooted and heaved off toward the locker room, fist held high overhead.

Benison stood frozen before the fear that Del had in fact perused the fruits of his hip hop hobby. He wanted desperately to know the truth, but should anyone have caught him shoegazing out here in the hall, he'd get heckled, so he kept on.

Blue duffel slung over shoulder, he pulled his hood up and butted the boiler room's door, spun off the latch—and stopped. As if waiting in ambush, a flurry of media types and their gadgets preyed upon his personal space, microphones flittering, fuzzy booms lording, and questions flying at him like a murder of crows, too quick and many to figure:

"What are your thoughts on your father's arrest earlier today?"

"What do you know about the charges placed against him?"

"Are you upset?"

Not that it stood out in his mind, but Benison wouldn't have been able to match one of these faces, thrust now into his personal space, to any of those present at today's post-practice presser. No, the rabble surrounding him now represented a different animal of reporter. The decals on their cameras and mics and booms betrayed big-name media brands—CNN's parallel red font, NBC's varicolored peacock, Fox News' brutalist block lettering. They vied for position like ambulance-chasers navigating a hospital's waiting area.

Benison had vaguely comprehended what was happening when the door behind him pounded open, bumping him nearer the slavering mob—but Coach took hold of his arm and pulled him through the scrum.

"We have no comments right now," he grumbled.

Coach plowed ahead, Benison in tow, looking over his shoulder as if being escorted from those he loved. Some-odd strides away from the scrum, Coach asked where his car was. On a dime they turned into a quadrangle of parked vehicles, across a lane, a yaw left, until Benison pointed to a white Audi sedan. He fumbled for the right key before the driver-side door. Finally he finagled the car key and, once seated, Coach bent into the descended power-window. He put his elbows on the sill, pausing as if to let the moment settle into the greater solution. Benison looked out his windshield, where a horizon of cars gave way to gray sky. "Fuck," he breathed.

"Best thing is to get home and don't talk to the press," Coach advised. "I'll tell Jonesy to hunker down with you. Make something to eat. Put in a movie. Do some homework. Just try not to watch the news. Benison," Coach said.

He looked at Coach, who'd turned to confront the swell of media cretins meandering nearer.

"You better go." Coach slapped the car's hardtop.

Benison made a parabola around the parking lot, watching reporters' faces go blank as if shut down by their central intelligence. New mist dusted the streets. The city's famously spired UFO hovered in shroud over the Seattle Center. At a red light, Benison opened Barz in his lap, plugged the aux cable into his phone, and, in picking a beat, jammed his mother's panicked texts in with the backlog of his conscious. Flipping through his notebook, he spat some syncopated scales—a *do re mi fa so dope* sort of solfege—and finally, hitting play, he slipped into the pocket of the beat.

The light changed. He fell silent. High synths droned on without him. Cars honked as he idled, his gaze caught in reverse. It'd occurred to him how absurd this was, the act of rapping, regardless of the circumstances.

Benison knew exactly what was going on. He just hadn't thought it would go down like this, with him finding out in real time, like every other asshole watching the 24-hour news cycle. Since adolescence, he'd been a stranger in his own home, the last to know—or never knowing—until it happened to him.

Julia flicked the spliff and watched sparks turn to ash. Loretta Lane's slanting cobblestones shone wet under the close moon. Her eyes followed streaks of cirrus, shorn from a sharp cold front.

Peter offered his jacket. In declining, Julia's show of defiance let her keep grip of the thick envelope stuffed with cash, tucked in her hoodie's kangaroo pouch. Two birds, a stone, and the guilt that attended blood money.

A couple approached, splitting their hands before the steps, circumnavigating this tense moment sensed by anyone with working eyes. The Iliad's front doors closed behind them with a dull metal thud. Peter hit the roach, one last crackle, and flicked it into a frowsy hedge. Elbows grinding knees, his mind making a moment into something soluble.

"Bet Brad's in his room, deep in Trappist fapping."

Julia looked at him askance. "He likes his beer. Give him a break."

"We could knock on 203," he said, indicating the couple just past. "See if we can watch those chicks scissor."

She scoffed. "Wanna say something of value?"

Peter punched his hands into either pocket. "You got pissed then just threw up deuces. What else do you want me to say?"

It'd been a whose-right-to-Jerusalem fight. You did this, well you did that, and all the way back.

"I don't know." Julia sighed, head dropping to the maroon block letters emblazoned in an obtuse arch across her hoodie's front: ASHBURY GRAMMAR. "My brain's done but I'm still kinda cracked out from Adderall."

"How'd you do?"

"Eighty-nine."

"Daaamn."

The way Myriadal College weighted their focus finals, an 89 shot Julia beyond earthly limits, pre-med or not.

Headlights surged over the street's crest. A car came down Loretta, its beams revealing her favorite building, brick, with spools of ivy reaching a roof from where one could see the whole city, all the way to the Puget Sound. Sitting on the steps in front of Peter's apartment building, they tried to see and understand things that were there only when thought of.

"Look. I'm sorry," Peter said. "But it's not something that's easy to talk about. So I make light of it."

"You make light of everything. But it's fluorescent, it's bullshit."

He *tsked*. "That's how you feel?"

"We can't keep doing it like this," she said.

And probably they couldn't.

Dave Lissener, a family friend from back home, was Julia's link to the University of Washington, over in the U-District. Which was where she'd found Peter, at Lissener's Halloween party. She'd been sitting by a coffee table, across which playing cards flew in sprinkler-shuttering rhythm. Sticking to social sips of beer, she watched Peter in Dave's kitchen. He solicited reactions without prejudice, from Thing 1, from Frankenstein, from Del the Funky Homosapien. At the party's edges hung a kid holding a body-sized poster board decorated with user posts, photos, interactive tabs, his face poked through a square window in the top-left corner, she understood now: he was a Myriadal Mates profile.

She watched how, when they weren't looking at Peter, neither did he them, nor ever, really, if you looked close enough. She watched ice melt to soggy pebbles in his third whiskey. He tolerated more than talked to a kid dressed as Superman, the generic social mechanics, same jokes in barely differing forms. She heard him ask, "Do you do hard drugs?"

"No?" Superman replied, confusion drawing his brows.

"Do them," Peter nodded once. "Do hard drugs, or too many will die of boredom." He killed his drink, turned to another kid, and said, "We're hanging out with him for the tax breaks right?"

Later he stood alone by the stereo. He'd taken off his jacket, and Julia caught a flicker of his costume: a white t-shirt with ORGASM DONOR markered in crude block lettering across the chest. Plus those black chinos she'd eventually come to despise, less for their appearance *qua* design than his failure to maintain the integrity of their original design via the advent of the washing machine. Peter swayed to a slurry trill beat, scrolling the device. She got up to make a move. En route to the tureen of jungle juice on the kitchen counter, she felt him sighting her, his archer's wink, or maybe he was just that drunk.

Just then a girl wearing gossamer wings, a tight pink tutu, and a spangled wand tucked into her fairy belt—"seething Toothbitch" would be Peter's description—got in his face with a fake-ass grin, glancing down at his shirt.

"That's a sorry pretense for meeting girls."

"The only pretense I see is your fat ass in tights."

Things got quiet except for some Gaga track mocking the moment. A pugnacious kid in Shawn Kemp getup pushed through. His face, from what Julia would recall, was all chivalry and valiance, while his eyes sought any excuse to turn things physical.

"Do I know you?" Peter said and stepped nose-to-nose, nearly whispering now, "white man can't jump?"

"Fuck you say?"

"Did I stutter?"

"Maybe I wasn't close enough to hear." The kid jammed his nose into Peter's. "Why don't you try again."

Which was when Julia, in the spirit of Halloween, wrung Peter's hand through the crush, toward the elevators, and down into the mist.

"So I'll be sleeping on the couch tonight, huh?"

Julia, wearing her little black dress, winced in the wet chill, huddling into herself. "You shouldn't start shit."

"You shouldn't get in the middle of it," Peter muttered into a cupped glow like a firefly whisperer. He whipped his hands away and hissed at his first drag. "What you doin here anyway? Stalking me or something?"

She smiled for what felt like the first time in ages. He remembered her from last spring, when they'd met at the pier. Well, of course he remembered her—as a human he had memories of shared experiences—but he seemed to do so fondly.

Now that they shared a similar zip code—a difference of one digit—nothing stopped them from continuing where they'd left off that night back in March. They skipped lectures to get high on Myriadal's mall during the last mild days before winter spun damp skeins of wool across cold skies. She snuck him onto campus after hours, using various alter-egos to distract security posted at Abrogate (Abrə-,gāt *n.* : the Jesuit school's sobriquet for the gated entrance opposite the admin building). They hung around Peter's place on the Hill, validating her feelings through the object art of his apartment—everything from his music library stacked with atrocious death metal to the sticky-note signed by Kaleigh, still affixed to his desk's frame, reminding him of a reminder that she'd been at a friend's for the weekend. Julia didn't ask, perhaps afraid of his answer. Or because there were his tawny eyebrows to gaze after, perfect as baseball seams. His gooey oxheart eyes. His body like a stick of butter, skinny-fat and delicious.

And of course, the drugs. Amid the besotted swirl of house parties, he'd slip off to disused rooms with this kid, Rameen, who always showed up late and never removed his thick-ribbed jacket, for which Peter called him "My Michelin Man"—for whom he ran marijuana across the border.

Julia Paolantonio was new to this city—but not to the land of the libertine. Not to a socioeconomic renaissance brought about by tech heads congregating from far and wide upon this incumbent bohemia, where Azalai's thousands of blue-badged coder-drones wielded the profits of online retail and web services to stake their global influence—beneath which the old world teemed, junkies scurrying at ground level, hustlers working the corners on 3rd, dope fiends creeping farther up the Hill. Corporate myths didn't fool her. Julia knew her phone's cobalt was mined by African children. It was all a racket. Or so she told Peter, whenever he sought assurance the night before a run.

One of those bent-up nights, they returned to Peter's place, absconded from an early shot of cold air dropped east of the mountains. Peter's heavy head lolled on the couch's back like a broken bobble. Perhaps accentuating her intoxication, just a touch, Julia let hers fall too. She rolled it toward him and said, "This stuff with Rameen. It's just temporary, right?"

Peter's shoulders could barely lift the air. "I dunno."

"You wanna do something real?" she blinked. His eyes were lowered to the zenith of his high. She added, "I want you to meet someone."

The next day, Peter Fosch sat in a stranger's kitchen, considering a Reuben from the swank deli down the street. His stomach had seen but a flask of hellfire over the past day (hellfire being an old Fosch-family recipe: bourbon with a splash of Louisiana hot sauce).

Julia's shower had begun threatening municipal water supplies. With nothing better to do, Peter found himself musing after the condo's decadence. He'd expected Italian chintz, only to be indifferently impressed by the black-and-white tile, alabaster armoire, and cream-colored couches. The place effused a wealthy Long Island vibe, though this was Mercer Island, where much of Seattle's Jewry resided. He didn't know how he made these associations. He'd never been to Long Island, though his best friend growing up—more like a brother, really—was Jewish. Remiss to reminiscing over such things, Peter was back to the Reuben idea when the front door opened.

A man in a pinstriped suit stepped large onto the sunlit landing. "You the kid who's neckin with my granddaughter?"

He lumbered into the kitchen, looming over Peter, until lunging suddenly, pounding a 10.0 on the Richter, his force of foot reverberating straight through the old polished tile and wood-strutted floor. Peter didn't react. Frowning, Julia's granddad said, "Maybe you got the right size balls."

He introduced himself as Johnny Raciti in such a way to make clear that, to interface with the guy, Peter would have to redact his short list of surviving values. For Julia's sake, Peter decided he'd tolerate the man.

Speaking in his home borough's ancient syntax, Raciti asked if Peter felt out of place. "You know, living on the Hill with all those flaming twigs." He asked what they did together, Peter and his granddaughter. He asked in a way that made Peter feel like he'd been fitted with a bulletproof vest, taken into a dark alcove, and shot in the chest.

"You know. Milkshakes and ballgames."

Raciti's cloying laugh trailed, leading to a strange silence. The quiet grew between them like a magnetic field, strong and invisible, until Raciti asked about the bike resting in the rubbled drive out front.

"We wear helmets."

"Like you wear condoms," Raciti flashed his yellow teeth. Then his grin contracted to a pucker. "You smart? You stay off the shit?"

"Yeah."

"Lie," he pointed. "Your eyes got more glue than Elmer's." Raciti leaned back, crossed arms atop his paunch. "But you're pretty good with that bike."

Peter's gaze said, Yes, I am fairly adroit.

"Those nos tanks," Raciti continued, "Only runners use those… You're wondering how I know that."

Indeed, he was.

"I know who you work for. Persian kid. With the jacket? His grass is garbage, almost as bad as his coke. I bumped better stuff in the back of dives that don't know they're dives."

"So you and Jules are close," Peter shrugged.

Raciti took his time sipping his water. "Listen, Peter, Pete—can I call you Pete? We ain't dealin dimes out your mommy's basement. You get paid in size. You fuck up big enough, you get fucked."

He let Raciti approach his proposition, and while he did, he thought how the truth of human relationships would reveal everyone as someone else's pawn.

As Raciti put it, a small wharf lingered somewhere along the coast north of Vancouver. By his description, Peter suspected it roughly 40 miles north of his drop-and-pickup point for Rameen. On a good day, from the port's quay you could see old ships wading Pacific chop in search of fresh catch. And on the third Thursday of each month, Peter would see a barge coming in.

"The captain's a grim sonofabitch, but reliable. Back in the '90s he moved tuna with coke stuffed to the gills. Now he works in a more niche industry. Special deliveries, you might say."

Raciti needed a guy to run a single satchel of unknown contraband for someone whose name was connoted by that shudder of inanimate things. "He goes by Mr. K. All you need to know is, he helped the CIA prop enough puppet regimes to run fifty seasons of Sesame Street. So don't fuck with this."

Peter ingested this information as he did his hellfire, with willful indifference. "The drop?"

"CubeSmart outside Bellingham. You'll get the unit and code later today."

Julia appeared in the kitchen. Her hair hung scraggly, not dripping but still damp. Peter watched her hand pledge allegiance to the back of her granddad's chair.

"And?" Peter nudged.

"Four per run."

The deal could've been four thousand punches to the dick and it wouldn't have made a difference: he didn't have a choice. He wished he cared enough to romanticize the matter, that you never had a choice. That he'd only love a girl with the nuts to put one on him like this. But he didn't. "Alright," he said.

Raciti seemed pleased. "Important thing is, these satchels? Don't worry about 'em. I learned a long time ago that sometimes half your pay is so you don't get curious, you understand?" A patter as the rubber-banded roll hit the table. "So there's for your curiosity."

Peter's unwavering gaze said that such a wad would do.

"From now on, you'll report to Mr. K's guys—and then to me, which'll be our little secret. Oh, and get a burner. This ain't Mulberry fuckin Road. Boys got eyes out."

Peter made to leave as though indifferent to whether Julia joined him. Nonetheless, she followed.

Julia was no longer cold—things had gotten heated here on the Iliad's stoop. Her voice wasn't hoarse, but sections of what she said were strained. Now came the time to punctuate her paper of grievances. Exhausted of her means to render exasperation, as her own sort of *intifada*, she brought up his apartment:

"I mean"—cutting a harsh chuckle—"why do we always have to hang out here?"

Because if clean is good, then 405 at the Iliad was pure evil.

Salt-and-pepper spliff ash was scattered in neat little hills about the carpet, as if undead ants had settled there.

Old food resided on plate and off, and dirty plates were many.

The smell was generally rank, insufficiently guised by industrial scent.

Opened confection wrappers now served the people. "The fly people," as Peter called them.

In particular, Julia detested the dish towel wrapped around the kitchen faucet's base—a rudimentary shunt for leakage that would otherwise spit and spray with unpredictable direction and magnitude. Said towel had cultured visible fungi, the growth's discoloration indistinguishable from that of smeared feces.

The bathroom's doorknob had broken off clean, as if guillotined for being resistant to turning. But worse than this oversized peephole: those who favored loo-room privacy were forced to pull open a bottom drawer as a make-shift latch. As for the state of the bathroom itself—best not to enter at all, if possible.

Found nowhere in 405: evidence of organic macronutrient. Rogue Peanut Butter M&M's, a 405 favorite, dwelt melted on the carpet, smashed by sneaker or bare foot alike. The M&M's, admittedly, could be attributed to Peter's roommate, Brad, who bought them in bulk at Costco and left them chip-clipped in the cabinet above the fridge, bowing to Peter's bottle as if praying to his habits.

A makeshift water bong presided over the shunting towel, just to its festering left. But not just any water bong. This was a smoke-fogged 2-liter 7-Up bottle with a tinfoil bowlpiece set where the cap should've been—a relic of the apartment's general disgustingness, but, more specifically, the prefab bong was of a piece with the kitchen's most ominous phenomenon:

The kitchen's faux-marble countertops were plagued by chalky dust, like a boardwalk swept over by wet sand or salt blooming on a flat. Not only was its presence inexplicable, but when wiped away with a wet paper towel, not but five minutes later would the efflorescence reappear in different patterns of the same striated form, all of which Julia deemed as evidence of incorporeal haunting here in 405 at the Iliad.

Crumbs and crust and crab-like yellow goop covered the stovetop. No one used the stove much. Also inexplicable.

Those of 405's guests that suspected rodential infestation were proven correct. A few days before today's focus finals, Julia had overturned a bowl—that is, a bowl for foodstuffs—only to find a mouse trapped within, dead for lord only knew how long. Its putrescence sent her rushing into the bathroom, forearm muffling her mouth, where she coughed up a few phantom mouse carcasses. Properly purged, she returned to Peter's room and dallied on his laptop, her presence meant to gauge whether he'd heard her retching and would he ask why. But he just kept on balling clothes into clumps that he then stuffed into drawers and so, sitting in his squeaky swivel chair, angry at his indifference, she tooled around the web until lured by Peter's Gmail tab, left open to a missive from almost a year ago sent by—George Fosch.

She forgot her stomach, along with the furious certainty as to why a dead mouse was left trapped under a bowl on the kitchen counter (he didn't care). She looked back, ensuring Peter's continued pursuit with regards to the folding.

In this *mea culpa* to his son, George explained some things for a piece:

George Fosch   Nov 4
to me

I want to say sorry. For everything. Sometimes things just don't go as you thought they ought to. Kaleigh says hi. Wants you to know she didn't know nothing about anything till the day of, and she cried and told me to turn back and get you else she's gone to run back home. She's settled down now, happier to of left. Go start somewhere new and forget.

Getting old is cruel. Its taken a heck of a long time just to get to not that long ago. Remember the day me and you went paintballing over by the Clark farm on 108? You was real young. Couldn't of been more than eight or nine. My old buddy veered off his truck rout just to see me and my boy. Remember how he thrown up the back of his truck and all them boxes of feed? Could of fed the Clark farm's chickens for a year. My buddy chewed me out about not knowing we were gone paintballing, and he wouldn't of wore his Mountaineers jersey less he wanted it tie-died. You made your old man real proud that day. Killed many an enemy. Then how about when we set down for a spell for a cold Coca Cola after. I hope you could try and remember that day when you think of your old man, and sorry again.

"What is this?" Julia turned to Peter, who kept folding clothes, his form captured by the rhombus of light blearing through the blinds. "Fosch," she said. "Hey, Peter."

Seconds passed. Him crumpling otherwise clean clothes. She watched him. She watched him calculate what she'd meant by "this." She watched mullions erect before his eyes, which could only see through the window of his cell, and Julia just wanted visitation rights. As if granting them, he spoke. The story had legs, took stride like something long trained in his mind—as only deeply grafted memories are.

Peter said he'd tried hiding the bottles sometimes, but decided to let Mom have her Svedka after his $3,000 trip to the ER for a broken jaw. "We had this insurance called Blue Cross Don't Get

Fuckin Injured. A whole social services thing," he said. "I was
what, maybe eleven? I fed the rep a bunch of lies. Left the real
parts out, like how…"

His father's snores permeate the wall dividing their rooms.
He put Kaleigh down in her crib a couple hours before hay-time,
yet still she lies awake, cooing at her mobile of the solar system.

Downstairs, a commercial's jingle cuts out.

Peter's in bed not to sleep, but to wait. Book in his hands.
Thoughts in his brain. Redskins pajamas on—but the lights too.
His English teacher at school said people fear what they can't see
or understand. This in response to some stupid kid's question—or
some kid's stupid question—as to why white people didn't like
black people back then. But when Peter's mother appears in his
doorway, she's no silhouette, no blank outline over which he paints
his fears, but the same mother he sees each day, or most days: a
wretch in broad lamplight.

Mrs. Fosch would leave the light on. She'd swallow. She'd labor
to his bed, her besotted saunter filling him with dread. She'd slam
the bottle on his nightstand, atop whatever fantasy novel he'd
read as a special form of escape. She'd lean over him, tease him
till firm—or berate him for his failures as a man, his failures as a
manboy, as a man stuck in boyhood, his father's snores rippling
the shared wall. She'd slip limp hands under his waistband that,
if drawstrung and knotted, would draw her redoubled ire. She'd
take him slow. She'd pinion his wrists to the emaciated mattress,
bellow at him to look at her, to behold the billion radicles blooming
across a bust sagging loose in her padded brassier like the udders
of a deranged beast. Her lowing. Him lying doe-eyed.

The first time he finished, she'd slapped him hard and asked him
what people'd think. So he learned to notify her of his outcom-
ing with a quarterhearted grunt. If he didn't—didn't at all—he'd
gotten hit. The deeply conflicted effort to finish dominated his
recurring memories—recurring *feelings*, really, as not even the most
evanescent flashes of stark imagery equated to the inarticulate
confusion and gaslighted conversations and fantasized reprisals and
all of that which rushed across his synapses in varying directions

and magnitudes as if mocking that moment when he did finish, finally, his head falling to the side as if severed, and when he looked back at that demon slaked, he imagined their eyes connected by charged bolts, an optical battle magic. In this way he transfigured them dueling visions. Only, in the morning, he'd find his fantasy novel tainted, a wet ring where her vodka had stood. To this day, his mental pestle could not grind this feeling into whit small and indiscernible enough...

...Julia's hands made a hospital mask over her mouth and nose. She removed them for just a moment to urge, "Peter...*Jesus.*"

"Then one night," Peter continued, "she came upstairs. And I...I finally realized...I just told her to leave. I told her she better leave. And that was it...And, you know, I lived. I survived. And doing that, I also realized..."

He stopped folding clothes and stepped nearer. Standing in the light, a darkened adumbration, he looked like an unknown species.

"I realized that maybe, in the end, it was God's plan. To be ready for you." He knelt and took her in his hands. "To be able to give you all I'd learned."

Julia's brain hitched. She wiped her face and mouth with the crooks of her wrist. She shared Peter's eyes, their mischievous saccade otherwise beset by stoicism.

She ripped her hands away, shot up, shoved him hard—"Fuck you"—and pounded out of his room.

How paltry this world must be that Peter reserved his lowliest jocular taste for the girl he shared bed with. That her original motive to meet him had been so inherently malicious, it gave him carte blanche to ply his resentment.

Motherfucker, she thought while storming down Denny and back to campus—the irony of the sentiment's phrasing lost amid her anger.

Thoughts of ending it dogged her, followed her every step panting like a starving pet—sent her into moral spirals. She required certainty, a firm course of action. She'd ruminate for hours in bed, often beside him, as he tossed under sheets sickly sweetened with the scent of ketosis. At one point she'd resolved to stay with him until he was irrefutably strung-out or cheated on her in a blackout. Then—and only then—could she leave guiltlessly. How could she even think such thoughts with impunity? How could she even consider continuing to imply her commitment to Peter by virtue of not breaking up with him? Peter wasn't exactly an emblem of honor…But she couldn't do it. More than loving this ragged pulp of flesh, she was terrified of what it would do to him, her heartbeat at pace with some diabolical rockabilly number.

…And so it went.

Despite the campus-wide fiesta during the four days off for focus final revision, she didn't see him. The night prior to Finals, Julia spent less time studying than dawdling. Her dorm room dark save for her laptop's sharp light, she surfed digital waves of polemic op-eds—her lowliest intellectual indulgence. Her fury swelled and broke with each capsizing page, every receding info-crash.

An hour's reading about the bin Laden hunt purged her anger for the moment. She leaned out her dorm's window, listening to the campus whir, or to Jackie McLean jangling from her laptop's janky speakers. Her phone dinged—not Peter.

The other schools had gotten Julia's generic tripe. Myriadal College, however, had been pleased to read about her father.

Distance was the deal-breaker. Neither Berkeley nor Stanford were far enough from her father, whose last function in life was draining their joint bank account to finance his freewheeling shot through the stratum of default consciousness.

It'd been her, not her mother, who'd done the driving, all the way to the Renton area Hertz. Julia feared her mother's volatile tendencies too much, in wake of they-knew-what, to let her operate the rented vehicle packed with luggage and left open to Route 1's switchbacks.

"Can you turn down the AC?"

"Can you, Mom?"

Her mother's wrist flashed pale. Julia imagined those wrists clamped by his hands. Imagined him demanding their lockbox's contents. Golds, silvers, stones of all shine—lapidary precursors to crystal, freebase, smack laced with fentanyl, everything under the autopsy's sulfur-lit sun. He'd hauled off with what he'd later pawn—and still called Julia later that night. He'd become a common lab rat needing to feed on a sharp tip. At least he didn't hit anyone, Julia thought now, as if some warmer principle had survived crystal's freeze.

"I still don't know about this," her mother said, curt, her eyes in her lap.

"Well, it would help if you looked up too."

"No," she shook her head and looked out her window. Crags. Scree. Trees. A scudding blur. "No, I need to stay. In case—"

"*Looked* up, Mom. I literally need you to help me watch this road or else I'm going to freak out."

"It's three months. Then you're at school. We'll talk every day, as many times as you need. If Johnny—"

"If he what? Because Dad made it pretty clear…"

"Your father made a lot of things clear."

"Mom, please? Can we not?"

"You're not going to sur*vive* with me until school starts. I won't have my daughter live like that. We're in the car. We're going."

"Why can't I stay with Dave until school?"

"It would get back to the family," her mother said to the cliff.

"And staying with Johnny won't?"

"Plus, Dave has a girlfriend now. Ginny told me. There wouldn't be room."

She'd never heard her mother utter "the family" in such idiomatic terms. Its kitsch lingered within Scorsese films and rap-culture references, lending a surreal aspect to her very real loss.

"We have to do this," her mother said as though convincing herself.

Julia was just a kid, a tweener, when she'd learned of the fiend living inside her father, alongside his viscera, his gut, his instinct, whispering seductive devilry. He'd guaranteed his monster's confinement. Promised that his slimy beast would go the way of Jabba the Hutt, whom they'd just watched in *Return of the Jedi*, turning that national treasure into a symbol for something utterly unrelated. Only in this world would her father's inability to uphold his promise be reasonable. That he'd come from a man—her granddad, Johnny Raciti—who'd draw off any lush implied that he and his father weren't so different after all.

Her mom flat wept at the rental shop. Julia told her it would be all right. But he was gone. They were left with this truth as her mother got in the cab for the airport, a truth that stretched all the way back to San Francisco with infinite elasticity, like truth itself—*still gone, still gone, still gone.*

Forever gone.

She found Johnny waiting in the Hertz shop, betrayed by his chatoyant black shirt. He pointed things out on the ride back, but she wouldn't raise her eyes past his pin-lined slacks. He showed her to the condo's guest room. As he fetched the last of her luggage, she shut the door, cut the lights and laid down. Some minutes later she heard his wingtips *whish* across plush rug, approaching her new room for the summer. He was a dark cutout in the opened doorway. Peering along her supine repose, a jeaned knee bent, she pretended to have been dozing.

"Oh," she murmured.

"So uh, look," fumbled his tongue. Perhaps reacting to her rise from the bed, he hit the lights. "What's mine is yours. I know it don't feel like it because we never got to know each other. But we're family."

"Like my dad," she said, opening one of her red suitcases.

"Your father's a deserter."

Her father's every past plunge pricked at her like bad voodoo. She'd have done anything to sunder that dark sorcery. But backing him here would make her no different than the unfortunate corpulence standing before her now. Worse than a hypocrite, she'd have been *lying to herself*—the locus of all things self-inflicted according to her fellow Al-Anoners.

So she said nothing.

"Sweetie. The needle don't poke from the inside." her grand-dad said.

Julia exhibited what she now considered her proudest moment of restraint, saying nothing, unpacking her clothes. Her granddad dripped glib answers like the tip of her father's works. Firm in her silence, she heard the door close behind him.

Everything about him, she deplored. His shellac-back chrome-dome. His pugilistic stick-and-moves. His racist rabble-rousing and caddish crap, which was quite charmed, thank you. His any decency dogged when sniffing an advantage. He'd left her mother—her only fellow Paolantonio—back in the Bay Area, where she wore low blouses behind a hostess lectern and hunted for overnight shelters walled with cracked plaster and the sick smell of stale smoke and dried come.

But whenever Raciti, rather than Paolantonio, rolled off his formal address of her, Julia shot back that he couldn't make her his granddaughter by force of syllable.

Her father had once framed anxiety as "levels of worry that induce delusional thinking," or some other such nothing.

But her worries had proven entirely undeluded, left to wonder what was it he'd wanted, exactly? To get high? No, intravenous relapse turned fairly unfun and fast, a fact addicts knew but did not accept when "striking out for more research."

And another of her father's famous *bon mots:* "Worry not *that* you should do or think something, but *how* or *why*, so as to *do* it."

But it didn't matter *how* or *why* her granddad ground and grifted. It was *that* he did—and *that* she was so close to it now.

She spent most days reading in her room until Johnny came home from his office in Renton. Over dinners served by a uni-formed staff, he romanticized his past…

"…I tell 'im my ma's up in St. Luke's. He says what for. I say to get her tits done, the fuck you think? She's fuckin old. She's got cataracts, gout, you name it. *But,* we both knew she was going to pick the next acting boss…"

"…He tells me there's ten guys waiting outside that door, armed to the teeth with autos. I tell him I don't give a rat's ass, I'll jump out the fuckin window. I ain't payin…"

Tales of backdoor card games, the day's dealings dealt across bespoke green baize. Stories about the Raciti-Lucchese war—the reason her parents had eloped. He talked about his first piece, how it was cold and dead and when he'd used it, it made other things like it was. He talked about guys gone soft, legit, limp in the dick.

Forced to sit across from him at dinner—or rather, *encouraged*—she was helpless to curiosity's anonymous tastes. Behind her guise of indignation—within the confines of her private mind—she lapped these tales like his cook's cold gazpacho. He regaled of suffered marriages, bullets taken, capers pulled, his lips slicked with extra virgin as he spoke. He pieced together an underworld's mosaic, a cascade of characters that she inhabited, she was them, making retrospective decisions through their eyes—until one day, the day before she'd moved into Compartment 56 on Myriadal College's campus, when Johnny's plot hatched over steamed mussels and warm focaccia dipped in coconut cream.

Though a story in the literal sense, this one lacked the past's immovable luster, its inevitable unknowns. This one unraveled before Julia's eyes. This one's ending remained uncertain. This was why her father had left the family: he'd wanted no part in these stories.

"That fuckin Paki he's working for—Rameen's the name?—he's got him under a no-trade clause. That's where you come in," Johnny said, eyes fallen on the gleaming linguini he prodded around his plate. A second course arrived. The waiters in white stood tableside. Her any enchantment lifted like a nictitating membrane against which she'd visualized his previous tales. He was fat again. Slimy. He continued, "They got campus just like yours, no? A bookshop? Kids study? Watch sports? Thanks Trish," he said as a starched arm eclipsed her granddad and revealed him again, wiping the garlicky sheen from his mouth. "Find out where he scanned his ID, what parties he goes to. There are ways."

"I'm just some girl."

"A girl he can trust. A girl he's…familiar with?"

Julia knew she wouldn't eat another bite. In Johnny's eyes shone subterfuge's white-hot fission.

"He likes you. Sends you pictures of him on his bike, right there near the dunes the fuckin idiot," he chuckled. "Might as well pose with a Mountie while holding his wrists out for 'em… You know your father wouldn't let me near you. You know that, right?"

Again he wiped his swinish lips, covered his rotten mouth. He made her mother sing for her supper and regurgitate into the maws of those envelopes she sent Julia each month. He continued. "Thought he knew everything, that kid. Wise-ass. Look at him now. Couldn't keep a needle from his arm if his life depended on it."

Julia clamped her inner cheeks like a bit. Seeing this, he set down his silverware.

"Why?" she asked.

He grimaced, and Julia realized he was computing the wrong question, but she enjoyed watching her granddad struggle over that which he'd so recently boasted to understand: why her father, his son, had indulged in hedonistic suicide. Not until his lips had played at the idea of a few poor answers did she clarify: "What do you need Peter for?"

Julia watched his torrential confusion slow to a drip, watched it run off the flaps and folds of his face, which resumed its hardline stance on unexamined sadness and dewlaps. He pursed his lips, blinked, and nodded.

"Life ain't fair," he said, flipping his hands as if to absolve himself of the world's inequalities. "You happen to be in this position, where you happen to be acquainted with the best drug mule in the Pacific Northwest. Now, it ain't ideal, but neither are your choices as to who you choose to associate yourself with. A chip off the old block," he winked.

Her granddad's clichéd reference to their being related fetched up wretched feelings. But wasn't the logical reaction to blame her mother, who'd made an executive decision to ship her up here? Still, she couldn't. Any conversation with her mother would hinge on whether she'd known, before sending her up here, about the assignment her granddad had in store for her. And if her mother had known, it would, for all intents, turn her into a fish like her father. Instead, like the cash sent north, Julia stuffed it all into her envelope of repression.

"So you find this Fosch kid, you bring him here," he said and wiped his mouth, "and then Demiurge Securities—my firm?—it's *boomin,*" he jutted his chin. "You believe that? Kid from fuckin Flushing." He resumed scratching at his dish. "Anyway, a chair on the board for your mother, fat salary, stock options. That's a life, and a huge breach of protocol on my part. But," he shrugged, "I'm trusting you, because I trust myself," he said, poking the prongs of his will toward her. "And you're my blood."

As he had three nights a week through two solstices, Peter awaited his graveyard shift outside Aspira apartments. A year ago he needed the job to supplement his livelihood. Now, despite what he told himself, he needed it to pass the time.

Twirling his bike helmet, he felt resolved by the strap's rhythmed *smack*. His other hand flicked a spent butt then thumbed his phone to glow. Time said twenty after ten. Amber alert in Renton, just south of Seattle proper, black Honda. A text from Julia.

Peter peered through the mist more than Aspira's glass façade. The concierge desk's premium cut of granite was abandoned. Cammy had most likely left well before ten. He himself hadn't parked and roundhoused off his bike until fifteen after. No one would ever know. Surely not the Puget Property team, who'd hired Peter for late-night security to bolster their realty site, or so he presumed.

Feathered mist sent tufts of steam up from his scalp. He woke his phone again, read Julia's text again, and again pocketed it. Matthew—second-shift security—was most likely filing his time sheet up in the management office, or getting one last nip of the 'nog left over from the holiday party. The guy'd drink curdled milk from the teat of a mad cow if it were free.

Peter swigged from his flask of hellfire and resumed twirling his helmet—*smack-smack-smack*, a metronome for his thoughts. His jacket was wet. He stepped back under the awning's series of flat glass panes buttressed by gunmetal steel. How uniquely genius it was to be out of the rain while still watching it.

A young woman passed to enter, her fob beeping against the door's read-light. Matthew held the door for the resident on his way out—"After you"—and went to stand abreast Peter.

"You're on, mate," he said, jangling the master keys.

Peter pulled from his flask, returned it to his bike jacket's inlaid pocket, and offered Matthew a cigarette. Peter did this without acknowledging the Greek Brit's jowls, his pores like a thousand puncture wounds, and worst of all, above his bushy black brows and anvil forehead, his hair, two sad islets of macaroni curls separated by a continent of damp pate. Just shave it off, mate. The fun's over.

"Nothing to report," Matthew shrugged.

Matthew was a walking gerund, always stating things that could've just been done in the first place. Like not reporting anything that there wasn't to report.

"The log I just left," Matthew began to guff. "Made a doodle of my fat cock in some right busty tits," he chuckled. "Make sure to deliver the papers tonight." He unclipped the master keys, tossed them, and raised an arm in farewell. Stalking off, his beige trench coat flared out from his ankles.

Peter secured the keys in his inlaid pocket and adjusted his security belt—gun, tazer, baton, flashlight. He stubbed his analog into the concrete next to the cigarette receptacle and rolled the cuffs of his Puget Property shirt. Hands trading the helmet, he went in.

Manning the concierge desk, his shift slipped into the dead hours of its name. He licked his flask for last drops and got up again for first rounds, for which he lit a cigarette. Nicotine helped him roam for interlopers that never produced themselves.

The drizzle whispered to all surfaces, reminding Peter of being a small boy. How, on some mornings, he'd lock himself in the bathroom off the school's main entrance. Pants still belted and no bowel to move, he'd concentrate on the grimy tile caulk, shoe-scuff, and small puddles of piss and mud. Sometimes, when staring hard enough, currents of whit would cut across his vision. He'd decide that these dotty currents were molecular rapids, atoms perhaps. He'd decide that he was the first person in the world able to see submolecular material because he had to be—because there had to be something other than this.

He reentered Aspira and tacked toward the loading garage, the complex's only space immune to surveillance. He hopped from the mezzanine, jogged to the lift, and belayed the outsized chain links until the garage door thundered shut. The chain *clinked* to silence as he slid down the mezzanine's concrete siding. He closed his eyes for a few hours, his phone's dings an accelerating metronome of indignation.

Peter sat in the office of Finnegan O'Reilly, MSW, undergoing the court-mandated process of emotional sterilization.

"What about the music you're listening to?" asked the ever-solicitous O'Reilly.

Peter's eyes crinkled, "I thought we were gonna talk about my shits. Had blood again."

Heavy metal blared from an earbud dangling at his hip. Absolutely brutal grindcore truculence on ten. O'Reilly made notes in the yellow legal pad upon his lap, bound to a manila portfolio personal to one Peter Fosch, labeled suchly on its tab.

"I think the music's important to discuss," said O'Reilly. "You haven't turned it off for our session."

O'Reilly's deliberate manner of speech lent Peter the idea that he was slow too in mind. Its cheap frills—*um, ah, hm, well,* etc.—put Peter into a great contemptuous sleep. O'Reilly spoke as if time was not of the essence and behaved as if essence was not engendered by time. O'Reilly sounded like a Garmin GPS trying to navigate his emotional nebulae. O'Reilly was, in Peter's estimation, a charlatan.

Peter hadn't much nice to say about his court-appointed counselor. During their first session, as O'Reilly familiarized himself with Peter's portfolio (previous charges, current summons, mental health history), Peter had asked him to remove his glasses. He'd peered, tilted his head, and whispered, "The eyes of sin," only to plug up his ears with more death metal.

"It's quite aggressive," O'Reilly pressed. "The music."

"A bit after school special-ish, don't you think?"

O'Reilly shifted in his seat, starched shirt bunching over his slacks, and scratched at his orange ringlets, a real Ron Weasley over here. Peter bobbed his head to the kickdrum in his left ear and took a sip of Red Bull.

"I saw you drinking that in the, um, lobby, when I called you in."

Peter couldn't be sure whether O'Reilly was invoking the drink *qua* the drink, or his violation of the lobby's placard, which read: NO FOOD OR DRINK IN THE WAITING AREA. But he knew, really. To the quacks, a Red Bull was never just a Red Bull. Silent, he watched O'Reilly jot Freud-wise the hidden meaning of his withholding.

"How's the graveyard shift going?"

Where to begin? For starters, there was the Top 40 blaring down from the lobby's firmament. By midnight, his jaw hurt from forcing non-frowns at dwindling resident passersby. And thank Christ for that dwindle, since nothing was worse than people saying things to him just to say them to somebody. He had a running bet with himself that, within the first hour, someone would make a painfully obvious joke about the inset display of barbwire shapes hanging behind the concierge desk. Yes, they looked like a bunch of rebarbative cocks floating in an orgastic sea of gold light—he had eyes. There was no better sound than the elevator's *whoosh*, whisking away another talk-bot with no off button. Then Peter could take quick sucks from his flask and feel a little better about things.

The late hours confused his drinking (and coking (and spliffing)) for the perils of sleepless nights. Before the security job Peter had been a nocturne, not an insomniac. Now he couldn't be sure. He slept only after drinking. His experience was strange, his timeline ticked by each run through the pines, the inscrutable weight at his back. And yet these runs—rare pieces of proof that he existed; that he was a thinking and feeling entity—they contaminated the only other thing worth living for.

But Julia was angry with him. Again. Over a joke. How petty this world must be, that she'd wield her mightiest emotion against Peter's sordid little riff. He'd sooner have gotten mad at time's perceived acceleration over life's void of fulfillment. An illegal fraction represented best how fucked this so-called sentience was—and yet here she was, brooding over an extemporized jest. Wasn't that why she'd fallen for him in the first place? His darkly comic sublimations? Or were those O'Reilly words…

Julia was just like any other chemical he put in his body. She stretched the world, revealing its vast intricacy, until the comedown snapped it back to smaller than originally packaged—a condom used for makeup coitus, as they had a habit of fighting then fucking, repeat. Only, these days, there was a marked downtick in the fucking department. This vacuum could only be replaced by more drinking (and coking (and spliffing)), which made it more difficult to fuck, and so on.

It was too much to put into words. Each element had evolved from an earlier element, the heliums and hydrogens of his trauma too transmogrified to track back to their quarks. Plus, O'Reilly had only asked how the graveyard shift was going.

"I manage."

"And school?"

"In the mode of the space-time continuum, it's going."

Lie. Sip.

"Are you having trouble with your, um, coursework?"

"My answer insufficient?"

O'Reilly jotted. Peter gazed about the room, at potted plants, stills of construction sites, beach portraits. Bob Ross aesthetic, with a clinician's sanitary touch.

It struck him: why should he sit here talking in circles with this man who sold psychological schlock that, among several other sick notions, maintained all men wanted to fuck their mothers? Why couldn't Peter go piss in the plastic cup waiting for him in the bathroom, have O'Reilly sign off on their session, and cease this charade brought on them both by some asshole in black robes to whom standardized education and jurisprudential connections had come easy enough that he'd been deemed an arbiter of justice? Peter was going to die someday. That day could've come last winter, when he'd almost killed himself with his bike, which made him nearly responsible for doing to himself the thing that he, and most reasonable humans, fear most. That shit like this could simply happen was inescapable. Acknowledging this didn't make him crazy, didn't make him depressed. He was probably more mentally aligned than O'Reilly, who, dimly aware that he'd one day cease to be, still spoke and moved with the urgency of a plant. Put simply, O'Reilly couldn't counsel Peter out of a box.

Except Peter couldn't express any of that either. Rather, he begrudged O'Reilly the session's twenty remaining minutes before gracing the en suite. He removed from his pants the small jar of piss he'd borrowed from Rameen and hidden in his chinos' pocket, concealed by his hoodie's baggy hem. He then returned with the plastic cup, labeled "Fosch," filled with a liquid indistinguishable from that of apple juice.

On his way out, he heard O'Reilly *ahem*. "Um, Peter."

Peter turned.

"Please don't bring food or drink into the lobby."

Hooking left onto Harrison, Peter bared his teeth to extract a cigarette. He patted his pockets for fire. Cursing, he searched his backpack while crossing Denny, dodging blaring headlights and flipping the finger.

He'd parked his bike in a generous employee spot on ground level. He didn't require much for runs. Just a full tank, and the improvidence (substances) necessary to perform this work—you couldn't confront risk while dwelling upon it.

He'd take the 5 north about 100 miles. Then he'd veer into what was known among other mules as the dunes—a hilly wend through the Canadian pines. Coast opposite the southern Maritimes, a grim s.o.b. in a wool toque would step off a barge and hand him a satchel of enigmatic mass, which Peter would spirit south, through the sylvan morning and back onto the 5.

Peter kicked his stand and revved too loud for these close cement walls. He ducked under the gate's slow lift and roared into the night.

But first, he'd meet Julia, who awaited him from his stoop at the Iliad, where they'd hash out their Arusha Accords over a spliff before his long ride.

At Lake Union's edges they fed geese as might a mother of spoiled children come home from school. Cumulus puffs trailed in uniform rows, the product of exalted steam engines. They'd done a lot of mushrooms, but until today, Julia hadn't fallen victim to the *bad trip*—yet what was soon to transpire would trump even the worst of hallucinogenic malfunctions.

They hiked up Westlake toward Denny Park, where gathered was a rabble of oddmen engaged in varying activities. The two guys oncourt playing one-on-one: one's white undershirt was all Zorro'd, cut up like a lancer's merciful lesson; the other wore an orange headband and a Latrell Sprewell jersey and shit-talked his opponent's every miscue. At a picnic table in the shade of an oak were two D-boys: one in a blue velour jumpsuit, smoking a joint; another over his shoulder, guarding or overseeing the flea market pharmacy spread across the table. A thin woman in a frumpy romper walked back and forth, just inside the park's open gate, immersed in a phone call. Peter's hand slipped from Julia's to the quick of her pinky, lingering there before he greeted those on the court. Julia leaned against the fence, admiring Peter's ability to control his language, let alone the agendas of strangers, as he regrouped the trio into a game of 21.

Lurid flowers exploded from the late-spring green. The basketball court's bitumen looked like Oreo cheesecake. Peter's aura pumped and pulsed in ineffable rhythm. But then he checked the ball, setting in motion the grunt and flurry of physical competition, and all the warm colors melded into mud. Peter, so far now. His laugh, once childlike, now complicit, almost diabolical. The pharmacists at the picnic table looked at her sidelong, whispering. Cars screamed by Denny and Westlake like imperial TIE fighters. The girl pacing the park's border, still on her phone, could only have been relaying Julia's position to a savage capo coordinating this two-front offensive against her granddad—all of which distracted her from the two burly ruds busting onto the scene, one sporting an oily mullet and ripped jean shorts, the other a torn blue tank bearing splotchy bandoliers of white paint as if this blanched X signaled rejection of the paunch protecting his essential organs. (rəd *n. Peterism* : a red-faced alcoholic contracted to perform undesirable or illicit work.) The two ruds muscled their way into the game, which beckoned Julia's paranoid attention, demanding that all spectators and the otherwise sidelined enjoin the fray. Julia shrunk into the crosshatched fence, praying that she'd become part of its backdrop. The mulleted rud's glare locked her in, along with the iridescent bruise spread from his right eye back to temple. Her heart shriveled into a knot and remained roped up like that as the mulleted rud turned to the girl on the phone and seemed to glean sordid joy from her presence. Just then the other rud ripped the ball from Peter and hurled it across the court. A sharp exchange, and Julia went rigid as the mulleted rud threatened those who dared budge a muscle. She saw his partner bear down on the park's gate, his tank's messy X like a target homing in on its projectile, something terrifyingly obverse, which triggered in Julia a surge of paranoia indistinguishable from that of the weeks prior to finding Peter at Lissener's Halloween party—how, in trying to find him, it felt as if, at any moment, she'd be swept up in burlap and tossed in a white van, *and now this was actually happening.* 'Shroom-delusions didn't come in high-definition. Stricken, she watched the smaller rud steal the girl mid-phone call and haul her out of the park, his mulleted partner backpedaling in his wake, guarding the gate, firearm brandished in broad daylight. The girl struggled against the rud's homegrown arms, hooked under her armpits, dragging her like carry-on luggage, her feet its broken wheels, grinding along the pavement. He forced a roll of yarn in her mouth, slapped her for refusing the roll, made her clamp on it. His accomplice kept watch by the entrance, his piece trained on anyone who'd move a fucking muscle. Near the van's rear, the smaller rud taped the makeshift bit, mummifying her mouth, and shuttled the girl through the drab conversion van's opened hatch.

The van tore off and the offending rud stalked back through the entrance and onto the court, that shear-sleeved tank X'd with scatterplots of white paint, their faces red with sun or drink or both.

"Four-on-three," barked the bigger rud with the mullet, who pocketed his weapon. He turned to the picnic table and called louder, "Four-on-three."

The D-boys didn't even pull a visual tarp over their wares before moving toward the court. Julia had collapsed, taking the form of her knotted heart against the fence.

"Check," the mulleted rud barked again.

"What's all that about?" said the guy in the Sprewell jersey, whose glances at the van's wake—where it'd been—turned the nozzle on Julia's fear, and she whimpered small at realizing she didn't want any of them to say anything at all.

"We ain't playin no four-on-three," said the guy with the lanced-up shirt.

"Check the fucking ball," Peter said, the D-boys muttering their agreement.

Julia sent her heart out to them. The 'shrooms had grafted into the moment, nearly imperceptible but for her eyes. Shapes and colors shifting, mutating, patterning fractal, lending possibility to the hope that she might dissolve into the backdrop or disappear entirely.

But the proceeding minutes proved benign—other than a wildly rife basketball game, Julia's writhen faculties, and the apparent fact that a young woman had been abducted before her very distorted eyes—until Peter bullied his way to the basket, leaving the mulleted rud on his back. They shared words there under the hoop, all sibilate and hiss, which Julia couldn't make out whether for her fear or the distance between them. Still she couldn't move. She cowered in her pathetic crouch. The mulleted rud shoved Peter away, signaling that his partner punt the ball across the court. Flashing their weapons' handles, the two strongmen backed toward the entrance, whereupon they sprinted to a car Julia hadn't noticed idling some yards away, down Dexter.

"We need to leave. Now."

Leaning up Denny Way's steep incline, they labored for the Iliad. He looked over his shoulder—she couldn't. Her world wavered like an optical windstorm. She wanted inside, *now*. Jaywalking across Bellevue East, she was sure they'd be crushed by that white conversion van. The situation was her inheritance, like a vexed heirloom she'd throw downriver, only to find it in her hope chest later that night.

Locked in 405, "Did you know those people?"

"No," he said flat, gazing out the window. "They're just ruds." He looked at her, gauging comprehension. "They do blue collar work, undocumented," turning back out the picture window.

"Sounds like you know something about them."

Peter winced—whether annoyed or aggrieved, she couldn't tell. "Don't let the 'shrooms go bad on you, Jules."

"Too late."

He went to the kitchen and necked the bottle from the cabinet above the fridge. She sickened at the sound of SoCo giggling along his throat. Perhaps he was paranoid too, afraid the ruds had tracked them up the Hill, tagged them as special liabilities. Or was his lack of words meant to gaslight her? She replaced his position at the picture window, folded her arms, and looked out at the Space Needle, hoping she was hidden in sunglare but unable to step away out of some sense of guilt or shame that she should stand there and look at her limpid reflection, reckon with what she'd done, or hadn't done. A hazy Mount Rainier rose up as the city's backdrop. She turned back and faced him.

"This isn't a coincidence." Being so close to the truth, she only had to whisper. "I don't know what just happened, but it wasn't a coincidence."

"So now we go through this again?"

Why didn't he understand that truth wasn't to be vied with like some rival dealer? Truly, she wanted to know, but he wouldn't tell her. He hardly told her anything.

The apartment was cleaner, refurbished even. Just some scattered clothes to call the mess. He'd hired a cleaning service. He'd changed. The abducted girl was too much to burden. It crawled along her intestines, stippled her skin. He wouldn't have done this. Couldn't have.

"I don't talk to Johnny," she conceded, going to him now.

He kept looking at the white rectangle where a poster used to hang—looked at the rectangle as if it were a window into something only he could see.

Couldn't have.

"I wish I hadn't done it—pulled you in like this," she said. "But I don't regret it."

"Right," he said. "I work for him. That's it."

"No I know." She rested her forehead on his collarbone, hiding her squirmed frown.

"If I wanted to take someone," he said, "I wouldn't run a circus like that."

She let out a cross of scoff and laugh, pushed his shoulder, wiped her eyes. Without looking he collected her in his arm. Her head rested hard on his bony collar, stiffly padded by his jacket.

They'd relished in their post-Halloween honeymoon, absconded in 405, synergizing their amorous buzz with all sorts of psychoactives. The phase had lasted long enough to cast an illusion that she was with someone.

By early June, the question had turned on a simple conjunction—no longer *if*, but *when* to quarantine herself. She obsessed over her protracted exposure to toxicity: that the relationship had bent her micro-thoughts and -behaviors into permanent maladjustment; that the drugs had burned through her brain; that she'd forever be destined for dissolute boys, desiring precisely that which made her sick. She woke with cold stomachs. She couldn't eat until dark, or not at all. Smells, sounds, all sense dulled. She knew what it was to be a fraud, and perhaps this was her true fear—in humanity, in herself.

Following the breakup—a final two-word text: I can't—Julia Paolantonio slalomed between boys stuck like poles on a frozen mountain. She traded up from cherried bowls at trap shows to key-bumps in club bathrooms, eventually graduating to the EDM scene. She scoped out mid-rung dealers with excess Molly and a weakness for pretty girls, which was all of them, chasing chemical interconnectedness under epileptic light shows. She shook to dub-step boomers, Schedule I neuro-nuggets climaxing in synchronicity with a dropped beat. Strangers were best friends, fellow love-travelers, partners-in-transcendence—before the skin-crawling come-downs and chilly walks back to campus. She begrudged her father a retroactive respect for his ability to withstand these comedowns, the addict's thankless work. She drank to ease down from the rolls, compounding her hangovers. She drank to ease down from the breakup, precisely where she'd started, where it'd ended.

It didn't help that it was summer. Students loitered on campus like burnouts outside a 7-11, but with money, or family money. Three bottles of English gin sat in a cabinet above the fridge, her roommate Layla's, a connoisseur—a reclusive village child of an Emerald Triangle commune who'd escaped by dint of mathematical genius though had yet to grasp the outside world's social formulas. Julia would pad out and peek for clearance, swipe the one she hadn't the last time, and replace what she'd licked up with water. Often, she'd swig right there in the common area, three or four healthy glugs, replacing a cold burn with a warm one.

She thought of the city outside. She'd sucked the summer into her heartbroken binge, crushing bowling nights at the Garage and hangouts at Gas Works to unhad dots. But making up for missed *experience* proved quickly to be a pretext for strange sex. She'd later diagnose (as was a psych major's wont) this phase as an attempt to defamiliarize her associative lattice of love. Her late nights bred a mild illness, which led to an STD scare. The battery of costly tests likened the act of fornication to that of its clinical syllables. Plus, these misguided *experiences* led back to drinking, only this time at bars, which cost money, and money made her reckon with the monthly envelopes from her mother.

But never the girl at Denny Park. This she couldn't burden.

Outside her compartment was *wholesome experience.* Within her compartment festered brooding, like incense from a carnie's tent, luring her with noxious omens. So she pried herself from bed, went to her makeup mirror. She stared in the oval glass, vaguely disappointed with what she saw. In the bathroom, she blessed her face with cold ablutions before heading out for a walk.

It was truly hot—for Seattle—a golden day irradiated. Under this fire-gilded August sun, the streets were alive with smells of cafés and breakfast stalls. People bustled in business-wear—aprons, autobody jumpsuits, black brews brimming hot in hand, thrusting headlong into their aspirations. With her phone she caught converse images: a homeless man handing over change for a fiver; a small boy pointing sternly at his father; an inverted traffic cone filling a pothole.

She peeled toward Denny Park and took to curved paths lined with flowers—and stopped at sight of a grizzled man in a flat cap readying his trumpet. Birdlike trills sounded off his warmup. Closer, she saw the high sun hit a face foamed over by scrofula, swollen and carbuncled like something you'd see sticking out of wet sand. He played a number she couldn't name but which compelled her to drop cash in his case.

"Don't quit your day job," she said, observing the dearth of friends for her munificent fiver.

"It's a Tuesday," he said, and she laughed. "You'd be surprised how much this hustle gets me between gigs."

"Why aren't you at the Market? Or somewhere more crowded?"

"Same reason you don't see your favorite band play at KeyArena."

Julia frowned and nodded. She glanced at a black Mercedes parking parallel in front of Azalai's Varzia building.

"Not expecting my fans for another hour or so. Lunch rush brings me my daily. Which begs the question of what you're doing here?"

"Summer break," Julia shrugged.

"Go to that fancy school by the lake?"

Shame compounded, with interest, Julia nodded and brushed a lock from her face.

"Seem sad."

She watched him clean his trumpet with a cloth stained like the shunting towel's. Shutting down the memory, she muttered, "You can tell?"

"Look like you just got a bad reaction from Botox."

"Wonderful," Julia glanced at the road, embarrassed. The Mercedes had abandoned the tight spot.

"Too young to be sad. That's for old folks like me."

"I guess." She worried the curled lip of her striped skirt dress—black stripe, white, try, don't try. Her unfed stomach growled at her. "I guess I feel like I wake up and go through the motions, but for what? Some point where it then feels okay to die?"

"Whoa now, back your bus up with all that morbid shit. What do you know about death anyway?"

"More than you think."

"I see," he said and threw the cloth down, wiping his hands. "Tell me about it."

It took a moment for Julia to realize he wasn't speaking figuratively. "I thought it was a work day."

"Told you I got an hour, didn't I? Call it an early lunch."

They sat at a nearby bench, under a willow's stringy shade. She told him about her father's passing, meeting Peter—but bowdlerizing the bits about the latter, like Johnny's role in the story. The busker added guttural flourishes, little grunts and drawn *sheeit*s, to show his understanding or commiseration, or both. Time twisted around the story's telling: the sun's angle seemingly unchanged. She assumed it near noon when her story spun itself out.

The busker loosed a long sigh and, rather than offering mild encouragement—or anything at all—he simply got up, walked to his case, and loaded trumpet to mouth. His opening notes filtered skyward. Lunchers gathered round. With every dollar dropped into his case, Julia's frustration turned to anger, futility, and finally, she understood all at once what he'd meant. Though unconvinced by the message, she too got up and made to move on.

"Hey little lady."

A funny series of notes coaxed her attention. His last luncher clinked a couple more coins. Julia ambled over and pretended to examine the gleaming doubloon.

"You know, I played with Miles once."

Now her eyes went to him, his graying muttonchops, his lank frame forming to function, stooping to this street music. His face, pocked and scarred, revealed itself for the liability it had always been for him. Growing up, jazz giants had haunted her house. In the kitchen as her mother cooked. Muted clips coming through the study's door ajar, where her father graded papers, whipped up lectures, or worked through the long-overdue book based off his dissertation. Major-moded jingles from Thelonious, unkiltered keystrokes from Mingus. Life music, existentially integrated. She'd almost forgotten this sound.

"He stopped in at my club," he continued. "New York. I was at the end of my rope. I knew it wasn't no ticket. To get as good as me, you got to realize you ain't as good as him. Plus, with my face and all. Times were different back then."

"Wow," she said. "'Blue in Green' is like my all-time favorite cut."

"Well he sure as hell didn't let me touch any of that," he chuckled. "We just kicked something in Drop-D, something that moved, shuckin and jivin, feed the animals, all that shit. Still, to have the greatest to ever do it sit down second chair and give you that kind of respect? That was *my* club. Played there almost ten years."

"Why'd you quit?"

He leaned back, absorbing this affront in good humor. "Got a horn in my hand, don't I? Too cold in New York, man."

She laughed.

"Look uh…"

"Julia."

Eyes popped, he reeled off another series of jaunty notes. "That's funny. Julian is *my* God-given name, but they call me Dr. J 'cause I can loop under a bass backboard like—"

"The basketball player. I know. A Knickerbocker?" she tried, one eye closed for luck.

"76er, but close. Look," he sighed, "there might not be a point to being sad. But you're also right. There ain't a point to anything. And the best games are the ones without a point."

Within minutes of walking away, Julia wondered how she would've reacted if his face weren't damaged—whether his condition lent him credibility to speak on managing tragedy. Were they the wise words of a brass-wielding prophet, or sugared bullshit? Was the busker an Isaiah, or another has-been nothing-of-Nazareth?

No, it was simple. Her father was dead. Peter was gone, dead too for all she knew. For all Julia knew, her mother hadn't been aware of his existence to begin with—only that Johnny had softened to their situation.

It was only getting hotter. Habit had her checking makeup before remembering she hadn't applied this morning. She strolled along the path and stopped at the fence around Denny Park's basketball court. Through the crosshatch, across Westlake, she stared at the Whole Foods, which leaked shoppers carrying eco-conscious bags laden with groceries. She checked her phone.

Her mother had replied to her photos with one of her own: a belabored picture, according to its hamstrung angle, of her new place near the Mission. Rich lavender walls and white crown molding were set off by plum pastels and white pieces, the perfection nearly unsettling in wake of what had happened. All thanks to Grampa Johnny.

Julia hadn't been back since Christmas. The new apartment wouldn't end her streak. Her job at the Myriadal Student Union co-op, which paid a pittance compared to those envelopes, provided the necessary excuse. That purple place, it wasn't her home. Plus, going back would only lead to an exhausting cycle of disclosure, row, catharsis, repeat.

No, her mom seemed happy—now in another picture she'd sent, waiting with a friend in the requisite 45-minute line for brunch at Mama's.

Slumped at the picnic table near the basketball court, Julia found herself deprived of her sought-after apotheosis regarding, well, anything and everything. The oak's shade offered cool reprieve. She looked up through the leafy dome, darker greens dappling the blue sky beyond.

That day turned over in her mind like a spit roast under arid night, a thought far from home. The girl's abduction, their fleeing, her head on Peter's shoulder...

...The sun was a glum red gumdrop plopping into the Puget's mouth, melting everything to plasmic dusk. Julia's head nestled into his bony frame. "Peter," she looked up at his stubbled cheek. "I have to ask you something. Have you ever...Have you ever hurt anyone?"

When he didn't answer, she asked again and he pulled away.

"So it's yes," she said. She felt her face twist into the shape of his irreparable wrongdoing. He disappeared into his room and didn't come out.

So she'd left.

Meeting the trumpet player, parked now at the picnic table under the oak—it could only have led to relapse, recalling the same tragedies, blending the past and present. She shut memory's crucible, whose power to weld the present was only there if remembered. Her mind held no jurisdiction over the envelopes from her mother, bloated by her granddad's blood money.

7 June 11ᵗʰ, 2012 → June 27ᵗʰ, 2012

Adolescence in affluence. $2 million bungalow. Goalrilla hoop.
Day-shift maid. $86,200 worth of baseball cards—Topps sets,
signed rookies, king of the card-show. Ten evergreen acres lead-
ing back to Lake Washington. White Audi sedan equipped with
subwoofer bass. Girls he couldn't see past a binary optics—did
their eyes sparkle when they looked at him?
  High-quality vanity.
  Low-fi malaise.
  Graduation.
  Europe.
  Okay.

Right on schedule, Ricky started getting Benison's goat. He drank
too much at arrivals. He called the cabbie "bro." He rolled up to
the hostel in Rome, his suitcase bloated by shoes, tech crap, and
ambitious boxes of condoms, about the latter of which he whispered while waiting in line for check-in.
  "Dude chill."
  "What?" Ricky said, striking poses.
  But Benison did join him in bodyweight workouts each morning—mandatory to their college-athlete mentality. Wearing stretch
briefs gifted during his visit to the U, Ricky predicted his stats for
each forthcoming ACC game.
  "Two-for-three: single, double, three RBI. One-for-four: walk-
off solo shot. One-for-two, two walks and a sac bunt."
  At tourist traps they grinned like fools in love over bottles of
Bordeaux, veal fillets, foie gras. Most of which they left over for
the wait staff, their dinner tables a torture-tray of steak knives,
corkscrews, and scalloped prongs surrounding dissected carcasses
of rabbit and fowl. Come fall of night, Benison watched Ricky "spit
game," made amusing by language barriers. By the blurry hours

they were drinking at the hostel, where Benison again observed as Ricky cooked lies like old bags of popcorn.

Cassandra was an editor from Brookline freelancing abroad. Her reason for visiting Rome interested Ricky less than her body, Benison knew, and yet such imbalanced interests would never be requited. He relished in watching Ricky crush after Cassandra's ombré ends, or her chest, over which her brightening blonde strands were draped. Watched him fidget during her turn to speak. Watched him use college baseball as a Trojan Horse for a time-shareish presentation about his scholarship to the U.

"Who's the you?"

She hunched within her words, bored and anxious, not that Ricky would've known.

"Wait-wait-wait. If you're 22," said Cassandra, interrupting Ricky's flaccid cock of a story, "then I'm getting hot flashes."

Her friend Sando giggled into his black leather jacket.

"Why are you laughing," Ricky said deadpan.

Cassandra pouted, "Aw."

"He's frustrated," Sando said all sultry.

"Yes," Cassandra took Ricky's hand. "Rick. If you can stop being such a depressive episode—and I mean like, *thee* buzzer of Killington's gate? Maybe just loosen up and have some fun?"

The next morning, Ricky announced that, thus far, the girls they'd met at the hostel were just those: girls. For these two striplings, in the war-scorched land of romance, it would be about the Woman. Or as Ricky put it:

"Real tits," he motioned.

Benison poked at his eggs. Glanced at gothic stone, the trim Italian suits.

"Duh yi-u und'r-thand?" Ricky lowed, slapping a limp hand against his chest.

"Oh I remember you," Benison grinned and pointed. "You rode the short bus back in high school."

Long before their arrival in France, Benison had begun thinking: this trip could mean more than a two-minute memory of disappointing a Frenchwoman in bed. Ricky, however, remained less appreciative of the architecture, the countryside's diagonal vines, or a Milanese's mellifluous skin as an aesthetic experience shed of desire. It was all Ricky could do to make correlations between homosexuality and Dijon's refined idyll.

A couple days later, under the Louvre's coppered light, Ricky tried rousing Benison from his fartsy trance. Too late: he'd lost himself in ambient serenity, the heel-clacked hush, the click of a Nikon. He went so far as to bust out Barz and take ekphrastic notes on Italian Renaissance paintings, captivated by renderings of transcendence and lust under a religious guise:

> Everyone has seen Cupid shoot an arrow, or Jesus in the manger, or whatever. But this baby is sucking on his mom's tits right in front of Jesus while other chicks lounge naked nearby reaching out for the baby. I also think the baby might be Jesus too. I mean, it's all made up anyways. ~~I think the artist is saying something about~~ I think the artist is using religion as a disguise to say something about sex, or suppression, or something like that. Jesus doesn't care that we wanna fuck. Society does.

Still amid the Italian Classics, he sat on one of the red benches that broke up the glass displays of royal crowns, jewelry, and small busts, and wrote a verse:

> Yea I'm a sucka for thorned ho's, dem Christ-worn throws
>
> Plaits and plaid skirts, a blouse on those

I'm killin the beat, they askin how he so cold

Fire off from the heat, the ice ain't melt it just floe/w

A killa for reala these skilla skillet skills froze

As chill as J-Dilla still shill a long-hooked nose

I'm Jewish don't do dis you knew a cooler man no

If you a neutered poodle against the cause—then FUCK JIM CROW

He'd fallen into his own flow (which for some reason had dredged up anger against institutionalized racism—or he simply couldn't let the rhyme go begging). Still, Ricky kept up the quips about "Babes he'd stick a few fingers in," or how "Serious everyone seemed," and stated that Benison had "Turned to the dark side."

"I'm not the one referencing *Star Wars*," Benison rejoined, scribbling in Barz.

"*Star Wars* is fucking awesome," Ricky said, bending to get a peek at Benison's page. "I'd be a Jedi over an anorexic loser with a paint brush any day. All these people are"—Ricky's arm reproving the Louvre's staid denizens—"are pretentious as fuck."

"Here." Benison proffered his rucksack by the strap. "Watch my bag."

"Why are you handing me your bag."

"Because, you're bitching constantly and I'm trying to see the Mona Lisa."

"Why're you being a dick?"

"Why are you asking questions like a three-year-old?"

"It's not like you know anything about art."

"Is this like an interrogation?"

"Quiet please."

"Sorry," they synchronized. The red-vested docent moved along.

Benison took Ricky's shoulders, their height differential making a low-grade ramp of his arms. "Look man, I just want to see this, okay?"

"Whatever," Ricky hissed nose-wise. "Chick's a four at best."

They were in Paris another two days, barely long enough to savor the senses. *Arrondissement* was both sight and sound, irregular polygons packed with triangulated blocks, bubbling voices and cold beers, their language like infinite iterations of the word itself—a word that meant Paris, whose police sirens were futile attempts at getting past the first two notes of *Jeopardy*'s theme song. These things he could not explain to his parents, arbitrary things of great importance.

Saving the two friends from fallout was their next and final destination: Amsterdam. Here, they rediscovered shared interests. Simply put, the Van Gogh Museum couldn't command Benison's attention as had the Louvre—not from Holland's adult playground.

They sipped Beck's at the hostel's wood-varnished bar. Benison eyed the smoking room, longing after pretty girls getting froggy on pot. Neither he nor Ricky were much interested in the greener side of the grass (not yet at least).

They'd lost any illusions regarding a slender French fashion designer in a bare-backed dress, which memory they'd have uncorked at opportune moments later that fall to up their sex-cred, or something. For his part, Benison had assimilated new features into his character, proven by the way he handled his resentment toward Ricky's flippancy and indifference—that is, he forgave him. Ricky was an eighteen-year-old kid in the presence of Australian bombshells with eagle eyes, which Amsterdam seemed to be oddly saturated with—or so he submitted while sucking his beer.

On the flight across the Atlantic, Ricky had proposed a pact: in Amsterdam, should three nights pass without cozying some floozy, on their last, they'd skulk the neon-lit streets and see about this legal prostitution. Benison hadn't necessarily agreed, but when time came, he adhered to Ricky's casuistic rule.

As they set off, Benison recalled what his father had told him: *Only sick, disgusting, deprived people pay for sex in sick, disgusting, deprived places.* At the time he'd assumed his father was defending

his own behavior, and Benison had responded with the sharp edges
he deserved. Yet, to himself, Benison couldn't help but revere the
power and control pooled at the foundation of his father's implied
success with women.

Regardless, his father's reproach gave Benison certain ideas
about the red-light district: that it was a petri dish swabbed with
salacious brine in which unscrupulous social scientists cultured
the embryos of their deviant subjects; that it was shadowed by
high walls separating these miscreants from the Netherlands'
decent folk; that it was a depraved place with cobbled alleys wet
with wankers' willy-juice; a hedonic hell teeming with crooked
characters whose remaining teeth were tobacco-stained, breath
reeking of the chlamydiatic deaths towards which they limped.
Benison imagined the details: spooky mists and food stalls run
by scammers; brothels with less-than-lithe lineups—a selection
of two-timing whores who'd reach for your unpantsed pockets
while flaying you, their forearms built from years—nay, *decades*
of working on drug-deadened dicks, all of which imploded on
Benison's conscience as Ricky handed him a small white round pill.

"What's this?" Benison asked.

"Oxy."

"Oxy…"

"-contin. Got it from my aunt. Put it in my sock when we were
going through airport security."

"This has been in your sock?"

"It was the only way."

"How was it the only way? I can think of infinite other ways."

"Just eat it, dude," Ricky smirked.

Benison didn't know why he obliged, but he didn't know why
he did a lot of things. Whatever rationale he'd required to accept
the drug turned obsolete once the Oxy took effect, whereupon his
neurons composed that rhetorical opus at cosmic rate and volume.
Within twenty minutes he was cheesing hard. He countenanced the
fear and confusion he felt when not on 40mg of hillbilly heroin. Too
soon did they come upon the district—he'd been elated by the small
river bridges the city seemed so fond of—yet too elated was he to care.

But where were the peg-legged creepers? The shadow-alleys in which ratty squeaks alluded to shady dealings? The pear-shaped prostitutes with raccoon eyes and slummy bloc accents? Where was the sickness? the disgustingness? the depravity?

Rather, the two striplings had entered Willy Wonka's Food and Fuck Factory. It wasn't classy in the colloquial sense—or in any sense, really—but Benison did detect all ranges of accent, which to him sufficed as a sort of worldliness. The cobbled streets were lined with glass-front venues of two varieties: cloned munchies shops and neon-red windows in which barely-clad women displayed their bodily wares.

Around one window was a thick arch of viewership akin to an Elizabethan pit-crowd, sans the wanton jeers and medieval malaise. And in this particular window was their *woman*. Perhaps not the woman Ricky had conspired to seduce, but a woman far above the girls with whom they'd fooled around in ancillary rooms of high school house parties. Her stoic lips and brooding eyes, Benison mused, seemed wanting for things she knew would never be available to her in this lifetime. Benison envisaged the woman's breasts hanging over him, slapping her sex pupil's face as he was edified from inside.

A drunken duo left an opening in the arch. Benison and Ricky stoppered the gap, and when they did, she laid eyes on him—no, her smirk was meant for Ricky. Her finger's curl beckoned his approach. Ricky stepped forth from the crowd. Benison stood beaming alongside the cheering horde of mainly males, but not as many as he'd suspected before arriving.

Benison hadn't the slightest inkling as to his location. The signs read like a fantasy language, something Tolkien. He was content to wander in search of love—love good for thirty minutes of opiate-and-condom-addled deep-throating. His climax was a strange conflation of pleasure and clarity. That, or the pill had worn away. Sobriety deconstructed the worker's façade, behind which bared capitalism's fangs, those of the beast she suddenly resembled—a bit broad at the shoulders and stern in visage. Gruffly, the worker suggested he re-robe and leave €50 on the nightstand, and now

Benison noted a hint of what was it maybe a *husk* in her voice? And he stepped out into the street with sirens of panic bursting inside him—*WAH-WAH-WAH-WAH*—for there in his periphery, beside the prostitute's door, stood Ricky, leaning against the brick in sharp relief under a buzzing blue lamp.

"Well well well," Ricky sang. "What are we gonna do about this Benny?"

Benison said nothing. Just watched Ricky uncross his arms, fit smug hands into pockets.

"This is bad, Ben. Very bad."

Benison's anger grids surged, overloading as they had each time Ricky taunted him with the prospect of rolling shame. This time, however, he recognized not only *why*, but *what* this anger did for him and, in the way axiomatic truths slip from us like definitional evanescence, he wouldn't recall that this fury—and only this fury—held the power to override his shame…

"Is it really that bad, Ricky?" Benison said, striding toward him and, before passing him, muttering low in his ear, "Is it, really? Or are you just an asshole, with nothing better to do than fuck your friends over?"

"You try and fuck with me again," Ricky said, "and I'll tell everyone."

…and then the surge slipped back to its unknowable source.

Though the school week had only begun, Benison proposed that he and Jonesy hit Capitol Hill for a spot of carousing. Moe Bar Mondays were a place and time whence they could evade the Hill's onslaught of "hipsters," which Jonesy referred to with genuine hate.

No one was this tall (6'3" and change) and sinewy (182 lbs.) without a reason for being so, and being a DI baller lent their flirtations, no matter how half-assed, a belletristic quality. Sometime after midnight Benison ran into a family friend he'd known since four or five, when Lily and her older sister had given him garish makeup and photographed the experiment. He'd seen her last at temple, Yom Kippur, maybe four years ago. An image of Lily throwing her mom some moue in the parking lot, to hell with holydays. He scrolled Facebook for a photo and found one of her and the rest of the Aiellos camping Yosemite. He moseyed until he happened near, tapping her shoulder.

In the cab back to campus, windows collecting mist like little crystal beads. Random movie on her laptop. They fumbled over each other for a time. Before she could remove his briefs, he struggled to excuse himself.

"Come *on.*"

Being seared by fluorescence, Benison tugged at his penis, its paradox of flaccid turgidity, a hung something, an inverted coat hook. Panic slatted his forehead. Biceps flexed. Abdomen moguled like a Breckenridge back-bowl. Fearing Lily's entry, glances toward the unlocked door (because locking it would've been weirder than her barging in) flung droplets of sweat from his damp ringlets. *Inception*'s harrowing single-note score really turned up the pressure. The sharp light flickered, distracting him from militant thoughts of Lily's nubile form, *Inception*'s score dousing it in all sorts of ominous shit he couldn't keep out of his head while he prayed to the God he didn't believe in (except following missed jump shots) that his dick'd just stand the fuck up so he could fuck the shit out of this very willing coed and store the whole vapid act in his bank of baselessly worshipped memories.

"No. No. Fuckfuckfuckfuckfuck," he whimpered, spurting rather impressive arcs that leapt the sink but spattered the mirror, its drip pooling near a bar of soap by Lily's toothbrush. Had he known that climax could be reached when only half-mast, he might've asserted his sticky efficacy in the toilet bowl, or her for that matter. If she got pregnant he'd at least avoid a big decision.

Benison plodded back to the bedroom. Lily's sidelong form flashed blue and white, her eyes unbearably aware. Crawling in bed beside her, he caught Pert Plus wafting off his deflated bone.

"What do you like?" she asked.

"What do you mean?" Benison said. Rather than playing dumb, he straight up sounded stupid. His pose was stupider, a swimsuit model's sidelong, tactlessly sportive. *Inception*'s credits roared from its perch on the desk chair drawn to her bed. He flopped over, squeezed his eyes, tortured the bridge of his nose. "I feel like such an asshole."

"It happens," she said, placating him, a fingernail playing along his hairless chest.

The credits faded to black. Some poorly pirated version of *Madagascar* booted next. An anthropomorphized jaunt. Not his speed. His come lingered on Lily's mirror like an implacable mousse smudge. He thought of the scene in *There's Something About Mary*, when Cameron Diaz quaffs her 'do with a drip of Ben Stiller's jizz. Lily kept on with the keratin stroke, trying to tickle him away from himself, but surrendered to sleep after a brutal stretch of silence.

He slipped out shortly after, her whistling nostrils giving cover. Back at 3309, locked in his room, he dug up images culled from deliberate searches: keyword "milf;" keyword "BBW;" keyword

"BBW milf." He'd printed them, preferring physical likenesses to the cold light of his laptop. He kept them in a bin as if embezzled from Bellevue High's PTA coffers, the money blown on rare fetish porn—like middle-aged buxoms, bordering-on-the-rotund, nearly broken water. He envisioned the names they'd call him: *preggo-my-Eggo; Mommy's little fuckboy; fambulance-chaser.*

He groaned over the cup.

Finally.

Following class, Benison hit the Commissary atop Comp 50. He sat alone, hunched over potato soup. Doughnut glaze of mental distance descended upon his eyes.

The Commissary band smoothed into another pop-rock number as he took notice of his unused fork. The absurdity of live music in a college diner, a plangent misplacement, eluded him in light of this utensil and its tines. He wondered whether his father was also given plastic in prison. He pressed his forefinger into the fork's back, slid it along. Thin fin-whited skin. It was possible that now, for the first time since the arrest, he was dislodged, rid of the reflexive muck that marred his aims.

Later, he ran. Was willing to release another round of lactic acid—benchwarmers weren't excused from suicides. He brushed Lake Union's lips, its prettified rail tracks and docked water homes, where he imagined the mentally unstable underwent their furtive senescence. On his way back, mile-five huffin', he heard triage units wail past, and he chased them.

Then he was back in 3309, waiting the return of Jonesy and their subs from the 'WAY, as they'd dubbed it. He imagined Jonesy walking along Terry, spinning off the latch into Aspira, up the elevator and in. He imagined his father being led along the block back to solitary. He counted off roughly twenty seconds. He braced for the lock's click, the door's unsuctioning.

Impatient, feeling an inarticulate frisson, Benison texted him: Yo. You wanna smoke tonight?

A couple quick licks at spliff's seam, and Jonesy brandished it. Benison flipped the light, moved some pillows, the fluttery moments before liftoff. His butthole clenched, heart pumping nervy. When he sat his left knee joggled.

"Ain't a thing," Jonesy said, admiring his work. He engulfed the tip, ripped something smooth, and shot a plume through concentric rings.

"Whoa," Benison said, sincere in his awe, the smoldering cone now in his fingers.

"Go on, now," Jonesy urged.

Benison pulled on it, coughed, was called a crude variant of vagina, hit it hard, eyes bulged, retched a bunch, blinked out tears, moaned and spat and sniffed and said "Oh God" over and over, wiping his eyes and hawking righteous loogies into a glass cup. "Dude my throat is the firebombing of Tokyo." Jonesy cracked. He had to concentrate on his feelings. Apologies to this throat, he took a couple more hits. It all seemed so masochistic. He wasn't above the belief that he'd already contracted cancer. A vague good vibe had arrived. His eyes glassine, glued to the TV. A mild enjoyment.

So he started smoking on the regular. Jonesy broke an eyeballed gram off the eight he bought from some kid in Comp 12, and Benison paid him time-and-a-half-for his troubles. When alone and deprived of his roommate's svelte cones, he'd roll the worst joints of the post-Vietnam era.

From a few dozen feet down Terry, Aspira's façade glowed nacreous. He'd lit his nubby little number when he saw a woman exit the halfway house across the street, which Aspira's uppitier yuppies called unfortunate or an eyesore or an unfortunate eyesore. Exhibit A: this woman, legs carbuncled and varicose, eyes like a Tommy Gun, inefficiently effective, leery of anything that might remind her of what she'd done to get here, what she'd done to get like this, and why she'd do it all over again. She clung to a streetlamp, under whose sodium light could be see seen her natty purple shirt, hanging knee-length. She wore nothing else. Her fear infected him and, potentiated by the joint, tripped strobes of red and blue paranoia—

Whup whup.

Just a squad car's jingoistic swirls—more the police state of his mind. He couldn't understand why they announced their arrival. Parked and loaded, the cops dispersed toward opposite ends of Terry.

The cold front brought bluster, puddles and stains rubbed cold from the streets. Benison hopped in place and hit the spliff—or was a spliff a joint? He'd never know. He started at the sight of both cops coming back north along Terry, the fled resident sequestered, limp as a whelp playing dead for a snow leopard. The halfway house's director (or manager, or whatever) came out crestfallen, a profusion of apology. Benison wondered if he only cared this much because he was smacked. Otherwise, he'd be incurious, or would just relate it back to his life. He was indulging in such guilts when he started again at a sudden voice.

"We got a fugitive."

Just late-night security, who joined him for a smoke. They watched the shorter cop start in with the pat-down. From the crotch of her panties she pulled a starkly coked dimebag, so escorted the flaccid resident into the squad car. As the other cop negotiated the director's guilt, Benison remembered seeing that kid at Whole Foods fake sick so his mom would ask what would make him feel better, whereupon he said, "Dessert!" That was this resident, only these cops didn't care whether she was faking or OD'ing.

The director seemed convinced that he was okay at his job. Benison chuckled, first at the thought, then at thinking the thought. (Thinking about thoughts made him anxious partly because he felt meta-awareness wasted his time—which anxiety and guilt marijuana reframed as curiosity.) Concentrating on the cops meant being aware of the watchdude's presence. The squad car hummed up Terry, and Benison breathed, quite frankly, better.

"Fuckin pigs," the security guard spat, flicking his spent butt at the base of the cigarette receptacle. Benison laughed before even processing that he'd imagined people seeing a cigarette at the base of a trash can for cigarettes.

"Peter."

"Benison."

Neither looked.

"They're frauds. Just like her friends, you know?"

"Oh yeah?" Benison said, not knowing what to say. He saw Peter push his holster aside, removing a flask from his right pocket.

"Those poet types," he said and sucked on his flask. "They think it's some monkish undertaking. It's Wordsworthian fuckin bull-verse..." he finished quieter, as if remembering himself. He muttered, hissing and huffing up laughs, sucking and dragging, dragging and sucking. His was Zeno's cigarette. Rebuckling his holster's fastenings, taking more and faster into his lungs. He smelled like a vat of warm spirits and sweat. Fortunately, perhaps inevitably, he polished his flask and shambled up the Hill. Not long after he'd left, however, did the door bleat open. Benison tossed the roach before the silhouette neared, trench coat aflutter—Matthew, the other night guy.

"Taking in the breeze, then?"

"Yeah, can't sleep," he said. "Peter on now?"

"Peter?" Matthew sneered, flapping his lips like a horse might. "Crazy fuck got fired ages ago."

Dicking off on Christmas being a proud ritual for sub-Reform Jews, Benison earned himself an early handjob, establishing temporal room for a second romp. He busted out Barz, wrote some seriously lacking material. He hit the bowl, sunk into the couch. The ceiling's decorative flecks reminded him of the Italian countryside's little stucco houses. He thought of his father, seated in his close steel cell, his only visual respite its small square window.

With the weed wearing, he opened his laptop on the glass coffee table and videophoned his mother. To his surprise, her cobalt eyes scorched his laptop's color sensor. He saw Angelica pass in the background, her arms become load-bearing struts for dirty clothes and dishware between the hours of nine and five—Benison couldn't fathom it. He'd pined after her throughout puberty. Finally his mother waved, her smile a teak taper.

Michelle Thibodeaux's disappearance swept the Deaf domain and its interpreting phylum. Benison couldn't be fucked by it. On the contrary, his mother couldn't be mollified—so there they were again. For all Benison cared, Michelle could've been doing sambas with Brazilian stud-muffins ten years her junior who fucked her like his father hadn't, wild and rabid and riddled with Portuguese expletives. Could've fallen in with Manchester spivs who'd put her on at the house of ill repute. Could've been struck down by their Lord and Savior Jesus Christ in lieu of Godly behavior, thus erasing this human stain from the otherwise sterling reputation of the Catholic Church. To Benison's mother, however, Michelle Thibodeaux had tucked TNT under the office's boiler room, lit the fuses, and ditched town.

People are just gullible, she signed. *Of* course *she's off somewhere with her fat reward check.*

You don't know that.

She shouldn't have talked.

Benison kneaded his forehead in frustration.

Your father is in serious trouble.

He deserves *to be,* just a hooked index and wrist gone limp.

Do you understand what he's going through right now?

I've made it a point not to.

He's in a federal prison, with real *criminals, and we* need *him.* This also a hooked index, homonym to his, nailing her imperative to the kitchen table.

Benison hadn't been home since the arrest. His absence sent a message, but a missed birthday would've declared war.

The Behrenreich household was a twenty-minute drive from Aspira—across Lake Washington via the floating 520, a modern pontoon bridge connecting Seattle and Bellevue by way of Mercer Island. Farther east, the mountains, and unfathomable sprawl.

Cars crowded the curb and stuffed up the driveway, at bottom of which loomed his altar: the Goalrilla basketball hoop, at edge of Giotto's blacktop. Prior to his sophomore year, his father had hired contractors to flatten a circle of the drive and smooth it with tar. His field goal percentage jumped 7.2%. His old man knew a good investment. Benison weaved between vehicles, taking the step of flagstones that led from drive to door, bordered by braces of violet pansies and yellow primrose.

He rang the bell, flashes of lamplight announcing his entry. He heard his mother's call, which he was ashamed to be ashamed of. He smiled through the foyer's crush of fanfare. Many little women kissed his cheek, the men hugging his hand. The bending was awkward. He endured his mother's oldest friend, Mrs. Goldfarb, whose mammoth hello trumpeted the elephant in the room. Accustomed to the sounds, a hearing aid's whistle, the moribund moans—the most honest noises he'd ever heard. He plucked hors d'oeuvres and obliged family friends, who inquired about school and basketball and looked at him stupid whenever those topics ran their course. Many commented on his height as if it were an original observation. His response to *How are you?* just couldn't fully imply that life was shit, end-to-end. From this milieu formed a riddle: they'd never know him for who he was, but they were many who knew him.

Time came to sing "Happy Birthday," murdered by a special sort of monotone—his cue to leave. He kissed his mother's cheek in front of her book club friends and whipped the Audi back across the 520. He'd placed her birthday card (from Papyrus) on the edge of her dresser like a restaurant billfold, complete with $200 to Nordstrom. Nothing said I love you like circulating laundered money.

Walls cordoned his mother's realities. In one room it was all bunting and birthday cake. In the other, she held vigil for her former life as if she were no longer solvent. She said they needed him—she didn't understand need, proven by the 33rd-floor penthouse Benison shared with Jonesy.

Whose panorama spanned roughly 200° of Seattle proper. Stand there long enough and you'd catch a seaplane materializing from low skies, navigating construction cranes and squirting white frosting along Lake Union's blue fondant, smooth as a planet seen from space. Vaulted ceilings, leather divans and couches arced around a glass coffee table littered with controllers and sports drinks and snacks, Jonesy icing his ankle, all in still and silent ode to the flat-screen set midway up the wall running *SportsCenter* on mute for the nth time today, its theme song accented by sleigh bells and eerie Christmas guitars.

"And you say Daddy don't love you."

Benison crunched a chip and shrugged.

"I ain't even gone home for Christmas. Why? My pop won't pay for *shit*. 'A man finds his own way,'" Jonesy said, all mock-stentorian. "That nigga find a Corona real quick."

"Self-sufficiency isn't such a bad thing."

"And you the one buying all this?"

Bugging Benison most was the *way* Jonesy interpreted his situation: that *way* being completely removed from any experience. He explained the differences between exaggerated threat and real pain: that most Americans feared the former and were oblivious to the latter; that Jonesy was most Americans.

"The hell you talking about?" Jonesy said.

Exasperated, Benison groaned, "Never mind."

"Nah man, explain it to me."

"Didn't I just though?"

"You speaking on danger," Jonesy said, limping toward his room. "Try walking East 109 after midnight. Man, you in a bubble made of your skin. You ain't got the first *inkling* of what it's like…"

…to cross into El Barrio, where the Upper East Side's rich infrastructure morphed into rain-cracked slag, corner guys' noses running down their chins, and the great expanse of bodega town. Poverty: a terminal illness one fights and dies with, every inch, no matter how much money one pours into treating it. After New York, they'd picked up and moved to Austin, where Jonesy's pop opened a body shop and preached putting your head down and doing your work, not blaming a system rigged for you to lose slow, insufferably slow.

"Being poor is shit. I get it. But—"

"Do you?" Jonesy sneered. Arm sweeping up 3309's sumptuous amenities, he said, "Cause I really think you don't."

With a fury so calm he felt removed, Benison said, "And I really don't think you know what it's like to have a gun pointed at you. So you can take all my pop's *love*, if that's what you really need. Cause I need that shit like I need a fucking hole in my head."

"You tellin me that's a hundred?" Jonesy pressed. "For a white boy from out there in Bellevue, I find that pretty fuckin hard to believe."

Benison turned to Jonesy, arms a stale braid of dough, eyes aglow with anger. "Fuck you."

Jonesy's head pulled back in mock appall. Eyes low and brows raised, he sang, "Well fuck you then—*and* yo daddy," and limped into his room, slamming the door.

Bruised by shame and anger, Benison seethed. Were black kids just the benighted product of their environments? Were Jews just an aggrieved shibboleth? No. Neither. *Obviously* black people had it worse. But they were also distinct individuals, each with their own unique circumstances, and Benison wasn't going to diminish his own dire environs for the sake of prevailing social etiquette.

About an hour later Jonesy hobbled out of his room and mumbled something about attaining sustenance. Benison wasn't ready to apologize. Jonesy still seemed too upset, which was unseemly and he needed to know this.

He fiddled with his laptop, flitted palled eyes at *SportsCenter*. Mainly he kneaded the implications of their lidded tiff. The mental undertow tugged him to the fridge. He cadged a couple cookies from the tupperware tagged by Jonesy's mom. Until now Benison had avoided the cookies like thoughts of treason.

He rolled a shit spliff, all cursory and over-licked, and *whooshed* down to ground level. The lobby's stale Christmas cheer mocked him from on high. The festooned lights. The massive tree in the middle, adorned with a thousand red and green baubles, topped by an outrageously intricate silver snowflake. He *clacked* the door open and, ambling down Terry, toward the cigarette post, recognized Peter by his black-and-yellow bike jacket, smoking amid the chilly mist as if averse to Aspira's glass overhangs. Benison stood behind him and lit up.

Peter turned to him, his face a shadow against the darkening sky beyond the halfway house. Benison's eyes bounced around his assessor.

"What?" he snapped.

"You seem pissed," Peter dragged.

"Oh yeah?"

"Oh yeah," Peter said in passive riposte. He joined him under the overhang. "What's getting your goat."

"Getting my goat?"

"The source of your anger," Peter said, rolling his wrist, smoke twirling in competitive ribbons, gorgeously choreographed.

"You my fuckin therapist now?" His periphery couldn't help but catch Peter's gaze. "*What?*"

"Think I underestimated you," he said, peering and dragging.

"And what was your original estimation?"

"That you were a pussy," he shrugged. "Your joint's out."

"Oh. Thanks." Benison relit, dragged, offered.

Peter declined, "I don't fuck with that small-time shit anymore."

"So what exactly do you fuck with?"—*sssss…hhhoooo*—"I hear you don't even work here anymore."

"Been around to pick up paychecks and whatnot."

"And whatnot…Sorry," Benison glanced. "So then what was with *you* the other night?" he chanced. "Couldn't understand half the shit you were talking about."

"Wouldn't expect you to."

Stoked once again, Benison said, "You know I don't know what you know about me, but I'm not just some rich kid."

Peter nodded, squinting into the smoke. "You play ball."

"No, I mean—" Benison stopped. Thought. "You ever thought you were gonna die?"

"Loaded question."

"Okay," he ceded, "I mean, you ever been held up or something? Didn't know what the dude was gonna do? So it becomes binary—he either does it or he doesn't?"

"Have you?"

"Yeah," Benison said, dragged, nodded. "Something like that."

"So…" Peter shrugged again, flicking his spent cig to the curb. "The fuck happen then?"

"Here's how the story goes. The boyfriend or fiancé or whatever, he has the flowers delivered during the work day. So the delivery dude calls from his shitty van and asks the girlfriend or whatever etcetera to come down and get her flowers curbside, cause there's no parking by her government building, she's a boring administrator of etcetera etcetera. She refuses to do this, she's busy, he should just figure out a way to bring them up. But this delivery dude, he's got like a billion orders today, and they're wilting before he can deliver em, which gets him absolutely butt-torched by his boss. Naturally, he hates his job and his life. Every day he's gotta bring flowers to people that are happier than him, which makes them happier while he just gets sadder, increasing the quotient between haves and have-nots, or whatever. So tonight's the night. He's gonna go home and take like, twenty benzos and wait for the light to shine on his God-fearing soul—but then with all this beauty rushing into these last moments, he decides he wants to *live*. The paramedics don't get there till it's too late. The lights go out with him all slumped on the couch in a pool of coughed-up blood that totally fucked up the leather so no one else can ever use it again, and what a waste of obviously not high-end but like, totally serviceable furniture," Quentin finished.

Vanessa and Jamie peered at him.

"Did your father leave?" Jamie asked.

"I bet he's uncircumcised," Vanessa wagered.

"No, this one of his shitty allegories," said Jaime.

"You really need someone," said Vanessa. "For your quotient, or whatever."

Quentin took out his phone, dialed some numbers, and put it to ear. "Yeah…Yeah hi…Oh…So this isn't A Big Fucking Deal? Okay see you later then." He pretended to hang up. The women made noises of disapproval to which he said, "What makes you think I need flowers to get laid?"

This trio of terps (tərp *n.* : industry term for sign language interpreter) were in Behrenreich Interpreting Services' lunch hall, an antiquated box of wood raised above the office pit and stuffed with medieval décor and knickknackery. Convincing flames blazed in rust-iron candelabras. Stained chandeliers pressed a drowsy glow. Lacquered wood tables licked up a burnt orange glare from the kitchen's open flames. The buffet line had shortened, soon to expire, and overpaid servers wearing faux sheepskins would mingle with overpaid chefs in white robes, clinking little glasses filled with lemon aperitif. The trio's repartee petered to a weak-worded pulse. They stacked their trays on the conveyor belt training into the kitchen.

They lingered outside the lunch hall's stained glass, elbows on railing, espresso shots cooling in their guts. Quentin's eyes fell to Boss's office—a vitreous box suspended halfway up the two-story knockdown. They scanned the pit below, the abutting call booths within green-screened cubicles. Zagging down the retrofitted fire escape, the trio lost it upon witnessing the bouquet of roses stuck in the VP's door.

"What'd I tell you?" Quentin said, laughing off the last step.

"Who's holding out on the laughing gas?"

Silence swept through the trio. Then Vanessa and Jamie peeled giggling into their booths, leaving Quentin to face the VP's sudden appearance.

"Couldn't get em curbside, could you?" Quentin shrugged

Though bewildered by his meaning, Michelle awarded his courage with a smirk and walked by him wordless. Rarely did she regard the puckish terp's pseudo-socialist commentary, but she often did his work. Last month he'd tallied almost 5,000 minutes, more than most Video Relay Service providers as a whole. Not a quantity easily reached using only one monitor, but Quentin was a dedicated 21st century grifter—perhaps too dedicated.

"Back to work," she called to Quentin over her shoulder.

Her minded strut—a strict sashay—created the very aisle between sets of VRS booths: post-industrial honeycombs dripping viscous money. Incoming calls warbled and neighbors chatted or fluttered translations, but most idled, doing crosswords, clipping toenails, reading trash romance novels, and snacking. Lots of snacking. This was how money was made. Lots of money.

Michelle went in with the flowers pressed to stomach, total eclipse. Her spacious glass office was lit like dusted gloss. She sat at a neat black desk dead center, on which sat nothing but a Macbook, simple remote, VRS equipment, and magnetic utensil-holder. From an upper corner of her office, her VRS monitor peered down like an outsized security camera, below which were her monitor and VisiTech's platform equipment, all suctioned to the glass wall.

She plucked the note from the flowers:

Important call, 1:30. Happy Valentine's Day

"Where's the vase?" she muttered.

It was 1:28—couldn't accuse him of not knowing her schedule. She thumbed the remote to activate her monitor. The hardware whined, the read-light dimmed.

"Fucking Raciti," she groaned. "New prototype my ass."

A light thwack had it up and thrumming, and she returned to her desk. The VisiTech decal materialized from the black screen, then faded, replaced by the interface: cam box; call-tracking; and contact list, replete with the numbers of her Deaf friends and colleagues. Mainly colleagues. Okay, so they were all colleagues, aside from her parents, to whom she spoke infrequently and with guiltless brevity.

She pulled the neutral blue screen until it stood flush behind her computer chair—force of habit from her years spent interpreting, but there was also some glare. Michelle Thibodeaux was Behrenreich Interpreting Services' VP, de facto despot of this buccaneer's brigade. She'd long ago left interpreting behind, with her five-figure salary. Except for Marc's calls. She was the only one he trusted.

One obnoxious ring. Before answering, she propped her phone against the utensil holder, the blacks blending, and aligned its lens toward the monitor. Imagined consequences harried but couldn't conquer the process. She answered. Long and shrewd and a touch sallow, black hair slicked back, Marc resolved on the cam-box. He drew deuces from his right eye: *Can you see me?*

Michelle nodded her fist, *Yes*, her other hand near her phone. She pressed record.

How's business?

She pulled back. *Great. The important call?*

Dreyfus says his marketing tier is getting shifty, this and that. But I think it's him who's nervous, quaking downturned hands. *Maybe cut him a check. Something healthy, for his loyalty.*

She nodded. During this morning's quorum, she and the admins had discussed the problem of the FCC, whose ineptitude never ceased to amuse or amaze Michelle, depending on the day. In the early years of VRS, the FCC had done nothing as unscrupulous providers ran amok, exploiting obscene per-minute rates, as if taking strategy from the League of Nations prior to WWII. Worse yet, upon their belated beach landing, rather than charge past the battlements, they simply stuck their heads in the sand as said VRS providers continued running minutes. The government, Michelle thought: where America put mediocrity to use. Anyhow, BIS's Director of Marketing, Casey Len, had led the morning quorum. Len was known about the office for his forward-leaning scowl, as if pissed off at whoever picked out the oversized Hawaiian shirts he wore each day.

"If we keep letting our terps idle..." he'd warned. The FCC was tightening regulations, beginning with the ban on hiring Deaf folks to call from within relay centers, effective next month. "We're all paid-up, so those wannabe T-men will audit the calls themselves."

Michelle had left the conference room before the others. Weakening her ability—no, killing her *motivation* to organize and rally was the knowledge that it would all be over, and Casey Len couldn't change that. Like how Sheila Leroux had let all the lawns grow wild on the eve of the neighborhood council election, back in '94. So she thought of her impending eight-figure check feeding a sumptuous spa in Bali, where some studded rod would rub her feet, put that green shit all over her face, give her cucumbers for eyes.

Is that why you're calling? she signed now to Marc. *Or do you need me to fix your Outlook again…*

That Marc was his company's sole PC-user struck Michelle as a twisted parody on a Mac commercial: *Don't be a Marc, a clunky letter standing in the way of the future. Be lean, sleek, sexy. Be Mac.* Cue the opposition's accusations of anti-Semitism. Oh, how much she'd learned since moving north.

I want to see you tonight, he gestured, all Sign-English, getting his point across his way, the turgid way. A Marc. *My surprise.*

Her jaw tightened.

Pink Door. Nine-thirty. You know I can't stand those cabarets.

Then why take me.

I'm taking you.

I'm at a loss, her hands dropping the metaphorically misplaced. *Soon, Michelle.*

You said when he went to school…

Like most colleges, Myriadal starts at the end of summer. He inhaled and raised his head, and she nearly forgave his quick slip into sarcasm. *You have to trust me.*

You're still fucking your wife, banging peace signs together then held up incredulous hands. *And I'm supposed to trust you?*

Tonight, I want to be with you. What do you think that means?

It means you're good at multitasking.

She ended the call. The remote clattered. She sucked a swath of air, swiveled her chair, angling at her long view of the Puget. Slowly, beneath her veil of awareness, her expression turned neutral. Thespian was the art of the long con, and Michelle Thibodeaux had grown up in Bayou slums, learning to conform her accent like Marc—better than Marc, for she had fully functioning ears.

Late modern capitalism didn't reward the company that smiled at every customer. It rewarded the company grinning at the knowledge that they couldn't be beaten. Thinking of those eight figures printed on a government-cut reward check, she almost broke neutral.

She took up Marc's typed note, along with her transcribed testimony executed by a certified court reporter. Her thumb crossed pearl glow's threshold and tapped glass—successfully transmitting to the SEC's Office of the Whistleblower, located at the Supreme Justice courthouse, the details of Behrenreich Interpreting Services' fraud scheme, which she'd utter into a coiled stenomask on June 28th, 2012.

She cut the recording.

Michelle would oblige Marc his Valentine's dinner. She'd even allow her stage character room for growth in the form of faux-forgiveness. Or maybe it would be the Italian red, the brown-dusted tiramisu, Pink Door's sumptuous fusion-fare—healing her of contempt, allowing flushed smiles, even a few laughs. Seated across from her, Marc would pet her hand and dole more wine, once more this dark lothario hooked by a Roman nose.

Roughly four months later, Marc would call an office-wide meeting. From his glass pulpit, he'd deliver a signed speech replete with trite invocations of Sparta in the face of fate or foe. For his finale, he'd flick aflame the freshly delivered FBI subpoena before putting it out with his piss, met with hundreds of fluttering hands, as is the wont of Deaf applause.

A week after the war cry, Michelle would supply her resignation. His office drapes lowered, she'd put on a fine performance, her wistful display made perfectly impervious by the Office of the Whistleblower's Protection Act, which guaranteed her anonymity, among other more lucrative things.

I know we've had our differences, separating her indexes like window-wipers. *But this isn't about you and me. It's over.* A sniffle here, a dab there, the subtle quiver of lip, the course of this elegy. His office dim. Tented hands hiding his mouth. He'd be considering, but exactly what, Michelle wouldn't figure.

I'm sorry, her fist rubbing heart.

He'd only keep looking at her. He'd know. His three-piece Armani suit, diamond-studded watch, the office's wet bar lined with smoky amber spirits and chiseled glass tumblers and a pointed crystalline stirrer—everything around her taking on these sharpnesses.

His right hand rising, hanging there, an unformed word, and he'd flick his fingers, *Okay.*

And she'd depart the office, the building, the company. Bali, here she'd come.

"Ten o'clock here at KOMO 4's studios, and we start with breaking news. We're only twenty miles from the VisiTech Platforms Renton office, where FBI raids this morning ended with the arrests of two administrators."

"Yes, Cathy, and three more are still at large. But just minutes ago the body of Demiurge Securities CEO, Johnny Raciti, shocked tourists and day-travelers when it washed ashore Bainbridge—"

Michelle silenced the stream and set her phone on the counter. She gazed out her floor-to-ceiling windows, glass of red gripped firmer than she knew. From these heights, at night, the shoreline to the International District looked like a city prepared for war, all bent metal and menacing prosceniums, waiting for ships crossing the marine. Dunkirk. Only this time, no one would make it across the channel but her.

She let herself be lulled by the orbital speed of a Ferris wheel perpetually attempting to roll off the pier and into the Puget. Behind her, the barrenness of a stripped penthouse.

The black leather couches, the cherub-pissing sculpture that turned on and off by clap, the sleek black technoids—all of it stowed in a storage building where Ethiopian immigrants sold African ceramics and totems out of their units. She'd never return for her things. Eating the unit costs was one of her celebratory decisions, a principled waste that scoffed at her childhood's paltry means.

Her phone growled at the island counter, rousing her from reverie. A text from Marc.

Cotillion-trained and good-boy-courted, Michelle had once revered the home and garden. Though reformed of swamp culture, as she thought of it, where Catholicism and children were her divine duties, moving to Seattle for a staff position at BIS had been a means to marrying an intelligent man utterly devoid of southern decorum. A northerly man. She'd frequented bars where fiduciaries loosened their ties, nursed their cocktails, and approached debutantes with legitimate sociosexual offers. A lithe little transplant from Baton Rouge, she sipped diluted mojitos comped by fuckboy VCs, waiting for that fresh sheet to be faxed her way. And yet, largely unimpressed by the mist culture—the Seattle cold front, as they called it—she made a paradoxical re-alization: she was a lot smarter than she'd thought. The notion seemed to free her mind, allow her to question everything, namely the institution of marriage: what could be more meaningless than something that had a 50% chance of working?

So instead, she'd bought herself a Marc. Not that they hadn't started up already—not that she'd have let anyone touch her for any sum of money—but now that she'd had him where she wanted him…People used their feelings to entrap once another in ways society accepted. And she'd had feelings, which she was reminded of a couple days ago, when he'd arrived unannounced.

The warrant is out, he'd signed, standing in her doorway.

"Marc. You can't be here."

It could be days. Hours.

"I've been seeing someone," she told him, "and I know how you get when your territory's been marked."

"*I would be jealous,*" he said and signed, "*but we both know Derekson's not your type.*"

Leaning against the doorframe, Michelle ran a languid hand through lush licorice curls. "I told you to get rid of my fob."

"They let me in."

"Don't come back again."

But he pushed the door before she could close it. "What did you expect from me?"

"*And what did you expect from* me*? To elope with you before a rabbi doing five-to-ten for embezzlement?*"

"Michelle."

"Marc," she mocked, cocking her hands once again. "*You expected me not to protect myself? They served me a* personal *subpoena. What was I going to do? Piss on it?*"

Then show me, thrusting a finger into an open palm.

Was he signing because he suspected the place bugged? She didn't know, but decided to play the entomologist if only to spook him. She turned toward the kitchen and he followed, closing the door behind him.

"I don't think you were served."

"What are you saying, Marc? Why don't you tell me what you're really saying."

I'm saying whoever blew the whistle had information only you had.

"*What makes you so sure anyone stepped up to talk?*" Michelle poured a couple healthy dollops of red. Handing him one, then signing with that hand, "*The Feds approached me. I don't know how it started, I don't know if anyone stepped up, but I told them enough to stay out of prison. You should be one to understand that,*" she said, swished her wine, leaned against the black marble counter.

"I hope you're right," he'd said, gathering his Italian threads.

Michelle sipped her wine, whose sweet stole her reverie once again. She wouldn't press a forlorn index to chin if it meant *missing* him less. She didn't. Not at all. Sip, sip, gulp.

Marc's text instructed her to check his email, which was cc'd to an address with vaguely familiar characters:

Marc Behrenreich   Nov 4

to me

A maze for the rat.

Her snort fell meek, merely filling her glass with daylong breath. Attached were files whose encryption she cracked using the company's codes. Only then did she understand enough: the attachments were proof of transfers between Behrenreich Interpreting Services and various tax-shelters, which immediately betrayed him who was cc'd on the email.

Resting her hind on the counter's cool marble, Michelle's thoughts shorted and sparked. There was no proper response. She should've abandoned the deposition as soon as they'd mentioned Stephan Klimnick. Surely, by the end of their questioning, she should've known. Not that it mattered. Not anymore.

This cocktail of fear and hate required bitters. She unpacked a bit, the rye, the bitters, but no orange peel: an old fashioned, to pretend at composure. She mixed another. And one more, goodly full. Lukecool acrylic cubes clinking in her glass, she leaned against the wet bar's marble. In the darkness, her unwell yellow.

Out there, across the lake, Marc readied himself for one last sleepless night as a free man. His white-collar sabbatical would go as followed: tennis in the morning; board games in the afternoon; conjugal visits in the evening. Wouldn't even have to spend the night with Ellen. Just bend her over the formica table, groan for a few seconds, and salute, *Bye-bye*. He'd wink at the guards and stroll back for another round of ping-pong with a fellow Yankees fan doing five-to-ten for kickbacks. Looking up at the TV between serves, CNN's tickertape would read: WHISTLEBLOWER FOUND DEAD, SUSPECTED FOUL PLAY.

The next morning, Michelle stared past her shower curtain. She saw a man obscured by shadows, flipping silver dollars for her life.

She blinked.

Fleeing required living with a sore neck, craning constantly to watch for phantoms—until one materialized and put three silenced holes in her skull, no longer privileged with feeling fear. The walk from her penthouse to the Westlake Transit Station, where she'd board the tram to Sea-Tac—the idea of all this exposure to fluid oxygen allowing for smooth passage of deadly projectiles.

She'd call for a cab. Leaving her suitcases behind, she'd step out into the gray autumn dome—but instead of the Yellow Cab she'd called for, by Harbor Steps' curb an idling town car, its passenger window bearing refracted buildings, lowering.

"Well if it isn't the whistler."

She blinked.

The shower had gone cold. The knobs shrieked as she shut the water. Changeling schemes dripped in rhythm with the shower-head, fast and frivolous, then slow and deliberate. They'd check JetBlue's registry—the Feds, Klimnick's fixer. Forgoing a towel, she tracked water across the hall, to her phone on the marble counter.

"…Hey, Jason?…Yeah…I need a favor."

Sundays were spent at Our Lady Mary of the Cross, down near the swamp, where swains went to neck. Where her friend Tina almost got bit by a gator, or just saw one, or just made it up, just 'cause. White lace and corsage, weddings she scoffed at from back pews. ("He hits her inside a month.") A cortege or two.

Her grandpappy, Elkin Laboulier, begrudged her veneration for the North, where Michelle claimed nobody gone and done nothing without first figuring it through. "Them intellectual e-lites got a fancy saying up there, in their fancy institution. Call it the paradox of choice. Meanin, God ain't put you on this good green earth to've known what's best fer ya."

Indeed, the North had represented freedom, the answer—the antithesis to the swamp's rote piety, where nobody gone and done nothing without first consulting the fairytale.

"Yer missin the point," Grandpappy groused.

Gangie stayed out of it. Time was, her granddaughter had worn the squirrel costume she'd made for her. Little Michelle would hunker in the backyard for hours, enmeshed in bushes slung with kudzu, waiting for another of her kind to come bearing tidings and break acorns with her. So as Michelle got older, Gangie let live her granddaughter's "phase," as she called it—all the glitzy magazines, those heretical books about the *real* history of the South. This was God's country.

One day Michelle received a letter from her mother. Why had she sent the it to the dentist's office, where Michelle worked Mondays and Wednesdays after school? How did she know? The letter's swollen enigma was put on ice as she ripped, removing a sheet of loose leaf riddled with barely legible screed. Michelle wondered how many edits it had undergone to achieve its sorry state. It took ten minutes to piece her mother's missive.

"Dad always hate hem," her mother wrote—her mother who, like so many of America's Deaf, had eschewed hearing culture altogether, including its written language. "Dad want me mary here man, but I dont spek! Then Dad fire hem. We did look for job for year at lest, went to cort and fight you. But no money."

Between the broken characters, Michelle gleaned that, after losing their daughter for good, her parents had shipped up to Coalwood, WV, where her father found work in a sawmill, then the mineshafts, and got sick.

The office was silent. She looked down at her calico shirt. For a trice, Michelle believed her mother's words. And yet, she'd found her place of employment.

"We are so sad not to send leter til now," its waning words read. "I want to right my self so you cud see how hard for us. No phone, no money. We are sad each day for you."

Michelle balled the letter and thrust her hand deep into the trash, punching there until her knuckles screamed. Hearing the jangle of a door jamb, Doctor Gerard peeking out at the disturbance, she drew up in her seat.

"Everything okay?"

"Somethin's stuck to the bottom," she said, forcing a smile, her blush hot on cheek.

After work, Michelle tarried none in confronting Gangie, who sat at the breakfast nook where she took her cigarettes before bed. She flattened the crumpled letter, which she'd recouped from the trash bin at the dentist's. Red asterisks speckled its upper corner like thistles pressed in a heavy book.

"Y'all said they *abandoned* me here. This *here?* says otherwise."

"Yer grandpappy didn't hate him. Not at first," Gangie scoffed. "Yer poppa was a boozer, through and through. Hair-a-the-dog kinda drunk. Made him puttier'n playdough," she said, sighing, stubbing her cigarette, eyes off toward the glass cupboard lined with cheap trinkets, figurines, a cuckoo clock here and there. She wrung her hands, lower lip trembling. "Look, yer father lost the job to a better man. Kinda man yer mother *shoulda* married. What was we gone do? Let you get raised up in that house?" she said, tamping her cigarette. She got up for bed and, with a foot on the first step, said to Michelle, "By the way, you left your unmentionables in the bathroom again."

Broken cookies swaddled in his shirt, Benison returned to the couch. He lay sidelong, lifted a limp arm, queued some YouTube. He watched Tyson savor a bite of Holyfield's ear. Viral dentist visits. Gnarly skateboarding accidents. An A$AP Rocky video that opened with the rapper-cum-couture hitting the joint—then Rihanna en route to his place—and *scene*. Now they were at the mall in new outfits, Rihanna in a zebra-print dress, molesting a metal mannequin for cheap laughs. A$AP suggested over the song's bridge that they leave forever. But why? To where? Were they in trouble? It was all so strange. Benison thought of them mid-take, dancing like that, syncing their lips for the cameras. The image was infinitely funny. He brayed so hard that, after a while, he could only have been laughing at the braying itself, laughs inside brays, his stomach knapping up in knots, and he rolled over to find Jonesy squinting down at him, concerned as a coroner.

"What you all geekin about?"

"You remember—you remember that time—"

"Look here for a minute. Man," Jonesy chuckled, "you ate them cookies didn't you?"

"Oh *heeeell* yea, son," Benison said with an OG's churl. "Ya ma's cookies are realer than Real Deal Holyfield. Mrs. Fields can suck a *dehck*," he cracked himself up.

Jonesy shook his head. "Them ain't momma's cookies."

"Hm?"

"What I'm telling you my brotha"—placing a surgeon's grave hand on Benison's shoulder—"is that you high as fuck. And yo eyes is *werewolf*."

Benison *felt* his face contort surprise before he'd fully developed surprise's idea, much less surprise *as* idea, which led into a hall of metaphysical mirrors. "Ohhh*hhhh* shit dude. Th-at's crazy," Benison simmered. "Why am I yelling?" Then he frowned, cupping his ear as if to listen for something. No, nothing there. Sounds just sounded weird.

"Yo it's cool, man," Jonesy smirked.

Benison flushed the color of relief. His mind raced out toward nothing in particular, anything really. His interest landed on his lips, how he could make them *plop*, which reminded him of the duck call he'd mastered at summer camp. Soon he was yapping rasping quacks at his roommate, chasing him around the apartment like his grandfather had during that last bad bout of sundowners, stalking them around the home's recreation area until a couple burlier nurses sequestered him, or this rabid version of him. Benison had been seven. The memory stopped him cold, Jonesy's giggles trailing off to a trickle of mirthful confusion.

Still relatively marijuana-naïve, Benison's first edible experience went: giggles and trippy-goggles; gross gastronomy; fork-gripped slumber.

Moving along stage one, Benison awed at how small was his personal observatory. It was all very profound until he came across the idea of it being profound, whereupon profundity would morph into absurdity. He hugged a pillow to his chest, as he'd once held his stuffed Tigger, rocking against waves of euphoric distortion.

"You want to hear something crazy?"

Jonesy stared as he sojourned into deep thought, forgetting all intention to speak. He had to reacclimate. Everything bright and buzzing. What were *things*? Distantly, he said, "No, it's…"

With his head in the green cloud, he'd missed his landing strip. He stretched for the dropped thread, groping, tugging whatever he could find. The yarn rolled out, unraveling in his head…

Right now, all around the world, millions of people were surviving just north of the poverty line, while modern amenities required but one prevailing expedient: money. Benison had access to money earned neither by him, nor those who'd given it to him, and was therefore complicit in the world's economic predacity. He'd been bestowed enough bones to live a bon vivant's three weeks in Europe—and he'd failed to get a gift for anyone he cared about, like Enid, his high school heart-friend. He worried about missed jump shots to the point where he couldn't taste his food, while there were people on this earth whose distention of belly was a result of not feast but famine. His penis malfunctioned. He was weak. How had his genes not been culled back when troglodytes were busy keeping their quality of living exactly one nanounit above the suicide line. These post-apes had fought for inches until they simply died, all so Benison could totally ignore his physics teacher's thankless digression into string theory on the second-to-last day of high school. Instead he'd imagined what shapes of ass Europe was producing nowadays. It was all about balance in life, and Benison *had* taken close note of his specious privilege. Yet with this knowledge he'd done nothing, nothing but ineffectively defy his parents and hang out with guys like Ricky, whose passion for the socioeconomic scorecard was tantamount to that of how many shits he'd taken thus far this week.

Wait, what was he thinking again?

He looked down at the thread, which, even if he could, he dared not follow.

He was blazed as a grease fire off "them ain't Mamma's cookies." Sunk deep into the couch, he stared at a spot a few feet southwest of the flashing TV. He stated his access to ripped money, unimaginable sums drained down labyrinthine fiscal conduits and, like a laundered Super Mario, popping out the other end, ready for action.

There was silence. Benison was caught in marijuana no-man's land, seeing between things, like the unsaid words in Jonesy's eyes.

"About earlier," Benison started. "It might sound tried as fuck, and yeah, I don't know what it's like to not have money…"

"Yeah, I mean, you was trippin. But I get you. And I'm a tell you though," he said, lifting and padding toward his room. "I can't tell if you should lay off this shit or hit the weed every god dang day."

Curlicues of smoke leaked like a defeated spirit from his nostrils. He blew the rest—*hhhhhhhhhhoooo*—a lush silvery billow rising and dissipating into an ambient haze. From his window, bladdered light pissed through the blinds, lifting the smoked motes.

This was the answer.

Pulling up the blinds, the light burst golden over his bed. He watched cumulocirrus rush like leaves over a porch in Pennington, NJ, where his mother had grown. A cladogram of evolving Ellens— yet no matter her age, she was Deaf, desperate to know, desperate to be guaranteed something she didn't have. The snuffed joint bled out the root beer, dead of light. From his long closet he chose cream cotton trousers and a blue shirt. In the bathroom mirror, he mussed his flaxen mop, made a few faces, *swished* Listerine into his woolen gums. He stepped out to find his roommate at the stove, flipping hotcakes, some sonata reporting from his room.

"Greenie, dude," Benison grinned, shaking his head, sprawled across the couch.

"Right?" Jonesy agreed.

Stevie Green—AKA Greenie Steve, a sophomore walk-on from Portland—had blown up the group chat with blackout babble and, eventually—though some would say, inevitably—a dick pic. Benison's quick draw on Dick-sheathed had dropped him a few lolz, plus the promise of more mileage on said diction.

"Erik Satie," said Jonesy. "Monsieur was up on some high-quality minimalist strokes."

This was the Austin in Jonesy, the originality, the otherness— this music explained it better. Being explained everything. Benison felt he could do anything, and it wouldn't matter. This wasn't the answer. He was just high.

"It's the contrast. Between sunny days like this…" Jonesy looked out toward campus, South Lake Union, North Seattle's coastal spread. "Pancakes?" he said, realizing himself.

"Sure."

"Hittin the weed again," Jonesy tutted, testing his eyes. "You know Coach gonna run us after Christmas."

Awaiting the cakes, Benison flipped channels. He stopped on Seattle's King 5 local news, having caught his surname on the chyron in the bottom corner.

"*Today marks the first in what will be a series of admissible evidence hearings—*"

He punched in some familiar numbers and clicked.

"—*now, HBO comedy hour presents, Samuel Kaufman!*"

Turned around by this metaphysical crossover, only after a full minute did Benison fall into the comedian's routine: he hadn't seen Sam in what must have been a decade by now.

"*... Thank you thank you thank you... Okay that's enough... You in the front here. Yes, you sir. What's the most important thing you did today doesn't matter you're wrong, it was to drink water, drinking water was the single most important thing you did because without it, you would wither from acute dehydration like the needy little bitch you are. So Deaf people... Let's talk about Deaf people... I have Deaf parents... Yeah, I have Deaf parents. That means I'm a CODA, which stands for child of Deaf adults, which is also what they called B-roll for* Children of the Corn, *and there's a fun fact for you. Anyway I had the sort of childhood of Deaf adults where I'd be high all the time in order to cope with my lack of signing skills and the resulting feelings-fuck of shame and sorrow and alienation. For example, something us CODAs get from our parents a lot is, 'What was that noise?' But I was never all that great with pantomimed farting euphemisms, especially whilst fadened as fucketh... My little brother, of course he's also a sworn member of the childrenhood of the Deaf adults—only he can actually sign. So, naturally, I punished him for it...*"

Roughly halfway through the special, Benison texted Robert— the younger brother—to validate Sam's comic prowess. By the time he hung his duffel's strap over shoulder, his evolved sadness had faded. He'd just been high. Now, just hazed. He stopped for a coffee at the Commissary atop Comp 50. Again he was brimming, a throttled beast, on the hunt for some imperative.

The senior class of Bellevue High's basketball squad sat around the Behrenreichs' living room. *Saved by the Bell* was interrupted by a commercial for the *Rocky* marathon, scheduled to run this Sunday. Not without fuss did they tabulate the marathon out to eight hours of sedentary achievement, for which Benison's contribution would be crucial: watching the marathon at, say, Ricky's house, where resided non-deaf parents, would prevent the cadre from untabulating fresh cans of Ranyay with effervescent freedom. (Răn-yāy *n.* : colloquial term for Seattle's local brew, Rainier.)

But then Benison remembered: that Sunday was Passover.

Slumped on a gold lamé dinner chair taken from the dining room, Ricky went after him. He called Benison a twice-a-year Jew. Said he looked more like a Hitler Youth than any sort of Hebrew he'd ever seen. Said he'd seen the Christmas tree they'd put up last year, must've been big enough to block the menorah.

Benison's stonewalling bid him change tack, which he saw coming, the kid was crafty. Switching the focus onto what they *could* accomplish together, Ricky painted a picture of watching the marathon during Passover. "We could sneak kosher wine. Get that one interpreter drunk and invite her to hang with us."

But Benison insisted that the cadre couldn't possibly watch (at least) eight hours of TV while a Seder transpired a free-throw away, with over twenty of the Deaf world's wealthiest lined along the tables for his father's shot at unabated elitism, guaranteed swish every time. "Plus," Benison added, "Manischewitz tastes like wine with like 50 packets of aspartame in it."

He regretted this ad hominem attack on Passover, which he should've known would only serve to galvanize Ricky's efforts. Ricky started quizzing Benison's knowledge of the Old Testament. (His father was a former verger and Ricky had gone to Catholic school before budding as a baseball star.) He pounded at him: the ten plagues; the four questions; which animal's blood marked the doors of Jewish slaves, informing God that these were firstborns of the Faith. Exasperated, when asked who Miriam was, Benison said, "Your mom."

"Someone's got Chanukah gelt," he said, punning on the chocolates wrapped in gilt and pronouncing the holiday *Cha-new-kah.*

"Funny," Benison muttered.

"When's the last time you honored the Shabbos?"

"Last time I was at your mom's house."

"This is very bad, Benny. Very bad."

Reeling from Ricky's overwhelmingly effective misuse of religious knowledge, Benison blurted, "The only thing that's bad are your puns you dick-sheathed holy-roller."

"WHOA," boomed Terrence Livengood, a spindly kid with a brighter future in pretty much anything besides basketball. "Someone's got a *lot* of gelt."

Benison shook his head, crossed his arms, and glared at Zack Morris. The cadre chanted—"*Rock-y Rock-y Rock-y Rock-y Rock-y*"— which culminated in an outburst of "Adriaaaaaaaaaaaaaaaan"s—over which Benison's frustrated rebuttals could gain no audible purchase.

The cadre got distracted by a text from Sarah Gertler about her party next weekend, and Benison slipped quietly into his mother's sewing room. She was bent over a silkscreen of book-pressed ferns, autumn leaves, and thick jungle grass as he excavated the big bin of art supplies from under the fusty armoire. He'd removed half its contents when his fingers brushed the booklet's cool spiral.

He brought the booklet into the kitchen. On its cover he penned CARE BOOK—and so began his nihilist's catechism. In blue ballpoint he toiled toward his truest apathies crossed with everything Ricky lived for and loved. He listed "college baseball." He listed "Brett Favre's employment status." He listed "Ricky's sister's cleft palate." He listed a lot of other things that Ricky talked about a lot and cared a lot about (except for his sister's cleft palate, which he only cared a lot about). Benison worked through two-and-a-half *Saved by the Bell*s before presenting to Ricky, still slumped in the lamé chair, the idols and deities of his unholy indifference.

"Open it to the back," he said, a hand gripping his friend's shoulder. Ricky searched the cadre for understanding as might a sea mammal through aquarium glass. "What are you looking at them for?" Benison asked, prodding at Ricky's collarbone. "What's it say?"

"Dude, alright."

"The last one." Benison clutched his nape and forced his face closer. "What do I care about least, *Rick*?"

Uncomprehending, Ricky's lips moved to no avail until Benison tested the taut flesh of his friend's neck and smashed his face into the CARE BOOK.

"Jesus!"

"Read it," Benison growled. For the moment, Benison basked in the cool fear pooling at his feet. The cadre budged not an inch from their frozen stares. "Huh?" he urged.

Trepid, nearly trembling, Ricky didn't refuse to read—he couldn't. A tear blotted the page.

The Seder had been said, the Haggadah read. Led by his father, interpreted by Vanessa Schafer, a titular figure in all senses: Vanessa—convex bombshell and manager of the BIS Cares initiative—lent www.bisglobe.com a hint of sex sells. Benison knew this because his father had told him as much. He'd long since routed to his room and pumped his dick to stereoscopic snapshots of her bust's supple adjustments. Onscreen, Rocky Balboa and the Soviet war machine were trading utterly devastating blows. Ricky and the rest of the cadre were probably drooling beer by now. Benison changed the channel. Along with the rest of the *Rocky* canon, *IV* adhered to themes of perseverance despite all odds, and this wouldn't do.

A meager two schools had shown serious interest. Both fallbacks. Though DII powerhouses, they were in Potato Town, Middle America, bumbling with bumfucks. He'd sooner start slamming heroin than attend either, if only to work his game and transfer.

"We saw your tape. It's obvious what you can do. You have the chance to take a great team a long way."

Read: playing at Podunk U would get him more recognition than riding the bench at U of Washington.

Who'd called, yes. In the 10AM tone of a man needing a new life, a Huskies assistant coach had asked him to walk on.

To *walk on.*

An *assistant coach.*

His bureaucratic air had implied no room to wander from facts: that he, an assistant coach, was asking Benison to *walk on.*

Of course he could take some time to think it over.

"We'd have you come in and do a workout…"

Yes, the call was a coded invitation. Big schools could award only so many scholarships, and to land a local talent without wasting one. It was some bullshit. Bullshit to think that a First-Team All-County player would *walk on.* He'd put up monster numbers this year. His only blemish? Losing in the first round of regionals, but there were eleven other guys to blame, half of whom couldn't guard a signpost.

Walk-ons paid for school. Walk-ons rode the bench. Walk-ons were practice pawns, sparring partners for the guys who got significant minutes. Walk-ons were scrubs.

It was some bullshit.

But he held out for hope. Gary Williams himself had attended his last game as a Bellevue High Bobcat. He'd blended in behind the parents. Having hoisted a huge line, Benison had expected a call, at least. Alas, his phone didn't lie: it was April 12th, 2012. Contact period had *been* beginning.

As though she were receiving his signal, Enid buzzed, asking whether he'd heard anything. She knew the time for that call was now, and now, and now. Every moment diminished his hope of receiving the call.

Some time went by like this, ESPN highlights a green screen for thought, animated symbols and figures like a weather forecast for his mind. He kept the closed captioning on, a security blanket for his viewing experience, or force of habit from having to turn it on whenever his parents were watching. Another episode of *SportsCenter* had kicked off when a knock startled his knee.

"Jesus," he snapped at a second series, pulling his belt a fathom tighter. "Time is fucking required."

Okay, Benison, his name a stiff salute, her face a contortion of torment. *It's rude to leave the table with the guests still here.*

Benison deplored the ease with which she discovered deeper wells of indignation. Just look at your life, he'd think, whenever his petty teenage negligence threw her into a state. Rolling cream into her hands, still wearing her checkered dress and fishhook earrings. Benison towered over her as if made of bigger atoms.

Okay, he flicked.

Her lips moved as if to say something. Angelica's vacuum ruptured the moment, and he watched his mother cover her cochlear, hidden under the late-wheat hair he'd inherited.

Your father wants to talk to you. She turned toward the hall's half bath, where she removed her makeup each night. Paused in profile, she leaned on her far foot, her face saying, *Huh?*

And Benison's face saying, *I didn't fucking say anything.*

She frowned and went into the bathroom.

He went to the study, shoved the heavy door, the wood's ledges like misericords, and saw his father sitting at his laptop. Sawed-off string notes floated like wood-dust from the low-fi speakers. An article from *The Wall Street Journal* claimed his screen. His hearing aids lay next to the laptop. Their wax molds gave him rashes. Benison stood there, perhaps three feet behind him. Did he know the music was still on?

There was his Dickensian desk, the coffee table spread with business rags. The walls all stills of Yankees greats. Never long for this room, Benison stopped to absorb the one of old Mick, frozen in follow-through, watching his work's wavelike arc, trajectory's crest surging skyward.

His father noticed him—the Deaf's compensatory sense; an undocumented perception—and swiveled his chair, a bionic-like piece of frippery. He spread a hand to the leather armchair, angled near his desk.

"I want to show you something," he said, a bit louder for his unaided ears. Darkness flooded the gullies of his cheeks and chin as he turned the laptop toward Benison. Before opening his portfolio (an Excel sheet with roughly a dozen stocks), Benison caught glimpse of the window tab next to the *Wall Street Journal* article: Beethoven's Op. 61 in D Maj…

"This is a list of companies," his father said, and Benison begrudged or obliged the offered seat. "Their trade symbols, current price, what I bought them at. Simple enough?"

What if they could understand music?

He nodded.

"Good," his father commenced in his low voice, dull and round and erudite, his nose like dripping stalactite. "I'm going to show you some stock options. What that means is I'm betting on the stock as an underlying, like a point spread in sports."

What did that make this conversation's underlying? he thought, then tried to imagine his mother listening for the first time to an absolutely rugged cut. Something off, say, *The Chronic*, or *Ready to Die*—maybe "Gimme the Loot." His mother caught him practicing once, back when he hadn't admitted his greatest fear. Never again at the kitchen table, running through rhymes as if this were the secret he'd invested for the long view, rather than a speculative gamble: what would they think of him, earphones plugged eponymous, Barz opened to the latest sixteen, spitting staccato as she came in with groceries.

"Let me give you an example," his father said, leaning back, ankle over knee, glint off his Roland Iten. Content to compartmentalize: his son as pupil; his son as asset; his son as expendable. "*Understand?*" he finished, flicking an index up by his temple.

Benison comprehended the basics. You bought one hundred shares of any stock on offer for the cover/call option. If, after a set period, the stock stayed under the target price, you earned a premium and sold the shares. If, however, the stock beat the target, you lost out on the premium and sold the shares at target, regardless of how much it'd risen. His father had always explained things well, just not often, and not the right things.

Benison watched him tinker with the spreadsheet. Angelica's vacuum ripped again and stopped as quickly. He'd once seen them on the patio, his father and Angelica, which his mother had designed. Years ago. Bottles of champagne littering the cane table, late-summer light radiating the green glass. "*Lo siento*," she'd whimpered, fist circling her breast. His father massaged her shoulder, urging her to quiet down. A bucket in her lap, dress's strap fallen to the slender, she stiffened, tried to silence her gag like a cat coughing up lint. Benison had set his baseball bag against the sliding glass. Rarely did heavy squalls sweep over the Puget, but lightning would always cancel the remainder of a little league game.

"…You should reinvest the premium to keep it untaxed…"

It struck Benison odd, how he acted one way around his parents, another with his coaches, teachers, friends. What if, right now, he undid his button-up, pulled aside his a-shirt, and licked his nipple, mewling, "Milk, milk, milk"? Would his father understand his frisson as the sojourn from the self that it was? Did his friends?

"…Here's how you write the trade." He turned the laptop so his son could better see. Benison straightened. "Place a 'buy-write' options order…"

The orchestra begged attention by carving silence for the violin solo. He imagined Ludwig's quill dipping in dark ink and scratching the cadenza. As learned in eighth-grade music class, Beethoven had gone deaf from typhus. Be him a CODA to remember this stray piece of trivia, when to him, Paul Revere was a Beastie Boys song. Had Beethoven composed this concerto during those deaf years? The solo's crescendo invited all strings into the chorused refrain, the hemp of a thousand horses reaching for some human ideal.

"…will net you a 7% annual yield…"

Intermission brought momentary quiet. The second movement began gentler. His father would never know this music, which, Benison believed, anchored his cheap appraisal of the arts. Deafness was his fearsome rook, a blunt instrument to guard against ignorance.

"…even if over the 46-day period…"

Pinching their mold, his hearing aids more screeched than warbled, as if desperate to avoid his hirsute ears. He let the concerto play, but Benison saw shame flash in his eyes, which turned to the whiskey sweating abreast his laptop.

"Easy enough?"

Benison's shrug seemed to bother him.

"What do you want?" he asked, leaning back with his Macallan.

"What do you mean?" Benison asked, but he knew. His father knew he knew, so waited. "To play somewhere good. Get minutes. Get good grades."

His father placed the tumbler on his desk with a disapproving clatter. The random lesson in options was a smokescreen for this moment. His father synthesized these teachable moments, only to grill him about something entirely unrelated, something related to nothing Benison could understand.

"A good life?" he said with another shrug, more malign than the last.

"No," he grumbled, shaking his head. "What do you *want*."

Benison's anger tripped, autocatalytic, in a way he'd never allowed before his father. Lured into another of these randomized tests, he decided to bubble a fat dick into the scantron: "To not talk to you right now?"

A fist flew down from the rook as if catapulted from on high, and Benison, stupefied, admired the blunt wad of knuckles that *thudded* the side of his head. His eyes flash-bombed. Dazed and unaware, he palmed the spot smarting at his temple. Then, from automatic mechanisms of language, "What in the fuck is wrong with you?"

His father was quavering. Benison considered standing over him, the huff of his chest demonstrating his might. He'd done this once. His father hadn't flinched.

"I should say the same to you," he pointed. "With a talent like yours."

"It's basketball you abusive asshole."

It was effective. His father's glare gave off hot fault—his, Benison's, the world's.

"My father gave me power of attorney. My brother still can't read. Which one do you think he hit?"

"What would you have me do, m'lord?"

"Pick up the phone."

"Oh yeah?" Benison said, palm milking the spot. "And call Gary fucking Williams? Make him an offer he can't refuse?"

"How about Jason Derekson."

Be him a Myriadal hopeful to know who that was. Now he did thrust up and loom. Now it was the armchair that *thudded* the wall. The act forced his father to ask himself whether he was prepared to experience the pain he was so content to instill in others. Reciprocation. Reprisals. Appraisal of his chances. Words that require fingerspelling. The problem was, the answer was always yes: his father was willing, while Benison wasn't.

"I will give you access to your bar mitzvah money," he said, looking up at his broiling son, without a whiff of fear in his voice or manner. "You turn a 7% annual yield using what I just showed you, and you will have earned the money for UW's in-state tuition," his father said, nursing his whiskey. He did this. Made you wait.

"Or," he continued, "you can take what you want, with the understanding that I might not always be around to give it to you."

Finally. Only three years after his father had first hinted at his potential imprisonment. Only six years after VisiTech's goons had gotten to them. That was how Benison's mind referred to the men who'd disabused his father of his desire to shutter Behrenreich Interpreting Services' VRS branch. Strongmen. Thugs. *Ruds*, as Peter would call them months later, showing interest in Benison's story, this olive branch of destitution. Peter's disagreeing eyes would make truce over this tale: that Benison was a weak, entitled kid who'd never set a willing toe in Peter's world, the world of wicked men, or men who did wicked things. Benison's response would be to tell Peter that he understood one thing about that world. He understood its language, its innuendo, its entendre. He understood it as if it could be learned through fear. Threats could chill you. Threats were cold as gunmetal. But fear was hot. Fear melted threat into liquid reality, muggy and swampish, the stuff that made you sweat: should it have been deemed necessary, those goons from six years ago would've followed through on their threat.

"…I might not always be around to give it to you." The words tumbled like rocks across the road as he swerved the Audi onto the 520, heading for Ricky's house. Not for the first time had his father's dog whistle dipped into Benison's rhetorical register, revealing the conversation's underlying: the family business had been subpoenaed.

VisiTech's fixers would now formalize the efficient threat made all those years ago—or wager on his father staying mum in court. He'd have pressed him for information had his father's promise to shut up shop meant more than six years of implicit welching—had his answers imparted something useful. To Benison, it was only a matter of time before he'd confront his old specter—now, and now, and now…

The Myriadal Gazette   Business

December 28th, 2012

KeyArena: The City's Financial Sarcophagus

by Roopa Mehta

Known around town as the Seattle Derby, the Myriadal Rapiers and Washington Huskies will face off today at 2PM. But the Derby wasn't always the Derby. As a new institution, Myriadal got walloped, year after year. The Huskies' established program had been turning out pro talent for decades. Not many outside Westlake's campus considered it a rivalry.

Enter Eric Dodd. You know, the founder of the world's largest online retail enterprise, Azalai, whose HQ is wherever you look out your dorm window? That guy. A longtime basketball fan, Dodd has been thumping to bring the SuperSonics back since their departure in 2008. Combined with his unprecedented wealth, he's the ideal impresario of Seattle basketball. But what do Eric Dodd and the Seattle Supersonics have to do with Myriadal basketball?

KeyArena is buried under the Seattle Center, the city's cloister of tourist attractions. Following the SuperSonics' move to Oklahoma City, KeyArena morphed from sports mecca into cultural relic. The strategy, city officials say, defers tax-heavy renovations or rebuilding. Dodd, however, has criticized KeyArena's economic mummification. In an interview with *The Seattle Times*, Dodd said, "KeyArena should be more than a glorified garage used for smoked-out music festivals. The city's willful negligence is happy to let its Coliseum become a 'historical landmark,' which is a fiscally irreversible designation."

Back in 2009, Dodd warned that, failing an increase in utilization, KeyArena was projected to begin losing money over the next decade; renovations were not a matter of debate, but necessity. And it was REACOM, the contracting megafirm responsible for Azalai's Westlake campus, that presented Dodd's plan to the City Council.

Not a day after the REACOM pitch, Dodd was hit with the *Times*' front-page headline: DISMISSING THE DISTAFF. Per the article, Dodd's reasons for renovation seemed conspicuously ignorant to the fact that the WNBA's Seattle Storm plays at KeyArena (not to mention Seattle University, both Men's and Women's). *Seattle Times* staffer, Joan Lillian, put forth her arguments against the relegation of professional women. Dodd fired back, calling the article an afterthought. He even went on to say the article "whored out the real issue of women's disenfranchisement."

Initially, local politicians sided with the *Times*. Mayor McGinn trumpeted women's rights and the "Preserve the Arena" campaign—until the fruit of outrage turned, and hardly anyone noticed when he and other city officials signed the REACOM deal to renovate the stadium. The next day, the *Times* printed a story headlined: PORK BARREL DELIVERY, CITY HALL. It was on page 11 of the business section.

Around the same time, Myriadal College renamed their business school after Seattle's digital magnate. The Dodd School of Business generates hundreds of millions in tuition revenue and alumni contributions, which has attracted high-profile professors from all over the world. Following the REACOM deal, Myriadal aimed this firehose of contributions at its athletic programs—namely basketball and volleyball. Within two years, the Myriadal Rapiers basketball program cracked the top-25. Within five, they were whupping the Washington Huskies. Gary Williams was poached away from Xavier. Legendary Tar Heels coach, Dean Smith, was coaxed into recruiting consultancy. Myriadal began earning premium TV rights with Seattle's local sports channels.

Let's go back to the turn of the century, when Dodd bought up South Lake Union's acreage in anticipation of Azalai campus expansion. However, to this day, not one Azalai tower has been built on that property. In the mode of Ray Kroc, Dodd realized he'd happened upon the real estate business. To pay for his Westlake HQ, he leased the SLU property out to the new West Coat Ivy, Myriadal College.

The *Times* spent months trying to unearth foul play, interviewing city officials about the commercial property tax reduction, passed back in 2004, just in time for the Myriadal build. More recently, several pundits pointed out the sudden deregulation of Azalai's grocery delivery services, Camelback, and its beta drones buzzing over private backyards. But these connections proved only that the city wanted Myriadal's money inside its borders—along with Myriadal clientele's money - and were willing to incentivize this.

Meanwhile, the city moved ahead with KeyArena's renovations. Rather than jack taxes, the REACOM deal stipulated that capital be raised by issuing municipal bonds. Wall Street's more recherché investors, anticipating a new pro team, began repackaging the bonds as derivatives, mainly futures.

On July 25th, 2008, NBA commissioner David Stern announced that two new expansion teams would be added to the league—in 2020, far behind Eric Dodd's schedule. The city had structured the REACOM deal under the assumption that NBA revenue would come by 2016, or 2018 at the latest. If the city couldn't fund the renovation, work stoppage would create controversy.

The onus to buoy the stadium's $1.2 billion renovation fell upon the bondholder; Everyman Joe and Thatlady Jane were caught holding the bag. Rather than scupper the ship, the city issued more bonds while hiking prices, which lowered bond yields. Bond yields fall as prices rise.

The antecedents to economic crisis were textbook. The *Times* excoriated the city, but the public seemed tired of the story.

The crisis kept rattling city coffer lids, so Dodd sought to squeeze additional revenue from the teams playing at KeyArena. In perfect irony, he started with a call to the Seattle Storm's front office, proposing that the WNBA franchise use Azalai as a surrogate for team merchandising. The initiative brought modest success, but not nearly enough to stanch the bleeding.

This was when Dodd pushed to move Myriadal home games to KeyArena, pushing to move the Rapiers out of their humble gym in West Seattle. He got the Rapiers a restructured TV deal. He hung Pac-12 banners from the rafters. He promised that the Rapiers would play in the new SoDo stadium by 2020. With Dodd's backing, Myriadal emerged, practically overnight, as the fifth-highest grossing basketball program.

But depending on existing college teams for utilization was a PR band-aid for the arm and leg the city had lost. Perhaps beginning to panic, the city organized a huge buyback of the reno-bonds. It was rumored that Dodd himself had bought almost a half of the bearer bonds, which many Seattle residents blame for the city's loss of financial agency.

Just this past April, a mystery investor seized nearly 75% of the bearer bonds. The new player's identity is uncertain, as they staggered their buy orders, purchasing the bonds from a series of distinct holding companies. The move was unprecedented considering the bonds were purchased at premium prices. Regardless of their motive, this shadow investor has made their presence known; their stake in KeyArena's reno-bonds equals 13% of Seattle's annual revenue.

At the most recent town hall meeting, dozens of Seattle residents lined up to speak out against the city's negligence. Many pushed for a lawsuit that would force the buyer to provide sound reasoning for their investment. But city officials were dubious on legal action, citing that the shadow investor risks defaulting on those bonds and therefore, by law, is not beholden to such reasoning.

At the time of this writing, Standard & Poor's gives KeyArena's renovation bonds a AAA rating—the financial service's highest bond grade—making Myriadal College's basketball program a fortunate little fig leaf for the city's dirty little secret.

By the time Benison finished the *Gazette*'s feature story, Jonesy had left to have his ankle worked before the team boarded the bus.

An hour later, Benison donned his Rapiers Polo and slacks, shouldered his duffel, and shuffled down Denny Way. His earbuds blared Juelz Santana, featuring a tweeange Weezy, evoking images of bandanas and Ecko jeans. Near Denny Park, Benison saw a stray dog in some brush, its piebald coat matted by mist. The dog was rolling a rock over in the dirt as if treasure were embedded within layers of sediment. Lil Wayne rapped: *Okay, let's talk about this ice that I'm carryin / All these karats like I'm a fuckin vegetarian.*

Benison would never know.

Such a rich history behind the Derby, and still the squad followed military protocol—first walking to campus, then taking the Rapiers' retrofitted Scenicruiser to KeyArena. Before their first home game, Coach Williams had said, "When y'all have 50-million-dollar sneaker deals, you can roll up in your Escalades and strut the gauntlet in your ridiculous costumes. For now, we play as a team, show up as a team. If you don't like it, call your local politician, which would be me, since I am the total authority here, to which I say get on the bus and shut your mouths. Any questions? Yeah, Del."

"Yeah, I mean, this a bit of a tangent," he'd said, "but can you get me out of biz-calc? Shit is fuckin up my average."

KeyArena was a sensory chamber—the megatron of sight and sound, smells of polished wood and sweat and hot dogs. Especially for the player standing center court, it was a spectacle, and Benison was still buzzing from a half-hit off the roach.

The stadium's busy expanse opened him to thoughts of equal proportion. Wandering the half-court line, dribbling through stilted legs, memories squirmed beneath his veil of awareness. (He couldn't sleep.) The Washington Huskies hustled out for warmups. (They'd had Bolognese that night, a big brainy pile of it.) Boos poured over the rails and onto their jogging line. (Benison had never heard them in the bedroom, where he thought they slept.) He scanned Washington's coaching crew for the *assistant* who'd called him back in April. (At some point he realized it wasn't his father in there with her.) (He'd never know.) Hip hop during layup lines. His right elbow smarted, the pain residual to an arthroscopic procedure back in seventh grade, something to do with the violence of his throwing motion. The local sports network's Shelly DeMarco provided dramatic preamble into a hooded camera. Outside Seattle, to the borders of the United States, this matchup of DI titans would broadcast on ESPN. Finger-roll, rebound, pass. Dunk, rebound, pass. His turn. Huskies supporters arrived like a flash-mob, fast, coordinated, purple trimmed in gold. One UW student wearing a *Teen Wolf* mask held a sign that read: POUR OUT A RAINIER FOR THIS RAPIER. He got tossed from the stadium, his poster confiscated, and Benison managed a smirk. The buzzer brought the starters out to center court. He remained pratfallen near the coolers. His mother couldn't make it today.

Myriadal won by twelve, going away. Benison subbed in at the very end. Dominguez inbounded to him as the clock hit zero, the harsh buzzer sawing game-time from the present like cheap scrapwood.

An itch irritated their skin of victory. The squad kept quiet as they stripped shoes and socks, applied wraps and liniments. They hadn't played well—just well enough to win. From the middle of the locker room Coach spoke in a disappointed tenor.

"It just won't wash, fellas. Oregon's got four guys who'll kill you on those open looks. We've got to close out on the perimeter. It's a matter of desire."

His sweeping gaze ended on Benison as though he should've done something better while the clock had run out with the ball in his hands. Or perhaps the look meant something else. He'd never know.

Myriadal's Sports Info Director, Jen Alderman, caught Coach's eye as he twisted to check the time. But his players required further admonishment, so she stood refastening her navy blazer's top button, adjusting her chamfered glasses, a blue pencil claiming her called blonde hair. She tolerated another minute before taking it upon herself to usher Jonesy, Del, and Gabe Griffin out to the conference booth. The other players showered and left. Now it was just Benison and AJ, who sat sulking by his locker.

"Austin," came Coach Wyles's voice from the hallway door.

AJ *tsked*, rolled his eyes, a slouch of disappointment. Bands of sweat bleached his forehead and the hollows under his eyes. He'd let his man drop 24 on him.

"Now."

"Aight aight," he groaned.

Soon after, Benison shouldered his duffel—the material form of his basketball baggage—and started for the door. From here he'd pass the conference room, cross an annex, and empty out into the hangar, where boilers roared, pipes clanged, and teammates waited for the bus.

But Benison didn't even make it into the hallway. Against the doorframe leaned Jason Derekson, who flipped the rubbered stay and straightened, hands clasped over his belt's notch.

"I was sorry to hear about the judge's decision. Denying bail."

Benison pressed his lips and shrugged.

Derekson squinted. "You should show some respect. The man was retained for his own safety."

Benison tongued his gums, shrugged.

A nasal scoff, and Derekson shook his head. "Anyway," he inhaled, looking over his glasses, "I wanted to make sure we're still on track?"

Benison looked at him and said nothing. A few beats passed like this. Then he secured his duffel and walked around Derekson.

He followed the hall past the conference room, through the annex. Coming out into the hangar, the bus idling in gray dusk, there squirmed beneath the veil of awareness that second night of Passover, sitting in his father's study.

"So what am I supposed to do," Benison had asked, "when you don't give him whatever he wants?"

Whether he *could*, this was buried under the fact that Benison *would* not make explicit reference to the NCAA Board seat promised Derekson upon his signing with Myriadal. Should he have unleashed the question, Benison would've watched it charge across his conscious only to die, like so many cognitive revolutions, at the impermeable membranes keeping separate his most flammable ideas.

"Nothing," his father shrugged, gazing at his son as if he were gormless.

"Nothing," Benison repeated. Indignant, despite the dearth of moral clarity when it came to welching on bribes, his father's classic alpha move. Clearly, however, he took himself into consideration. "Explain to me how that's gonna work again?"

Deliberately—almost mockingly—his father bent and pulled a drawer open. From a quire of thick paper he peeled a single municipal bond certificate, bordered by blue garlands. He'd handed Benison the bond certificate and said, "Because I own this city."

Benison was ripped from sleep.

Bzzzzzzzz...

Bzzzzzzzz...

Bzzzzzzzz...

Bzzzzzzzz...

Groping for his phone, he wondered when he'd gone under. He was hazed. Blocked number.

"Hello?" he answered. His voice sounded like someone else's.

"Yes, Mr. Benison Behrenreich?"

"Yeah?"

"My name is Joan Lillian. I'm with *The Seattle Times.*"

He swung up on his bed, legs dangling over the edge, blood quickened and viscous.

"Mr. Behrenreich, I apologize for the hour. This is in regard to a story that will be printed tomorrow."

Benison stood now like an ancient beast at the bluff, peering beyond the earth's curve, birds wheeling scattershot. "Okay," he said. He heard a keyboard's clacks in the background.

"Are you aware of the nature of your father's evidence hearing?"

"…No."

"Then she was right…"

"Who was right?" Benison asked, looking at his lampshade.

"Mr. Behrenreich, are you familiar with a Michelle Thibodeaux?"

"Yeah, she worked for my dad. She's been. Missing." He wasn't sure he should've said this.

"Ms. Thibodeaux contacted me, personally, using embassy cables. She claims your father's hearing tomorrow regards a paper trail that incriminates a syndicate head connected to high levels of US intelligence."

Benison's jaw pushed outward, straining, thumb and index pressed into either eye. A lot of words. She kept saying them.

"Were you or your mother instructed to buy up municipal bonds?"

"What?"

"I have a source who spoke of an encounter between you and a member of the DeCavante crime family."

"Who told you that?" he gritted.

"Could you tell me a little more about the incident?"

"No," he growled. "I'm hanging up now."

"Alright now, Mr. Behrenreich. I understand. Please take down my number, in case—"

"I have it in my phone."

Benison stared at the ended call until the screen went dark. He realized his tight grip when it started hurting, his knuckles blanch-white, whereupon he stood and hurled his phone against the wall. A smudgy comma curled where it hit.

He snuck under the covers, still in his Rapiers Polo and slacks. Restive, he straightened, splayed, condensed. He wanted to hit the weed. He worried whether Jonesy had heard his phone hit the wall.

He wouldn't tell his mother about the call, or Michelle Thibodeaux.

PART TWO

There's Peter Fosch. He blends into the family room—a common area for people who happen to share his DNA. The dented empties. A hamper that threw up its clothes. TV dinners congealing over their stink. This is where he's learned about uncleanliness, ungodliness, being close to nothing.

He pulls knees to stomach and sniffs up some drip, his eyes following father, who hunches center stage, breath ragged, broken by pulls off the fifth he chokes at the neck, belaboring unintelligible accusations at his wife, whose wayward finger thrusts into his retina.

"CUNT," he bellows, hand over eye. He knocks into the TV and up the stairs.

His mother staggers, wet coins of vodka dappling the front of her shirt. She looms. "Fuck're you lookin at?" she asks Peter, and her eyes, like lolling glass, make the question seem literal. "You ain't shit. I'll cut yer gas line you look'me."

She staggers off.

There's Kaleigh Fosch, the next day, returning home from a friend's house. She's wearing bell bottom jeans and a white peplum blouse, flowery lace at the cuffs. Garments beyond her years, both past and future. Café au lait served up along the inside of her wrist. She's fixing a martini for her old lady. Broken-down beer boxes lean against the sliding door behind their mother, eyes hooded in the kitchen's slate light. Peter's in the family room, keying bumps from his cling-wrapped eight of yay.

There's his father, appearing at the foot of the stairs. His parka's swollen at the paunch, his face at the cheeks, the night with gaining dark. "Kaleigh," he grumbles.

Without looking to their mother, Kaleigh abandons the half-made drink, brine dancing helicoid—DNA drifting in booze—and shuffles to the door. Her bag waits among her father's things near the front door.

"Saw it in your email last week, George," she spits, referring to their Amtrak tickets. "Fuck you think I'm not surprised right now?"

Ushering Kaleigh out the door, their father looks back to Peter one last time. Cold air rushes in to replace them.

There's Peter, later that night. He finds his mother in her usual spot on the couch, fifth of Svedka sweating on the coffee table. He wants to know where they've gone to.

"Off with that whore of his," she slurs. "Don't worry, yer sister'll be back."

Swollen nights, when she'd cornered him and whipped his cheek until his head walloped the wall. "You wanna eat don't you? There's yer dinner yer hidin you little shit." But now he's the one shaking her, the fear of no god in her eyes, just vacant terror, as if witnessing oblivion itself. He shoves her into the couch, swipes the Svedka, his keys off the rack, and wakes up in a ditch not too far from his house. He doesn't recall the drunk tank.

There's Peter, picked up by his buddy Robert Kaufman. He has nothing to his name but the shirt on his shoulders, his black chinos, and court papers. He's that hungover sort of hangdog, watching his own feet crunch over slabs of refried snow and slosh and mud. Mr. Kaufman's arm wraps his wife's shoulders on the doorstep.

Peter's welcomed into their big box of blueblood brick, but it's useful space, the house's is, allowing for communication from its farthest reaches. Behind the house spreads the bean-shaped pool surrounded by flagstone and flowers and beeches and pine. Like all the good in Peter's life, the Kaufmans' is more refuge than home.

He and Robert spend the weekend playing videogames in the basement, where a 65-inch TV chamfers the far corner. Not but a few years ago, Robert's dad lingered in isolation, properly varnished, lacquered, shellacked: Robert favors shiny euphemisms for his father's recovering alcoholism. The controller is passed between them but seldom a word, as if *shiva* is being held upstairs. Onscreen, Peter's avatar is brutalized by one of the several advanced war machines programmed to seek its demise.

"What is this, amateur hour at the Apollo?" Robert grimaces. "Gimme the sticks."

Dinner in silence. With Robert's brother off chasing his come-up in New York, Peter takes his seat, Robert and his father at either elbow. Chewing hot sausages and sweet peppers, Peter nods his fist, *Yes, the food is good.*

After three days, or maybe it's ten, Peter laughs. His laugh's impishly staccato like he's driving over mounds of dead mice and finding it much too funny. He starts talking again, too. About Dio and death metal and dirt bikes. About how he used a littered coffee cup to pick up Dodger's shit this morning. There's Peter, lurking behind a corner and scaring the pants off Robert. There's Peter ramming his fist into his friend's asshole and yelling *Jail simulation!*

There's Mrs. Kaufman, scolding Peter's empty diet of Red Bulls and processed carbs. There's Peter's rejoinder, "B-Vitamins," he enunciates, brandishing the can. Mrs. Kaufman squints and leans forward to better understand him, which seems to help despite its absurdity.

There's Robert setting the table. There's Mr. Kaufman, reading the evening news on his tablet. There's Peter, copying Robert's history homework. There's Mrs. Kaufman's default frown as she works an angry pot of beef stew and sizzling latkes, stomping for her husband, who asks if the boys will help. His tone assumes them deeply remiss to do such things, and he's right, they are, but they do them, and Mrs. Kaufman finishes cooking, and there's clapping and hollering and flailing. There's Robert, rapping his knuckles against the table and asking his mother, *Why doesn't Dad get shit for wearing a hat at dinner?*

Because he can't hear me when I tell him not to.

Mr. Kaufman plays innocent. Then, facing Peter, his finger traces crocodile tears.

There's Peter—*ptt*—fake spitting on the dishes he hands Robert to dry. There's their nightly TV session. There's Mr. Kaufman idling by, hands in pockets, perhaps missing the days when he was his son's favorite person, perhaps remembering what he's done to rattle his trust. There's his stunted English. It's robbed of articles and transition verbs. It says "fucky" instead of "fucking." It complains, "Man, the Dodgers sucks this year," meaning the baseball team, not their dog.

There's Peter, alone in the computer room as the unmistakable sound of Mr. Kaufman's gait breaches the French doors.

"Dodgers, what is he doing?"

Peter hears him fuss over their golden retriever before knocking and entering.

"Listen, Peter. If you need anything for school. *Money, books, whatever.* You take out loan, but we will *help*," he says, cursory signs supporting his words. "And look, if you ever want, we go to *meeting*, we be happy to have you."

Peter frowns and offers a stolid *thank you*, that backhand drawn from chin. His smile tight, Mr. Kaufman takes his leave, and Peter's head falls into his cargo fatigues. He isn't ashamed of Mr. Kaufman's offer, but that his gratitude is dressed in this black Gojira shirt.

There's Peter in the shower, leaning against bloom glass tiles, turquoise and teal and aqua marine. The water's gone cold but he doesn't notice. Mr. Kaufman's words reminded him he's going to college soon, clear across the country. And that he isn't their son.

There's Peter, getting high again. For whole nights he rides with Bryan Quackenbush, his skinhead connect who's basically Peter plus two years of coke abuse. They blow lines off a pocket mirror through rolled Washingtons. He endures Quackenbush's strength training diatribes—"And I say to him, You call that a fuckin set? You gotta go *parallel* bro. And this dude starts givin me lip about a knee injury and I'm like well you wouldn'ta gotten injured if you'da fuckin repped right the fuckin idiot"—because the coke's plentiful, especially during chiseling season. In the small hours Peter fumbles through the window he left unlocked, and sleeps through the day.

He plays suburban roulette, lucky every time he spins the chamber. He's dared to stand in the middle of Centennial Lane at the height of afternoon traffic. He tries for high fives from driversby. He pleads temporary insanity to Principal Macintosh—"I was in a fugue state from all the learning"—and is suspended three days. Not four days later he solicits a fight on the quad during gym. Their physical educator, Mr. Sullivan, bores into the scrum and takes the brawlers into tender headlocks. To Peter's fortune, he doesn't report the incident.

There's Peter's GPA, flirting with the 2.0 minimum required by most collegiate admissions offices. Teacherly cautions flatter him with platitudes.

"You're too smart for this," said his math teacher, Mr. Thomas. "Talent minus hard work equals destitution," said his chemistry teacher, Mrs. Stoltz. "I taught your father here. He didn't have half the mind you do. You want to end up down Frederick Road, like him?" warned his English teacher, Ms. Neidig, who always encouraged Peter's love for bikes. "You want to wake up hungover just to pour cement? That kind of life might make for a good short story, but take it from me: suffering is a whole lot less worthwhile when you're the one undergoing it."

There's his scrunched baggie dotted with little green ribosomes, which Robert finds on the kitchen counter.

"Dude you can't just leave your bud out like that. They're Deaf, not blind," Robert says at the foot of the basement stairs.

Peter's still but for his thumbs working the joysticks. "My bad," he mutters.

The next morning Robert returns from the bathroom wrapped in a towel. "Forgot my—Dude, what the fuck?"

The towel seems to release Robert across the room. He grabs Peter's wrist and blows the powder off the wood stand. An elastic stillness, then Robert asks why he's doing this. Peter says he could ask the same thing, and is Robert going to compensate him for these losses.

"You mean Quackenbush though, right? Your sugar daddy?"

There's Peter shoving Robert where belly meets breastplate. There're Robert's small eyes glinting angry. There's a struggle. The lamp's knocked onto the bed. Peter uses Robert's collarbone to create distance before throwing the first punch. This ends the fight. Seconds later, Peter says he's sorry, but it's removed. He says it as if offering his friend an anagram, the meaning all scrambled. He says it in a way Robert can't refuse, without entendre, without hope for returning things to the way they were. Peter says it— "Sorry"—like glue applied to a broken toy.

There's Peter Fosch, a vacant form borne by his borrowed suit. He and Mr. Kaufman exit the Howard County Courthouse with expected results: license revoked for a year; 120 hours of community service; and a year of drug and alcohol counseling, followed by another three years with a general social worker. Without a word they get into the car and head back to the box of brick. Along the old Clark farm, where he'd gone paintballing with his pop, wheat grass and cattails and corn stalks bending in the wind. The trees along Breconshire menace them, their boughs snarling, boles shuddering, buds swaying like a newborn collective intelligence. Turreted stormclouds darken the sky. Drops drum up some business, bargaining by a thousand liquid bullets. Mr. Kaufman touches his hearing aid and glances at Peter as if to affirm the downpour through secondary sources of sound.

Trust in thine own eyes, Peter thinks, and nearly chuckles at the absurdity of it. He reaches for the envelope, Mr. Kaufman rapt at these exalted moments—hoping them exultant.

There's Peter Fosch, ripping open a letter, handed him prior to leaving for court that morning and propped atop their takeout coffees like a makeshift table. There's the University of Washington's crest above its masthead, the notary seal down near the dean of admissions' signature. Sandwiched between, the letter begins…

We're happy to inform you…

Only when the Southwest 747 began its descent into SeaTac did Peter stop concocting plots to beg for booze from one of the attendants. At baggage claim, he thought of a racket for pawning luggage stolen off the conveyor belt. On the Light Rail, the cityscape emerged with an elevated carom, rising in concert, all gleam and glare under the crisp August sun. He detrained at the U-District station. He hadn't known a summer day could be crisp, but this was the technocratic coast, where, for Peter, possibilities could be choices.

Four days after signing the lease on a 15x15 ft. U-District apartment that he dubbed his shitbox, he was back at the Kaufmans', packing his modest belongings. Their farewell was drawn, from family room to front step, embracing and, on the part of Mrs. Kaufman, effusive. He couldn't compete with two flown sons, not amid summer's moist turd, but their concern was osmotic.

Robert had set off for Palo Alto for an ambitious summer seminar in aeronautics, his sedan stuffed to the bungee-strap with still more stuff. Peter's bike, however, carried only him, his backpack, and one suitcase, borrowed from the Kaufmans. He'd decided to wait tables with Quackenbush in Ocean City, where the breeze licked like the salted rim of brackish Kraken and Cokes, which was what Peter would be fixing when the screen door whined, in stumbling Quackenbush, followed by a gaggle of girls who'd be in town for Senior Week.

(Sēnyər Wēk *n.*: East Coast tradition during which freshly graduated high school seniors spend a week at the beach with their friends; beta test for independence and college durability.)

Propping himself on an elbow, sickly, strung-out, like the stratus clouds in his window, he tried to recall the previous night. He couldn't—not even as his eyes fell upon the body beside his, slathered in what could only have been his personal upchuck.

Too nauseated to cope, he groped for the deck and lit a spliff. Some minutes passed before footfalls struck across the kitchen. Too much noise. He stubbed the spliff into the deck's scabrous railing, flicked the roach, and watched it twirl out and drift back toward the shack. She flung the door and stomped onto the deck.

"You're just going to stand there getting high? It's eight in the fucking morning."

Looking at her, his first thought was that he'd done something drunk. The rustle of paper towels in her crevasses, the seagulls squawking, the ocean's rushing breaths—he threw up over the railing, smirking at the word that entered his mind, uninhibited, much in the way that it made him:

Alcoholic.

"I see you didn't get it all out on me last night."

"You got in bed with me...Right?"

"You *are* a fucking asshole," she said, a caustic epiphany.

He stared at the spliff's chalky orts in little piles on the wood railing, listened as she plodded off, exhausted of indignation, he hoped. Down the splintered steps and along the blacktop, her purse's jangle was metered by slaps of thong sandal. He sat where he was, leaning over the banister. A splinter threatened his forearm as he shifted to answer his phone.

They spent a thousand seconds thwacking through the thickets grown over their untended friendship. Perhaps exhausted by such unpleasantries—lord knew Peter was—Robert bared himself:

"I'm not having a good time out here."

"No talent?" Peter tried at a quip.

"No, it's—" Robert choked.

"What's going on?" Peter tried to sound interested, which he hoped would lead to genuine interest.

"It's...my dad. He's uh...been indicted on fraud charges."

"*What?*"

"Yeah."

"Shit, man," Peter drawled, shocked by how soon he'd struck interest as much as the topic of interest itself.

"Yeah."

"He gonna get time or something?"

"Not if he cooperates."

"Color me shocked," said Peter, who, interested in his own candor, realized he'd been smacked by the spliff. "Never would've guessed he had it in him."

"You didn't know him as well when he drank. No one did," Robert added. The annotation was an indictment: that no one knew Peter. Not Robert, not even himself. This interested him for another couple hours, until he passed out on the old corduroy couch, springs pushing through the cushions' stuffing.

If nothing else, one thing was clear to Peter: college was easier than high school.

If UW's evergreen utopia credited him with such virtues as responsibility and independence—as convention would have him believe—he couldn't tell the difference. Attendance seemed optional. Minimal effort could pull you Bs, or even As if the class was easy, yet most students wasted hours. But most students wasted hours of their actual lives on memorization and mnemonic devices. He didn't even need clear goals, much less a major. Electives were a joke, their punch line the class you chose. Peter likened Ethnomusicology's rigor to that of Matthew "they stay the same age" McConaughey's approach to the bongos. If stuck in a real gelatin of a jam, he'd show early for exams and find a good angle. No one cared.

The real challenge was sobriety. One particularly ratchet Thirstday began by himself at the Monkey Pub and ended somewhere he'd never be able to tell anyone because he himself would never know. He'd made it home unscathed, passed out perpendicular to his mattress, his dreams just variegated blotches. The coke ringing his nostrils worked like smelling salts—but then, coming to, he caught a *rank* whiff.

They were leavings. A whole trail of turbid runoff leading to his computer chair. He'd voided himself over vast stretches of his now all-too-literal 15x15 shitbox. Over the next twenty minutes he searched as if for bodies under rubble, only it was shit under which nothing worth keeping could survive, wincing and retching whenever he turned up another goop of sultry evidence. Six hours of violent drunk-sleep had desensitized him not a single dram to his own brand of compost.

The forensics report: he'd tried to pull down his pants, shat in his computer chair, and wiped his ass on softer surfaces. Only then had he surrendered to what can only be called unconsciousness, since sleep implies rejuvenation and, currently, he felt like "ding dong dick," which he muttered now on the cement stoop of his shitbox.

He shambled to the QFC in ambulatory limbo, a barely-bipedal movement long relegated to primitive iterations of his species. People stared. Those near enough wrinkled their noses. He couldn't blame them, only himself. He ransacked the supplies aisle's rows of Lysol, wet-wipes, Febreeze, scented paper towels. He draped a stealthy arm over his bin. He asked for help at the self-checkout kiosk. The checkout clerk's expression explained with unequivocal cogency that he, Peter, looked like a hobo investing in a cleaning business, and that perhaps he should avoid the hypocrisy of a proof of concept that neglected his own hygiene. In a way, he was inverting expectations. These thoughts weren't helping.

The smug lady's smile took on tones of fear. He thought he caught her startle as he dipped a hand in his pocket, from which, along with his wallet and keys, he drew a receipt from Little Darlings. $20 on lap dances—and $148 on Diet Cokes? Then a strobed memory. Hard to see—just gaudy lasers. Railing talcumy coke off a dancer's stomach. Stumbling back. A dancer taking a key bump, claiming it keeps her figure. "A little Diet Coke with dinner," Peter had shrugged, flicking at her nipple ring…

Fuck.

He braced, ran his card, and expelled an acrid breath as the machine bleated approval.

Back at the shitbox, Peter reviewed the scene, cracked a beer, again setting to work. He couldn't subdue the stink that then lasted weeks. He wore a hospital mask to sleep. The story became the icebreaker for meeting his mind. In fact, it spurred a stint with total sobriety. For a while at least. That was the thing of it, right? Everything was only for a while.

His freshman year nearly through, Peter had made acquaintance-ships like loose threads of spit hanging from his maw over porcelain bowls in punkish bathrooms. He was embarrassed. Embarrassed that he'd shat where he ate with himself in his 15x15 ft. shitbox. Embarrassed that he'd become a questionably more intelligent version of his father. Embarrassed to be alive.

Once the shakes passed, he kicked the Red Bull for coffee. He rediscovered masturbation. He studied more than forty minutes for a Calc exam on which he lost all seven points for failing to show his work. At a Thai place on Broadway, he put a vegetable in his mouth: the carrots in his red curry.

He met someone while working the concierge desk at start of his shift. Slumped in one of the lobby's three velour couches, Dylan's lunky head sported a baseball cap whose old-school Orioles logo interested Peter less than its fit, the bill's slightly crooked angle blurring the line between douchey and louchey.

"From B-more?" Peter chanced, half disgusted with himself.

The dude seemed to require eye-contact before registering the question. "Bel Air."

"Sorry to hear that."

The dude's croaky chuckle prefixed his self to Peter's deprecating quip, marking him worthy of conversation. "Dylan," he said, striding the lobby's width and offering a hand. They talked until Peter's first rounds. Rather, Dylan did, Peter listened, and for once, Peter didn't mind.

Dylan was one of those weekend warriors, fifty or sixty grueling hours fueling his heights and trips, moonwalks of the mind. His numinous rituals were many and included: ruminating over peaty scotch; shredding slopes of uncut coke; art that was patentable as a novel aesthetic (really, Peter would never watch Fellini again; if that's what people called high comedy, he'd rather be a pleb); and, always, doses of acid ranging from micro to massive.

In the mirror, Peter suspected, Dylan saw a hedonic monk, a social martyr, depersonalizing in psychotropic secret. His roommate also fashioned himself a hermit, but Peter saw Brad for what he was: just another JavaScript hardon. So was Dylan, if you subbed the JavaScript and social ineptitude for responsible drug use and oil-business acumen. "The paycheck, mon frère," was

Dylan's answer to the otherwise lengthy ethical dialectic, and no one wanted that. "The payola." Peter appreciated that, rather than revel in, Dylan tolerated his raucous office. There were beer kegs, there was a pinball machine, ping pong tables, a stripper just the once which everyone felt super weird about, even a fleshlight Dylan said they found dried come on once—"on" and "in" being quite distinct within the context.

Peter didn't want to seem a gadfly in the ointment, so he hit the lever that got Dylan good and interested. "Yeah but I make money, too. People with half a dick make money."

"Well, I shan't lie, mon frère. One of several perquisites is the monthly pilgrimage to distant lands roiling in oil you see—*sssssssssssssss...hhhhooooooo*—you take a trip out to Afghanistan, for instance. You ask about mustard seeds. They know what you mean. I fly company private, no security, I can bring back a pound of pure, no problem."

"You in business?" Peter said, eyebrow lifted.

"Heh-heh," he looked off, face thronged with guilt of greed. "Nah, man. Nah…"

They savored this moment of tacit understanding. Crushing a butt and getting up for another glass, Dylan said, "But I know someone who is."

Peter shirked his session with O'Reilly—the court-appointed shrink responsible for obtaining his piss on a bimonthly basis. In claiming illness, Peter struck gold on plausible deniability: if Finnegan O'Reilly didn't believe him, he was a hypocrite (why would he need to treat a healthy person?); and if he did believe him—well, then Peter would've read O'Reilly for precisely the credulous rube he'd suspected him to be.

Peter's thinking was such: why drill into his emotional core, only to risk cracking his psychological crust? Wasn't it healthier to just go buy some shit, like any of the blind capitalists the O'Reillys of the world seemed to uphold as paragons of mental health? Still, perusing Holy Smoke's wide selection of shapely glass, he found himself extending his lie to the clerk.

"Head cold's going around, man." The clerk shook his head, chewing on the end of a Black and Mild. His Ray-Bans were harsh with afternoon light. "I got something for that."

Peter watched stretch-marks like efflorescence bloom from his chest as he reached into the display case.

"Kratom," the clerk proclaimed, placing a baggie of verdant herb atop the vitrine. "South Asian plant. Feels like someone dropped a Percocet in your coffee—except it's 100% natural."

"Legal?"

"For the moment," the clerk grinned. "First five g's are on the house."

They talked pharmacology—μ-opioid agonists; cold water extractions to remove acetaminophen from prescription pills; etc.—and Peter bought ten grams of Kratom on top of the five: White Maeng Da; Red Bali; and Green Malay.

Back in his shitbox, Peter followed the clerk's instructions:

Mix a teaspoon into water.

Play some Coltrane.

Ride the wave.

The first five did nothing. An hour later and the fifteen g's had dwindled to dregs. The last bit he toss'n'washed and, inexperienced in the method, his throat revolted against the crushed plant. He coughed the clot out at 405's picture window, breathing an infinite green rose, a sick magic trick. Coltrane's Eastern phase turning his stomach, his head hung over the fetid toilet, green boluses chunking from his throat like fairway divots.

He was gripping a pint glass of whiskey and ginger, hold the rocks, when he first heard the *swish* of that overstuffed duffel jacket, ribbed like the personified stack of rubber tubes in those tire commercials.

The newcomer dropped a redolent bulge of bubble wrap amid the silver tray's cornucopia of paraphernalia. Other than the table on which this drug-tray rested, Dylan's things were relegated to the floor. The TV, the unmade mattress, the bookshelves, which were just stacks of books.

"Rameen, Peter. Peter, Rameen," Dylan said, dashing his whiskey with water.

"Sorry I'm late, yo. Saw this insane bike in the garage."

His Persian burr battled an urban brogue—born in Pakistan, raised in Brooklyn. Peter mistook his use of the word *insane*. Having heard them all before—suicide rider; murdercycle; crouching tiger hidden death wish—he took it literally.

Catching shit from this walking pile of tires confounded his deepest assumptions about the world. "You mean my bike," Peter asserted.

"The fuck it is," Rameen said. And when Peter didn't respond, "What's the license plate then?"

"Fuck yourself."

"Knew you was lyne."

Peter recited his plate, "F-K-Y-R-S-L-F: Fuck yourself."

"Ho *snap*," Rameen guffawed, curling into the couch's arm. "I just got styled."

"Great plate," Dylan said with significance, bringing the tumbler of whiskey and water to his recliner—or, as he called it, the captain's seat.

Rameen appeared not to hear him. Rather, his eyes hinged on Peter's security belt and Puget Property shirt, gathering data about his person—*thinking*. This perm-and-all Persian who still hadn't flensed his rubbery blubber—he had *ideas*. He leaned and fingered a joint from the tray. "You race or something?"

"Feels like racing time." He wasn't sure why he'd said this. He was holding his first drink in three weeks.

"Nah I feel you bro," Rameen sniggered, then composed himself. "Really though."

"Slows time," Peter shrugged.

"Like I like my books," Dylan proclaimed. "A lifetime's fractal."

"So how you pay for the bike then?"

"Loans."

"That thing go off-road?"

"Probably…"

"Souped?"

"No…"

"Yo really though. Can you ride?"

"You want a demonstration or somethin?"

"If you wanna pay off that bike…"

Rameen had turned earnest, an expression Peter hadn't thought his physiognomy capable of. Peter glanced at Dylan, who was smirking like a jackass. "This dude wants me to *ride* his shit," Peter shook his head, growing his own grin. Rameen had his ear, so he disclosed of some work needing doors into the States, mainly marijuana. "Figure you could strap say, fifty pounds on that bike. Easy. My cousin, Ravjeet, he's got a grow up past Vancouver. Super smart."

"Don't they do that on foot?"

"Game's changed, homie. Fuckin Nucks, they got watch towers, hella personnel, all types of shit now. That sneaky shit don't work no more. You gotta *bust* that shit through."

"Aren't bikes kinda noisy?" Peter glanced at Dylan, who deferred back to Rameen.

"A good runner these days?" Rameen milked his moment. "His engine gives away where he *was*. Racing time," he added as if perfecting Peter's aperçus.

Peter didn't like his pace. Guys who spoke fast and offered emotional sops were guys with an angle. He pressed him, "How come I haven't heard about this?"

"Cause it *works*, bro. And you think the Mounties are tryna broadcast their failures?"

Peter set his drink down to better assess Rameen's any fauxs and faults. Dimebag dealers were idiots and liars. It was possible that his cousin, Ravjeet, dabbled in bud while moving serious stuff in larger numbers—then again, Ravjeet could be some pothead tending a farm marked off by eminent domain, two weeks away from a motorcade of contract crews and squad cars rolling up on his half-baked operation. And historically speaking, runners got caught. They got greedy or imprudent, and Peter couldn't keep seeing O'Reilly for the rest of his life. He'd just end it.

But thirty pounds per run? Maybe even fifty? Fuck, it was possible. The compartment beneath his passenger seat could hold twenty, easy, and the rest he could strap to the girders. He'd only run Rameen's stuff. Cop his cut and duck until the next run. No expansion, no greed. Boycott human nature.

Running could get him out of that 15x15 shitbox. Running could defray tuition statements. Running could pulverize the concrete ceiling that was his $14.75/hr security paycheck, his circadian arrhythmia, his fitful sleeps and waking dreams.

More than any fiscal pragmatism was this *feeling*. For the first time since making that ground turn on his old bike, going nearly parallel, kissing the road's heat, he was excused from justifying the next moment. He was sick of sucking fumes from life's exhaust pipe.

"What's my cut?"

Rameen slid the joint back onto the pyramid, a prop leveraging his presence. "If you're serious, you'll get that bike hella sprung. Then we talk numbers. D's got my digits."

Peter slept past 4PM the next day. He arrived at MATH216 thirteen minutes late, ratty Adidas sounding off his tardiness. Just as he was lowering into a seat in the back, his earbuds were yanked out, the classroom's silence bum-rushing his canals. The professor leaned over him—white muttonchops, porous scowl, tweedy coat with stitched elbow patches.

"This discussion begins at eighteen-hundred hours each and every Tuesday of the quarter. Which quarter lasts from January 22nd, 2010 until March 24th, 2010, broken only by spring break—which break, it appears, has severely taxed your temporal processing," the professor sneered. "What say you?"

What a bunch of bitter bones, when the world was chock-full of opportunities. An "I'm sorry Professor So-and-So" would've calmed the old cod, but Peter hadn't a solid grasp of surname. The other students were brimming statues.

"Let's take a listen to this drivel you're so attached to, you can't turn it off to save your future." With bitter cheer the professor put a bud in his ear. "My lord," he awed, dropping the earpiece and walking away. "As if it could get worse than Jonestown, with all you runts drinking this audible poison," he grumbled, and turned back toward the chalkboard.

"Yo, you're a fuckin clown," Peter drawled.

The professor stopped, shuffled in place, and turned around. "How's that?"

Imparting deep impatience, Peter looked away, shaking his head. "You act like we're halfwits, when we made it here. So fuckin teach us." He flung an arm, "Dude Cory over here?"—indicating the named student—"still pronounces hyperbole like it's a verb for bowling on amphetamines. Mainly because you've given zero examples to the contrary. Prolly thinks asymptote's an archaic noun for *butt-bag.* So why single me out when the whole class is proof you can't teach?"

Someone giggled an *Oh snap* as Peter collected his things and started toward the door.

He wouldn't attend another class at UW.

The bike shop brought him well north of the U-District. Flush with a general auto mechanic and burnt-out Radio Shack, its shotgun style led from a large garage, along a hall of offices, and ended at the reception desk, where a haggard secretary processed intakes and receipts, but spent most of the time texting with a stupid grin on her face.

Peter perused the catalogues fanned on an alloyed stand. Most of the models he glossed over pro forma, uninterested in baggers or other bikes lacking agility. But in a Yamaha with handlebar fairing, Peter found his (b)ride. The head technician, more of a grizzled Harley type himself, came out from his office minutes later and stood over his shoulder.

"Funny you take a liking. The R1's coming in later today. I could give you a ring. Trucks aren't always, well, reliable."

Rather than go back to his shitbox and hospital mask, Peter nipped his flask and ambled. The area's blue-collar vibe roused him from a trance—UW's evergreen bubble, Fremont's boring tourists, downtown's pretentious bustle. Here, in north Seattle, weeds triumphed concrete, clapboard boxed storefronts, and the smell of exhaust reminded him of home.

As a rule, Seattle's January sun came with cold, high pressure banking arctic air against the mountains. Peter's shoulders tightened under a t-shirt and brown hoodie. Returning to the shop, he came across a Motorstore, whose wares ranged from NASCAR kitsch to coat wax. He watched the silver mannequin in the window, which wore black jeans a black leather jacket slashed with fangs of yellow along the arms.

His card went through.

The shop's tinted panes tossed glare. His first hangover in weeks was a good honest gut-check. And, sure, it rasa'd the 'ole tabula. But he'd start to atrophy soon enough. Relapse wasn't a matter of object permanence. With ease he could remember his state of disfigurement—his Dickely dewclaw—following the last bender. The problem was, unlike calls from the head technician, which Peter answered now, he ignored such memories.

The head technician questioned Peter's desire to soup a perfectly absurd bike.

"Trials," Peter replied. This sounded like proper synecdoche.

"Hm," the technician crossed his chubby arms, his legs splayed in the way squat men's do. "Who's your sponsor?"

Peter looked at him. "So I lied."

"Hm."

"I just need the thing to go between trees."

"I don't take blood money, kid." He picked up his pen and pointed. "And what I mean by that is this: I don't care why you want to take your little excursions. Don't even want to hear about it. I'm no saint myself. But I'm not gonna help you to throw yourself headlong into a great fuckin pine, or get shot by a cop or a mule, or some asshole who chased too much scante and got lost. Those are the ways this ends," he said, pen tapping Rameen's specs.

"Sounds like you've got a pretty good idea about all this."

"I've made a living keeping my ideas to myself," the tech retorted.

"Look, we both know these bikes aren't coming off the racks in Japan."

The technician's eyes went sleepy.

"I can prove it under the hood, go and snitch to the suits in Iwata. I may look like I just killed myself last night, but I know how to negotiate this sort of thing," Peter said, placing a loyal wad of bills on the edge of the head tech's neat desk. "Or you can just come out and level."

The technician pulled on his beard, squeaked his chair. His rummy cheeks flushed rummier. His nose twitched, eyes gelling on the wad of Jacksons.

"We'll make it bounce like a six-four."

Rameen's specs went to a tall and tatted mechanic who: girded the supports; infused fork oil; recharged the shock with nitrogen; recalibrated preload and sag; and clicked the suspension looser. The bike sat like a trampoline. The techs jeered as he popped wheelies, did doughnuts, jumped gas lines. The head tech stood a human stricture, but he didn't stop him.

Later that day he met Rameen and his cousin off one of the 5's lesser-used exits. The pine trunks along the embankment were painted white—guised in the color of bark protection, these blanched boles marked the dunes.

He tacked and slowed his matte-yellow Yamaha. The cousins watched as if they hadn't expected him. Closer, Peter confirmed what he'd anticipated: his new bike inverted their expectations, of him, of his seriousness. Ravjeet offered neither hi nor hand, and Peter appreciated those who eschewed niceties. Both cousins helped labor his bike into the woods. A good start.

He made the workouts seem pedestrian. Like his bike was hooked to a gondola cable, purely sure over slope, between crag, down-hill. Then he jumped the embankment. The high whine of his engine, the braced landing and seamless acceleration, as if his wheels had gained friction while still midair. Ravjeet's jaw was all awe and freefall. He ceded: his cousin had done something right.

Peter revved up the service road. With enormous pride, Rameen looked at his cousin.

"Where'd you learn to ride?" Ravjeet said.

"My dad's left nut," Peter said within his helmet, tinted visor hiding his eyes.

Ravjeet switched to Farsi, a burrier version of his cousin's. Then, jutting his chin, he said, "You pack?"

Peter shook his helmet.

"Washington's open carry," Ravjeet explained, "but you need a concealed license to hold in a vehicle."

Lifting his visor, Peter squinted against the low sky's exposure. "How much does that matter with fifty pounds of bud on my bike?"

"Your call," Ravjeet shrugged. "But there's a whole lot of ride up to my farm."

"Yo this kid getting held up? Fat chance."

Ravjeet reeled off a Farsi of insults. Rameen rolled his eyes.

"First run in a couple weeks. We'll work out the details. In the meantime, get a piece. None of that Rambo shit, okay? Go to the range, get some practice."

"Gladly," Peter said.

"Lay off the fuckin sauce," Ravjeet said, head tipped toward his flask.

Peter shrugged, and that seemed to satisfy them. He'd nip enough to get right. It'd be good for him to moderate. With just one night under his belt, he'd already seen blood in his stool.

"And look," Ravjeet said gravely, "don't think you can fuck with me. I've got five other runners and forty trimmigrants. I'm legit, and I'm fair, but if you fuck me, I won't hesitate. They'll find you in a ditch with your arm sticking out."

At the King County Sheriff's Office, he pored over an application that would practically condone arming him for drug runs through the border forest. A bored cop pressed his fingers onto black ink. After a short wait, the processing clerk called him back over to the counter. He stood there as she held the application at arm's length, glossing it. Peter wasn't optimistic. His answers must've convinced the clerk he was on some sort of list somewhere.

"Change these to 'No.'"

He hesitated. Then, "Huh?"

"These three. That I marked with X's," she added, concerned with other work. "Your DUI's been washed and it's not a felony. And this therapy"—she seemed nearly indignant—"it doesn't constitute confinement in a mental health institution. So, that'll be $57.89. For the application fee," she laughed, flashing the pink gum shriveled in her molars.

Peter was incredulous—if a pants-shitter such as himself could get a gun…Then again, it was possible that this was the best feeling of them all. Getting away with something.

Less than a month later he got the letter. It seemed counter to the aims of a just society that a kid like him could lay claim to this laminated card, with his suspicious visage right there in the corner.

Less than two hours later his bike was exactly one Glock-nine and twenty rounds heavier. He'd placed them at the register like any bulk package of potato chips.

Three days later he made his first run, ten pounds of premium Nuck bud strapped to his back. By his fourth, he was running forty pounds for four-large. He hadn't known a summer day could be crisp. He did good work, which was eventless work—work that required neither permit, nor that for which he carried it.

Her father was a professor of postmodern literature and moral philosophy at Berkeley's Moses Hall. Her mother didn't work. They lived near the Painted Ladies. Since kindergarten, she'd attended private school. Bay Heights High, however, would offer her courses in "reality."

"Through its fecklessly allocated public subsidy?" was her premeditated retort. She'd lifted the mouthful from a blog.

The argument ended much as it had begun—without resolution. With every moment, the image of her at Ashbury Prep—the private high school that Ashbury Grammar had groomed her to attend—faded like the photo from *Back to the Future*, which she turned off now, flopped back on her bed, brooded.

What could possibly excuse her father's hypocrisy? It was he who'd spent her childhood waxing poetic about Ashbury Grammar. He who'd held forth about education adapting to the professional ecosystem. He who'd lambasted public school's rigid curricula and standardized testing. But then, during Julia's last winter break at Ashbury Grammar, he started with the glancing comments about Bay Heights.

The comments coincided with talk of money woes, hushed, but Julia heard from the upstairs banister and rushed down to challenge him. It was war. His parley charged Ashbury Grammar as "sheltering" and prompted her with "facing the real world."

Crackpot theories of public school as a wormhole into hyper-reality? Really? And here she'd thought his tweaker days were behind him.

Alas, her father did seem down in some serious doldrums. One morning she found him slumped at the coffee machine in a polka-dot button-up and silk blue trousers. Glasses pinched at hip, he stared at the machine doing its gurgling morning work.

"Watched pot never boils," Julia said, and narrowed her eyes. For a moment she thought his spot of white hair had spread. Then she swiped the shaving cream from above his ear.

"Thanks," he said. "Mr. Coffee is sad." His arm indicated the machine's belabored brooking.

"First day back," she said to say something, straining for the bag of steel cut oats in the beveled corner cabinet.

"Every day is the first day back."

"Right, Dad."

Footsteps announced her mother. "Honey, I need to you to pick up my prescription."

"Ma," Julia cawed.

"Morning sweetie."

Adding milk, Julia craned over her shoulder and saw a sleeveless black dress and scarlet cardigan. "You look hot," she said to her mother.

"All of this could be yours," she sang, twirled, and modeled her arched profile.

"Meh."

"I wish you'd wash those jeans."

"I wish you would, too," Julia said.

"Okay my little guns and roses." He capped his thermos, strapped his messenger bag, kissed his wife curt. "I'm going on a commitment tonight, out in Laurel Heights. If I'm not back by dinner…" he called.

And Julia responded, "We'll just wait longer."

His steps receded, creaking porch stairs, clopping dry sidewalk. Watching her oats fatten, she listened to her mother's morning bustle.

"What's up with Dad?" she said into her porridge.

"Not now, sweetie."

"So there's something up with Dad," she said in descending notes, leaning on the oven's handle, licking her sticky finger. "You're mad at him."

"I'm not mad at him."

"You're *upset*," she fluttered up.

"Sweetie, please? No wiping on the dish towels."

"I'll wash my jeans if you tell me."

"Ha!"

"Come on."

"It's his father," she waved, flipping through packets, flippant.

"Okay. Mom? This is where you keep speaking."

She straightened the packet stacks, three surly clacks of ream on marble island. "He called the other day."

"Really?"

"This isn't a joke, Julia."

"Who's joking? I'm not joking. I'm deeply interested."

"Johnny got power of attorney." She flattened the papers, breathed. "He's cutting us off."

Amorphous, but Julia's insides seemed to understand. "Oh... But...So why are you mad at Dad then? Upset?" she corrected.

"...I know you wanted to stick with Ashbury."

"...So you agree with me going to Bay Heights this fall?"

"It's not that—"

"Do you. Agree. With me going. To—"

"Julia stop it," she pointed. "This is difficult for us."

"You mean like, right now, right? Because I'm calling you out on your bullshit?"

"Okay you're grounded. No TV. No computer. No friends."

"Great, since I won't have friends anyway. Let anarchy reign"—a rueful battle cry.

"Julia Mary Paolantonio."

Pen hovering over their daughter's birth certificate, Julia's father had insisted his daughter and wife share titles. Her mother disapproved this faith to family traditions. Custom also called for avoiding the names of the estranged, including their mistresses. Its evocation indicated her mother's true anger, which worked against her: high scarlet cheekbones, all burlesque ire and angry beauty, were an aesthetic experience save for the subject matter.

"You need to learn to appreciate what we do for you."

"What *you* do for me? Or what some ancient *capo* does for *you*..." she laughed, looking away. "Man, you guys are full of shit."

Her mother's cheeks shrieked like a kettle.

"One day you're going to realize the whole world is full of shit—yourself included—and that your father and I are pretty damn good parents."

Julia refused eye contact.

"After school, straight to your room."

As her mother left without the PTA packets, Julia didn't stop her. Ashbury didn't need them anymore and, apparently, they didn't need Ashbury.

Her first day in Ashbury Grammar's junior high wing had ended precisely a couple minutes earlier. Adolescents, skins bright with overproduction of hormones and collagen, thronged the pickup curb, which she avoided in favor of crossing the playground, where K-6 kids met their parents. Beyond the junior high wing, she heard the whistles of pickup proctors, the honks of minivans, the bustle of kids boarding buses. Her head down, she tracked the asphalt underfoot, staring at gravel pocked with pearlescent grits like stony salami. In her broody ruminations, it hit her...how she was *here*...doing *this*...right...*now*.

Time and space was *weird*, but...not as weird as *existing*.

Was she the one thinking, or was her brain thinking? Or both? Perhaps the jump to sixth grade was jarring. The hallways were clinical, medical, dire, though absent were the grammar wing's color-coded routes to classes, which had always made her think of the variegated lines directing them to the room in which Aunt Ginny's mother had passed.

Junior high was newfangled. She was supposed to enter through the *side* door, where 7th- and 8th-graders loitered, some of them speaking on things she thought only high schoolers did. The teachers had all conspired to remind them that things would be different on the new wing. They were no longer entitled to certain amenities. The welfare system was banished. Their grades would reflect the intersection of intelligence and effort.

Tiger-economy of tweenage endocrine systems.

Pedagogical fearmongering.

Teeming fear.

Skepticism: if things are not as they seem, who can be blamed for what they see?

But Julia was certain: her father was stepping out. Her certainty was that of a prophet's, the certainty that signals birds south. The certainty, according to the media she consumed, of the male biological imperative—XY. The certainty, according to Julia's more progressive instinct, of human nature—A, G, C, T.

Each Sunday, her father attended mass, alone. This past Sunday he returned in a slick white coupe, which *whizzed* past the stop sign at the corner after dropping him off.

"How was it?" her mother asked at dinner.

Awaiting his response, Julia's eyes swung like an owl clock's.

"Pass yours, hon." Meatballs *squished* as she ladled them on plates.

"I'm twelve," Julia announced, taking the bowl and ladling her own.

"There was a ceremony for Father Dominic," he said. "Everyone lit a candle."

"So sad."

So *sad?*

There was a woman. In a speedy sports car. Dropping her father off *well* after mass had ended. If he could rationalize Catholicism, his mind could perform the somersault into another woman's bed.

The next Sunday, Julia told her mother she was going to—um, shit, she hadn't planned the finer points. She'd procrastinated inside *To Kill a Mockingbird*, her first book report not due until mid-October.

Standing in the kitchen—her mother making tea, her father grading essays—Julia prepared words that would convince them to condone an unaccompanied trip to the Bay Bridge. She stared at them, much in the way she did when poking fun at their throttled focus. No matter her angle, the proposal sounded insane to her mind's ear. She was twelve. Organizing solo excursions went far beyond her jurisdiction. Asking for a ride to Chelsea's or Shayla's—who were barely even school friends, let alone weekend besties—would risk her mother seeing her to the front door.

Unless…

"Hey Dad?"

"J-Dog," he semaphored. "What is proverbially up?"

"Please don't."

"Got it. No means no," he X'd indexes.

"Oh my—Dad. Gross much?"

"What's up?"

"Can you drop me off at the Bridge?"

His pen paused over a teacherly flourish.

"Coach Jack wants us to do a long run today but I'm not gonna do all these hills."

"How about I drive three hours down the 5 and drop you off at a checkpoint? I'm sure you'll make friends with the rest of the sex slaves."

"*Jonathan*," rang her mother's appall.

"Come on, Dad. If I have to do my loop four times I'll go crazy."

"Let her go, honey. It's only a few miles away," said her mother. "It's a nice area."

"What is this, the voice of reason in my head?"

Her mother added, "The voice of reason says, it's like two minutes from the church."

"I am very concerned for our daughter's safety," he said.

He meant something else, something she couldn't understand.

"Of course, honey," her mother said, returning to her work.

As did her father. Julia waited.

"You have two minutes," he said. "Your father's late and he's speaking today."

She leaned into the open window and kissed his cheek. He revved off, leaving her near a bike rental shop. Farther, a trail led to the Bay Bridge, whose upper trusses were shrouded in fog. She was three miles from home—but only a bit more than a third from the church.

She ran the gauntlet of eclectic tourists and less-varied locals. The latter grew, per capita, as she wound away from the water—dreadlocks, frosted spikes, loud band shirts. Lots of Zoo York. Metal. Epidermal impalement. Pungency. Skates and their dense soughing. This was what normal looked like, Julia told herself—except for where normal looked.

Their heads like camera dollies, tracking her with clinical precision as they passed.

Off Lombard she cozied into a stoop's cove. Along the curb nearby, technicians fed wire into a truck with an impressive cross of haste and care. Past the truck, across the street, stood an Inky Blots and a Spencer's. Again she referenced the directions, pulled from MapQuest. She looked up. Inky Blots, 431. Spencer's, 435. Bookending 433, which was definitively not a church.

An evanescent thought moved through her, as only the deepest and most uncomfortable truths do: that, much as her mother had described men's desire, vindication emptied itself shortly after it was won. Julia was cold in her spandex, shivering within the stoop's cove. She hugged her stomach.

Then she saw his burnished profile, eclipsing that woman's, walking beside him. The frosted glass door closed after them and Julia was spurned forth into the street, gull shadows flitting overhead. She made of her hand a hat's bill, squinted through the opaque entrance, seeing another door down a short hallway. She waited outside another few minutes, peeking every so's to ensure the coast's clearness.

Motel? Brothel?

She crept inside, along the drab hall, held her ear to a board wood door. On the door's brass placard was a circumscribed triangle, illuminati-like. Having a cult leader for a father was perhaps worse than a cheater. Just a few lines in she heard, "…and as Committee Leader, nothing pleases me more than to present to you Jonathan Raciti, who's here to tell his story."

Modest applause dwindled to rustles and restives. An amplified screech, an adjusted microphone, and her father's voice.

"Hi, my name is Jonathan, and I'm an addict and an alcoholic."

"Hi Jonathan."

"I'd like to thank Miranda and Julio for advocating this. They're two of biggest reasons I keep coming back."

"Keep coming back, it works if you work it."

Through the door's fake wood and the death of certainty, she listened to a story…

"Where I was born, if you didn't lock your door, you deserved to get your shit lifted."

The crowd laughed nervously, nearly cloyingly.

"Luckily, before I was even playing t-ball, my pop moved us from our apartment near the Hudson, into a gablefront outside Yonkers. One Sunday my pop was out of town. My ma was talking with girlfriends on the phone, which meant I could sneak some TV time, when the doorbell rang—twice, I remember. My mother yelled at me to get it and that set off baby Danny more than the doorbell had. I opened the door to a short man in a windowpane suit, charcoal with white crossings, and tortoise shell glasses. A lot like Meyer Lansky. He asked if my pop was home. When I told him he wasn't, Meyer said something about that being convenient, and asked to speak to my mother. 'You can speak to me,' I said to him. I was trying to keep my mother on the phone so I could keep watching cartoons. He told me to let him know he came by and turned away, and I caught a glimpse of something I'd never seen before outside TV or a movie: a semi Glock. On impulse, I said maybe one of the dumbest things I've ever said. I said, 'What's that?' Meyer, he's amused now. He peers down at me and says, 'You know what a vig is, hm?' I didn't even know what a live pair of tits looked like, but I nodded. He was less than convinced, and rightly so. He crouched down, that Glock's handle poking out his waistband. 'Your father, he owes a little money,' he says. 'For what?' I ask, and he says, 'For taking the Chargers with eight points.' At that point I squared up to him. 'He's a Giants fan.'…He stood up and said, 'It doesn't seem like you know what he really is, guy.'… Now I was scared and pissed off, which always turned me into a smartass, or made me more of one. I started explaining to him that the original guy—Guy Fawkes—was part of a conspiracy to blow up Parliament with gunpowder. I told him how, in the end, Guy and his boys all got caught. That they were drawn and quartered. Now, they say you can be too smart for this program. I think that applies to life in general. You think you know things. After I told my little parable about Guy Fawkes, I realized he'd use his piece if he had to. Not on me, and that was worse because of me.

"I told Meyer to give me a minute, I'd go get him his money. I hightailed upstairs, soft on my feet to keep my mother focused on her friends' gossip and whatnot. But once I got to my room, I heard her Coney accent, which could cut through a cinderblock. 'Can I help you?' she calls to him, and I hear him say something about, 'That's okay, ma'am. Your son's been kind enough to donate a dollar to the synagogue,' and she's all, 'That's sweet,' and whatnot, sucking on a Turkish Royal. I can still smell those. Anyway, Meyer knew what he was doing. Made a living doing it: shaking people down. I was aware of it, but what was a kid to do? I had no choice. I packed every cent since my first allowance. Didn't even know how much my pop owed. Just brought it down, assuming it was a sum I couldn't count to. And when Meyer opened the knapsack, he just smirked at me like, it's this easy for him. He tipped the brim of the hat he wasn't wearing and whistled his way off the porch. I cowered in my room for hours before I heard my pop come up the stairs, then his voice, just beyond my door: 'Office. Now.' Those were very bad words. Then again, the things I'd gleaned about his dealings earlier that day, they granted me some sort of amnesty. Plus, my mother was upstairs putting my sister down, and he couldn't kill me with witnesses in the house. In his office he was pointing at his chair. He would've whupped me if he'd found even the imprint of my ass in that chair. Now I realized this had less to do with the seat than what I could find out about him while sitting in it, and this pissed me. The way he talked about his job, he'd always called it 'human resources,' never a company, agency, institution. Still, I sat in the damn chair. 'You gave away two large, Jon. Two grand,' he said. 'Is that what a man does? Hands over his livelihood?' I tell him he had a gun, and he's worried about my allowance money? He said to me, 'Look, Junior, if you're a sailor, you're tryin to get home, but the wind don't change, what do you do, do you throw yourself overboard? No, you wait for the fuckin wind to change back.' As a kid, I felt like the less others knew about you, the more power you had. Maybe my pop felt the same way. I couldn't understand what me being put in danger had to do with sailing, so I got up, and I slammed the office door in his face. In our family—to disrespect your father like that? But I didn't care. I went to my friend Christian's and played Atari.

His mom made us grilled cheeses. It was nice. One of my last memories of normality. Later that night I snuck back into the house, and my pop was waiting by the fire. For the second time that day, he requested that I sit, on the couch this time. He rolled up his sleeves and paced. Then he surprised me. He said it wasn't the world that made me who I was. I did.' At that moment, in my kid's brain, I was wondering what my mother knew about what he did, and I just got angry again. I didn't think about what he was telling me. I just asked him, straight up, 'What do you do?' I saw him caught between explanations. 'It's a way of living, of knowing how to survive,' he said, and just then, my ma appeared at the bottom of the stairs in her nightgown, ready for bed. 'Danielle's out,' was all she said, and went back upstairs. She knew. A few years later, my pop and I were watching The Godfather, which to my pop was a documentary. Sounds cliché, but that's the thing, I'd try to ruin it for him. I remember watching Sonny get word about his sister getting beat up by her husband again. You know how Sonny races over in a rage, but the tollbooth's staked out by Barzini's henchmen. I'd been drinking quite a bit—toleration juice—but I remember saying something like, 'Had there been EZ-pass, Sonny would still be with us.' My pop just told me to get my feet off the table and put his beer there. I thought he was just displacing my smartassness, but after setting his beer, he paused the movie, right as Sonny was getting laced up. Maybe it was the sight of a son's death. I'd graduated that morning. My mother had come with Danny, who was a stranger to me even then. My pop was under house arrest so that anklet kept him from the ceremony. Still, maybe he was sorry to have missed it on some level. Maybe it was its own rite of passage. I'm still not sure why he chose this moment, but either way, he asked me if I remembered that day, giving away all my money, and what he'd said about the sailor. His eyes were on the movie. I thought for a moment, more to seem like I was trying to remember than actually remembering. He said it was the principle of it, that I'd been taken, and I begrudged him that. He was drunk. Or he was getting there, the happy rising action. He was that gleam-to-mean type. Anyway, there would be no better time to ask: I asked him what happened to the collector—to Meyer Lansky—and he just shrugged and flicked his head toward the TV, which was still paused on Sonny's last breaths. I was gut-checked, like a boxer taking a haymaker. I could no longer pretend what he was—what I was. He pressed play, releasing Sonny from his suffering. Then he said to me, 'What you don't see in the movies, is how they shit themselves.' He and my ma had split, so we were watching the movie in his bachelor pad in the city, a closet that cost a million bucks. For my ma's sake, it was just pizza, two-liter Coke, bottle of Jack. But he'd already shown me around, introduced me to his guys. He wasn't a conscript anymore, but full-connected. Crew to his name—guys collecting for him now, his own little Meyers. Guys paying him protection. Goombahs coming in and out. Stories about stupid conversations with John Gotti, like he was Bill fucking Clinton. The show-and-tell was a proposition. He'd remind me I was good with numbers. Send me off with uncomfortably thick wads of cash, his way of communicating what I could have. When the pressure really started building, I started using, half to cope but half to spite him. Kinda like treating a girl like shit to get her to dump you. Ran away upstate, where the meth was cheap and plenty. He'd still send guys to check on me where I was squatting in Rochester, doing all the standard shit to support my habit. But he'd wait till I begged. His guys'd come in kicking the other squatters, berating me for a bit, then leave me with a twenty, just enough to cop something to come off the crank. Like he wanted me back but had to humiliate me first…One day one of his guys tried to prove a point and went too far. You would've though this guy was on speed. A fuckin zealot. He was furious, screaming about how we could've been brothers, how I was throwing everything away. All the while I'm on the nod—nothing, just nothing, glaze over my eyes, you know. Not that it would've worked, but he couldn't beat up his boss's son. He could come up there and berate me, tell me I was a piece of shit, but he couldn't touch me. So he found the nearest junkie and just choked him out. Right there in front of me, and I did nothing—except get clean, the very next day…First meeting

I went to, I heard about Mikey, found dead after two years sober...
We'd split a bag and I hadn't even gotten his name...I wasn't planning on telling that story...Sorry, everyone...Anyway, this is not
when I stopped being an addict. There's never a singular event
that drives one to drink and smoke glass and shoot up for three
years, and there isn't one that ends it. But there are signs—or, in
my case, explicit acts. Addiction is in my blood. It's in my pop's,
and it's in mine. It's...I'm sorry. Thank you very much."

The audience's response—"Thank *you*, Jonathan"—knocked
Julia back to presence, staggering from the door. The folded map
slipped from her fingers. The rattled knob—the door opening.
She was stuck in mental mud. She watched him lean down to
drink, slurping the fountain's limpid stream, lips gleaming as he
straightened and saw her. During his pause his eyes shifted, from
singular shock to plenary hurt, and he went to her, his arms two
bulky snakes, eerily restrictive. Her understanding caught in this
vise, she couldn't help but think, *I don't know who you are.*

Born into and defected from his Sicilian sponsorship, Jonathan Raciti Junior was programmed for deep ambivalence. With Julia now privy to his past, he openly raged against America's historical oppression of Italian immigrants—or harangued his heritage for their venal means of combating such oppression—only to trace this violent tribalism back to their savage tip of the boot—but didn't that make them cowardly barbarians unable to inspire a proper coalition?—then again, they damn well did after getting their fill of foppish dictators—and this pendulum swinging for a while before her father finally tuckered out.

A professional employer of the Socratic method, the Italian topic polarized her father's mind, a personal polemic expressed without much ado—until his decision to "assimilate" her education.

The truth was, he hadn't changed his mind about Ashbury Prep and the efficacy of its private model. Rather he'd been scared to tell her the real reason they were sending her to Bay Heights. And that's why she was mad: in hiding their money problems, Julia sensed his disease—as the cult deigned to call his immensely complex and long-latent habit—rearing its irascible head, baring its infectious fangs, drooling is slavering drool.

Perched on a browning slope, Bay Heights High's supports hung like schist legs over its hillside seat, facing opposite the water. Built on arid land where fell little rain and fierce sunlight, Bay Heights was idyllic, with a view toward the urbane: from classroom windows students gazed out over the city, which Julia did throughout her first day, longing for Ashbury Prep, which she'd idealized for over ten years, from two hundred yards away, across a parking lot divided by more than age, but an unofficial border between Ashbury Grammar's raucous rabble of preteens and

Prep's existentially initiated. It was all in their posture, their relative nonchalance, a knowing that eluded Julia if not her *cooler* peers.

But Bay Heights was loud. Colossal. Individuality included cleavage and spiked bracelets, cussing in front of teachers, testosteronal scuffles like reruns of some Discovery Channel show about primate hierarchies. And they were some of the smarter ones. The last bell unleashed the student shoal, which swept her downstream, emptying into a parking lot's flat tarn of tar. Midst this lake of blacktop Julia recognized a couple girls from her last period. One of them was gawking at her hip.

"Hey. What's that?" the gawker said. "Your book."

"Oh, something my dad gave me."

"Your dad gave you *this*?"

The book slipped between her back and pack—a gesture more awkward than the embarrassment of being addressed—Julia felt heat rise up her turtled neck, cable-knit and black. But her classmate was kindly insistent, and Julia relented.

"*Killers of the Dream* is like all-time," she blinked, returning the text. "Are you also descended from the queenly Negress?"

"Shut up," her friend said. To Julia, "She's fucking with you."

"Yes," Julia said, still stunned.

"She's obviously Italian. Paolantonio, right?"

"Yes, I meant—Yes."

"I'm Liza."

"I'm Shazni. But all my bitches call me Shaz."

Shaz's caramel complexion was sprinkled with freckles like caster mocha, both hers and Liza's frames more muliebral than Julia's.

"Ms. Hastings *hates* me already," Shaz said and resumed her strut, which Liza then Julia fell in with. Where to, Julia couldn't know. "I can see the lump in her throat, coming up…MULATTO!" Shaz mimed an epithetic retch. "So. Julia. Is you a down ass bitch?"

"Uh."

"Doth one blazeth?"

"Do you like to get high," Liza clarified.

They slowed amid a row of cars, stopping when Shaz leaned on a worn sedan—what Shaz would refer to as her hooptie—fingers drumming its faded green pastel.

"Oh. No. My dad is an addict. Recovering," she added quickly.

"Oh, damn girl."

"Well, we don't have to…" Liza assured.

"No, it's totally cool. I'm totally not against it. Totally a personal choice."

"Totally," said Shaz, amused.

"Well," Liza said, "we were gonna hit up In-N-Out if you wanna join?"

"Blunt-ride the whip," Shaz sang, thumping the hooptie's husk.

Late summer's afternoon blast of fog was forming just offshore, ready to roll over the city like the lot's rising din.

"Sure," Julia shrugged.

The duo dated back to kindergarten—once upon a time, when friendships could be forged by the simple fact both having zeds in their names. Though Julia didn't think much of it, only now had they invited another to join their duo of heavenly creatures.

To them, Julia was lucky. She was an only child. She liked her family. Liza and Shaz, however, described their folks as products of bygone eras and cruder worlds. Everyone, thought Julia to herself, was deprived of perspective, public or private.

Liza Abdilova came from Czechs who'd escaped the Sudetenland. Her parents were punted Jews without a pegging among the Bay Area's corporate frontiersmen, Castro gays, and unapologetic potheads. They insisted on practicing the Shabbos, "Even though it's like, *obvious* that I'm tryna hum depressing Yiddish hymns on my Friday nights."

Shazni Zabwe hated her father in the deep way daughters can. She hated him for their truncated surname, bastardized from its original form and meaning. ("The vestige of our assimilation," Shaz spat.) She hated him for his mandate that Zabwe females remain faithful to tribal gender roles ("Oppressed woman things," she muttered.) Fela Kuti was Shaz's Eminem—"Fight Music" replaced with "Roforofo Fight"; desultory urban rage with rage against the Nigerian machine—which infuriated her father, who was a former attaché to the Nigerian Consulate in Atlanta. Her mother, a landed South African, never stood a chance. According to Shaz, she'd succumbed to her country's guilt complex in marrying an Igbo patriarch pledged to the Motherland's despotism. Her brothers? She got along with them well enough, but their friends? They just wanted to fuck her, or her brothers' friends whom she actually wanted to fuck hadn't fucked her when they'd had the chance.

Freshman year deepened into late fall. The fogs less fickle, porch thermometers bursting with mercury. Julia too made a transition, from triune curio to truant enigma. She'd disappear for a week only to return unannounced, corroborating her father's recent lecture at this symposium, on that obscure subject, and so on. Or she'd cite a weekend spent with the 'rents. Such behavior was odd at best, subversive at worst. But once back together, Julia's absence was quickly forgiven—or rather, forgotten. Together, in Shaz's glorious jalopy, Julia watched blunts cross the lacuna as they sputtered streets long known to them. She'd come home reeking of pot but not having partaken, until she did, as the months, and years, went on.

Low-lit and cozy, the Raciti-Paolantonio living room was the home's only without a window. Homework in one hand, bowl of oats in the other, Julia stood on thick ruffled carpet—all the benefits of shag, sans the sleazy connotations—awaiting her father's attention, which was trained on the textbook in his lap. Behind him, a bookcase claimed the wall—general literature on the left, his little slice of academia on the right, limned by his published treatises, propped atop this pedagogical section.

"Philosophy is 99% illusion," he said, eyes still on his book, "proven by its theories being at the mercy of modern amenities and science—never the other way around."

"Then how come religion's still around?" she grumbled, sitting on the leather ottoman in front of the couch, slapping her math homework on the coffee table's mahogany. The bowl too followed, blotting out this kaleidoscope of precalc problems.

"Leibniz's monad might've been replaced by a deeper understanding of atoms and quarks, but no one's proven the absence of God."

"God is like math," she groused. "I mean I don't know how a microwave works, but I'm honestly okay with never knowing."

"Well, it was the Pythagoreans," he said, closing his text, adjusting his glasses, "who came up with the monad number series—a geometrical proof that everything has a center—which Leibniz and Spinoza appropriated, claiming they were God's intangible building blocks for the universe," whose mystery her father illustrated through broad-armed gestures. "So without Pythagoreans, we'd have no precalc, no mathematical advancement, no modern philosophy. But without Leibniz and Spinoza"—a smirk quivering at lips' corner—"we'd have no fun."

Her father's ability to parse these little antinomies had once sparkled under his self-abasing spell: his self-proclaimed charlatanism lent him only greater credibility. Yet ever since that one afternoon, following her first day on Ashbury Grammar's junior high wing, her awe had genuflected to *skepticism.* She began viewing his intellectual modesty as a rhetorician's parlor trick, as if conjuring up counterpoints for the sole purpose of proving a concrete point, which philosophy seemed so hell-bent on avoiding. Lately—as she would moments from now—she'd given voice to such doubts, calling upon their interpersonal contentions as would a psychotherapist during analysis. As early as now, she was Myriadal's psych major-in-the-making.

"So I'm heading out. Once I finish this shit."

"Oh?" his brow piqued. "And how are San Francisco's most promising debutantes? Still holding paint swatches to the glass ceiling, I presume."

"It's almost like you don't like them," Julia sighed.

"Liza's alright."

"Hey."

"I am but a young goat," he started.

"A kidder," she continued—this game of theirs kind of like the vocabulary version of six degrees of Kevin Bacon, the rules equally understood and undefined.

"A jester."

"A harlequin."

"Oh, very nice."

"No stalling," she pointed.

"Merry Andrew." "Movie."

"Talkie."

"That's a synonym!"

"Is not," her father sang.

A second passed, an arm akimbo. Then she leaned and stuck her tongue in defeat.

"A snake?" he said.

"What's for dinner?"

"Ask your mother." He placed the book on an end table.

"She in her culinary cell?"

"Christ."

Her mother called, "I happen to enjoy being objectified."

"Um, ew?" Julia grimaced.

She appeared from behind the partition. "Will you be joining us at the table, m'lady?" she said, and curtsied.

"Depends if I'll be subjected to the nature of my bastardship."

"Watch it," her mother pointed a spatula, flinging a globule of oil.

"What? I'm just speaking my truth."

"Your what?" he grinned, squinting.

"Shaz," her mother gruffed, shook her head, and returned to the stove.

Julia watched him watching her. He pushed his horned-rim glasses, buttoned his blue cotton cardigan, and pulled his bluer board shorts. Their rowhome was purple. Nothing in this city was satisfied with subtlety. It was all a baroque carnival.

"Your mother's right," he said to Julia.

"Careful. Those are the sort of words that carry the fourth wave."

"Okay, honey? That's enough snark for the evening," he said, retrieving his pipe from the end table's drawer. He loaded and lit. Tobacco's fug could almost fill her spiritual cavities. Combined with the scent of garlic crackling in olive oil, the vinegared tomatoes and capers on flatbread, this was home.

"Give her a break. Her home life isn't exactly pleasant."

"Her dad makes good money," he shrugged.

"Here we go. The currency of happiness in our society. Regale me, again, in the metric?"

"I didn't write the book."

"Actually, you did. It's right behind you."

"Oh yeah." He mimicked the Michelangelo laugh, then mocked his own work: "Her parents, being blind capitalistic minions, can't connect her rabid sociopolitical passion to any sort of financially stable future."

"And you'd be okay with me if I were her?"

"That's like asking if I'd be okay if you weren't okay. That girl needs help, Jules. Despite or because of her parents, environment, or whatever."

Julia dropped her head and peered. *Skeptical.*

"Am I saying anything you're not thinking?" He squinted over a pull on his pipe. "She's a good girl with a good heart. All those exculpatory clichés. But here's another cliché: You can't help someone that doesn't want help."

"She's also sixteen," Julia said. Slumped into the Zelda couch, her feet pushed and fetched the ottoman like an ab-roller. "You're more like your dad than you admit."

"I resent that."

"Her dad performs *exposure checks* before she leaves the house."

"That's between her and her father." Then, "Does he really call them exposure checks?"

She sat up. "How about the fact that she can't date boys until she's in college?"

"Personally, I don't agree. But it's his choice."

"Her brothers could date when they were still in high school." She was blinking like Shaz now.

"You're arguing with someone who agrees with you, which means you're arguing with yourself."

"I'm expressing myself. If we were talking about her race, you would too."

"To be anything but white in this country is to be culturally predisposed to anger. But we're not talking about the validity of Shaz's anger. We're talking about the nature in which it affects her and how she can better cope with it." He tugged from the pipe. Musky vapors shrouded his face. "Okay, this conversation has taken a turn for the clinical."

"Paging Doctor Raciti," Julia inflected lowly.

"Aw, that's the first time you've referred to me by my proper title," he said, hands clasped over heart.

"Dammit."

"We don't choose who we love. Take your mom. She can blow a house down, but I adore her scarlet flush."

"I heard that!"

Maybe he was right. Shaz was an angry person. No matter how virtuous, her ideology was beset by this anger. Then again, as her father had said, oppression *created* anger, and Shaz did contradict her feminist agenda. Her self-esteem seemed dangerously dependent on romantic attention. She often acted as if she had no say in a relationship—only during their blunt rides.

Weeks wasted wending Haight streets, the weed more than Julia's well of generosity helping her endure the fallout of Shaz's abortive trysts. Tears, tirades, and coughing conniptions delivered into an unplugged blunt, the roach sucked out like a snake's venom. Shaz wept as if ditched at the altar. Each treacherous boy had made promises and preambles—was what Shaz claimed in the aftermath. Julia tired of reminding Shaz, over and over: that she'd been ambivalent about these boys to begin with; that power was surrendered from the moment she "decided" to "let" a guy fuck her.

Her melodramatic presentation—inexorably jilted—took time Julia would never recoup. She began to resent her. One day, a particularly drawn consolation sesh forced Julia to acknowledge the soapish imbroglio as an overplayed rerun: she outright accused Shaz of hooking up with someone for whom she'd expressed disdain. Liza had to mediate their texts for a week.

During that week, Julia weighed Shaz's wit and spontaneity against her patent histrionics. But she couldn't gauge the scale's reading. That, or she wouldn't.

By the end of junior year, the blunt ride had long stood as their ritual séance, their need to contact deadened thoughts after the school day's tedium. Shaz learned to let Liza throw out the idea, whereupon she'd chide Liza for "pressuring" Julia. "She hasn't hung out with her daddy in what, two days?"

Liza's arm reached around her gnashed headrest. Julia whined down the window, accepted the blunt, and pressed her feet against Liza's seat back. She lipped it and ripped, held, gazed at silvered wisps leaking from the roach. She hit it again from a quarter inch. Cannabinoids across a synaptic cleft. She took smaller hits after this, tiny ones. The hills rolled like topographical frequencies studded with the pastel façades of San Francisco's garish homes. She got an idea.

"We should start a site."

Two birds, a stone, and the desperate hope that a baby might save their marriage.

Liza's eyes flickered in the side mirror. "What kind?"

"I don't know. But we do this every day. We slog through school. We cram for tests. We wipe our RAM," she said, flipping a hand at the blunt. "We wake up and do it again. If we're going to organize our lives around getting into the schools we want, why not start doing something we like?"

"Ruth Bader Ginsburg back here."

"I learned C++ at that summer camp last year," Liza said.

"At least *some*thing productive happened there."

"An advocacy site," Julia said, paying the blunt forward. "Liza writes the code, we design and curate. Or Liza can do both," she added quickly.

"Uhmygod. I have a name already."

"Yeah?" Julia said, leaning into the lacuna.

Shaz continued, "My brothers legit cream their jeans over college basketball, and there's this old commentator they love named Dick Vitale…"

"And?" Liza prodded.

"So we could call it like, *Vagina* Vitale."

"Or," Julia said, receding into the backseat, hands clasped behind her head. "*Pussy* Vitale."

"*Yes*," Shaz agreed. "We have *Pussy Vitale* written in like noir-ish script. Then below that, some busty-ass *femme* fatale caricature whose vagina is like, swallowing Dick Vitale's head."

"Genius," Julia moaned through gritted teeth—a real boiler-room frisson.

They drove another couple hours. In a moment of seemingly unmitigated joy, Julia proposed *Pussy Vitale*'s portal tabs be labeled by puns on white male artists. Among them, a blog (David Foster's Hospice) and found art (Betch Banksy).

Then there was Joanathan Stanzen. Which started as a general poetry forum. But then people started battling each other, this mix of rhyme, rhythm, and verse. Users built their own competitions, their own culture, their own ethos—us against us.

So Liza cobbled together a sort of sharable live-stream .doc, plugging a randomization algorithm for passing the "mic." Whoever received the mic had three minutes to drop a stanza. Of the page's volume, roughly 89% were there to watch (and vote, and comment), with only 11% queued to participate. The triune posted flyers wherever they went, targeting co-ops, nonprofits, cafés, dispensaries, gay bars, more gay bars.

Tagline: *It's gonna be a bra'nfire.*

Just days after launch, username: Blax Americana lit Joanathan Stanzen with a poem that classmates passed around Facebook like a sultry note in math class. A reworked version, published in Berkeley's journal, went on to win a Pushcart. Thus prompting Shaz's demand to spin off a journal of theirs—a glorified zine.

"Clearly we deserve credit for this," she said and, ripping a hit, voice choked with smoke, repeated, "Clearly."

Liza's silence only deepened Julia's incredulity. How could she ignore Shaz's ignorance?

They may not have been *McSweeney's*, but *Pussy Vitale* was worth more than another glorified zine riding the literary zeitgeist's dick. Far more than another arty webpage, they offered what few URLs could: a viable platform.

Proof: a Pushcart-winning poem's unlikely rise was originally drafted—or, according to some, *allegedly* drafted—on Joanathan Stanzen. *The TAV* (owned by The Avant Viral, Inc.), a media startup in New York, covered the poem's provenance and it'd gone viral. *The TAV*'s piece spent some time lauding the poet's tropes ("… Blax's slant-rhyming parody of a rapper's day-in-the-life reads like Lil Wayne breaking his diary into sixteen bars…"). But they spent more on the site on which Blax penned it ("…*Pussy Vitale's* most popular forum has gained most of its traction in a niche feminist culture. One can't help but draw parallels to another social media platform—except this one sprung from exclusivity. As an open-source platform—Joanathan Stanzen—their features and promo and physical events have helped catapult two dozen-odd women into the literati's manor …").

A couple weeks after *The TAV*'s piece, Julia threw an advocacy event at Borderlands, a used bookstore smarmed in polished wood scattered with ratty rugs. Any worries concerning turnout were wiped away upon entry: not exactly packed, but people were scattered to the bookends.

Local authors read their work. A few girls got everyone up with some slam poetry. An older woman read some relics from her activist days. Julia hawked raffle tickets at a buck a ticket for feminist artifacts and sex toys. Liza's groupies—programmers, Internet prescients, sex-starved bloggers—seemed to swoon over their own compliments and questions, or compliments guised as questions.

And then there was Shaz, who begrudged the whole affair. Who stood cruciform in the corner. Whose curt introductions were aware of their angst to the point that the crowd, Julia sensed, could only question why they failed to rein in said angst, so she seemed the exhibitionist. Who took ten to hit a blunt with the bulls before the store window and accepted a shotgun from a gorgeous young man who happened to possess a pussy. (This wasn't the first time Julia felt past her controls.) Who got miffed when a white elderly lady, following Shaz's talking points surrounding intersectionality, spoke out about her experience with being old And now, Shaz appeared apoplectic as a small girl interrupted her motion to conclude the event.

"So thanks again, and if no one else has anything to share…"

"I do have something to share."

The crowd's chuckles chased her up the stage, redoubling as she struggled to lower the mic. Accomplished, smiling, she stated with startling surety, "My mother named me Lynn."

Lynn looked thirteen going on nine. But she had the lungs to breathe a carbon-based story into life. The only attendee to speak without reading, Lynn told of the first woman to fly a military aircraft. Many years ago, the US Air Force had commissioned this nameless woman to test-run automatic piloting systems for carrier planes. After two successful intracontinental flights, Air Force brass commissioned a flight over water—from which she never returned.

Lynn scuttled back to her seat before "embarrassing herself," she'd later tell Julia.

"Sorry we had to cut you off."

"Oh no," Lynn assured, making room and smiling for a bustling young girlboy in plaid and overall jeans. "I wouldn't want any more time than the others."

"So what's the story behind all this?" Julia tipped her head toward Lynn's ocean-blue tunic and grassy-green robe with gold trim.

"Well, I woulda told this too if I'd've kept my shit together. My dad used to tell us ghost stories about Mom getting lost in the Bermuda Triangle, like fairytales with happy endings. The blue is the one about her getting lost underwater, the green is the jungle one, and this," she opened her robe, revealing gray inlay crossed with black barbwire. Julia bent closer. "This is the scariest one, about her being a prisoner since she could've landed in Cuba, but *this* is my favorite one," she said, excited, peeling back a seam that hid fabric dyed by fiery yellows and oranges. "This is the story about how she flew into the sun."

"Oh, Lynn," Julia offered. "I'm so sorry."

She nodded and, eyes lowered, pushed pursed lips off-center in the universal expression of unfinished acceptance. You never totally do, Julia would think years later.

"You made these?"

"Mm-hm," she brightened. "With my dad."

"You're a brave girl."

"Oh. Well. Thanks."

They beamed at each other for a bit.

"Hope to see you again soon," Julia said. "If your dad lets you come back," Julia winked.

"He drove me here," she chirped, sprung up on her tippy-toes. She wore a pine green pair of those Crocs that looked like shower shoes.

Julia found Shaz and Liza outside, where a cool fog hung low, halving the stores and houses. People stuck around and talked about it. Shaz's spirits had lifted following a long conversation with one of the published poets, and the triune left the café in high spirits.

But then, later that night:

pUSSY vITALE

Why the pimp-ass font? Read Our Story

Virals   Phantasmagori   Betch Banksy   David Foster's Hospice   Joanathan Stanzen

THE PUSSY'S PUMP

Was interrupted during our open mic at Borderlands by a white lady who wanted to one-up my intersectionality with being old. #whitewomenaretheworst.

A baby certainly hadn't made things simpler. Their differences were like splayed haunches, a boggy crotch of contention that bestrode poor Liza. Hostile arguments, growing archives of mutual grievance, less after-school séances. One argument started over a small site detail and ended with Shaz accusing Julia of exploiting feminism for attention. O, the irony.

And yet she heard herself regurgitate Shaz's fanaticism to her father.

"Why do you bring me these complaints," her father questioned, "if you're just going to turn around and defend them?"

Because in defending Shaz she defended being friends with Shaz.

But, then again, Shaz kept her trapped in the amber of their freshman year. The unambered Julia had evolved. Julia the person—not the artifact—was jealous of Shaz's bust—and *liked* being jealous of Shaz's bust—and *liked* her body for its sexual function—and didn't see this as a slight against her comprehensive function.

This fluid Julia could like *certain* high school ostentations—parties over pep rallies—and still be privy to her privilege. The unfossilized Julia liked *people*. She liked *things*, like clothes. She'd spent her childhood in sweats, boyish jeans, t-shirts, until blossoming into a cis-woman with sartorial savvy: any unlocked thrift store. She liked rolling up to frees (frē *n.*: underage party absent parental supervision) at midnight, decked in Catholic school chic, ass-high plaid skirts and crew-necks unbuttoned to le décolletage.

Julia mused at the cliché about precocious kids being sponges, soaking up all the stuff. Shaz followed this platitude to its logical terminus: her sudsy learnings wrung out over an intellectual drain. Her sense of injustice was circular—360° of condemnation—and you were only safe at the center, beside her. She lumped every grievance, every trauma, every piece of malaise onto the archetypal male animus. If he or it deserved her criticism, he or it deserved to be stripped from the world. Julia feared what she couldn't articulate: that Shaz was *addicted* to the anger. One day, Julia put this notion to the test.

"So what are we going to do?"

Shaz's eyes flittered in the rearview. "What do you think we should do?"

"I mean it was all in good fun but now it looks malicious."

"Or accurate."

"The dude did hang himself," Liza said.

"That will be $11.45. Please pull around."

"It's cashed," said Shaz, passing the blunt.

"You have to pull around to pay, ma'am."

"Uhhhh it's definitely still cherried," Liza said.

"No, I meant—" Shaz started into the drive-through speaker. "Never mind. Thank you."

"We at least have to put out a statement or something."

"Put it out," Shaz ordered.

"I'm looking at the fucking stem of this maraschino."

"Uhmygod *fine*."

Shaz paid, passed back a holster of fries, and pulled out of the drive-through. The hooptie ticked its portents: a Chevy truck

T-boning Julia's side of the car; her building tolerance to bud, the drives dulling in a back-seat haze.

"It'll look bad if we don't," Julia kept on.

"I'm not really concerned with how things look. I'm concerned with how they are. To claim that David Foster Wallace was on our side when he was the poster child of the white male-dominated literary institution is naïve as fuck."

Julia hit the three-second timer, after which any response would taste stale to Shaz. "Have you ever even read anything he's written?"

"Yeah, a couple things."

"Like what?"

Liza's head fell to her window's sill. "Can we not?"

"I read the pool one."

"So not really."

"Oh my God. *Julia.* Is this your way of telling us you have a secret shrine of the dude in your room? I mean, he does kind of think like your dad."

Julia kicked Shaz's chair—kicked it hard—and Shaz slammed the brakes, horns blaring by. She glared in the rearview, all appall, as she pulled into a CVS parking lot. Fluid conflict ran hot. Her blood rushing to stop her heart from legislating an apology. The blunt giving off its dying gasps. Were you supposed to just let things die?

"Is you a down ass bitch or you gonna pass the fucking blunt."

Silence stretched like contrails in wake of Julia's outburst. They looked at each other in the mirrors—and then geeked out. But Julia felt her laughter's fakeness, its plastic cast in the mold of fear for what she'd lose, along with Shaz.

"I *is*," Shaz requited, and passed the blunt back to Julia. "Well I don't think we should take Hospice down. That says we did mean ill by it. Like, now that he's crow meat, maybe we shouldn't've."

Liza cut in quickly, "But we do say something, so people know this isn't a charnel house for non-females."

"Seconded."

"Fine. But you're writing it." Shaz looked at Liza, then the rearview. "Blood?"

"Blood," Julia and Liza chorused, miming slashed palms that they then smashed together.

"Uhmygod this burger is a fucking gastrogasm," Shaz moaned mid-chew. "You know we're basically eating corn meat right?"

"And manure."

"Jules, ew much?"

"Up past the hooves," she demonstrated then toked.

"I've thought about going vegan," Liza said, and they all looked at each other again.

"Nahhhhhhh."

Julia's US History teacher, Mrs. Desmond, was a self-proclaimed veteran of the second-wave. As such, on the day before winter break she put on an inspired revue of the suffragettes.

As her peers numbed out, Julia scowled, scoffed, snorted, exasperated by Mrs. Desmond's tale of incorrigible human behavior. What bothered Julia most was how so many *women* had opposed their own right to vote, like the Benedicts in Elizabethan bonnets— those fucking Brit-chicks had been the worst. Only humans could turn a simple thing like basic rights into something so complex and protracted.

That night, Julia paddled out into some serious webular chop. Hoping to find morsels of optimism, perhaps hope itself, she researched the following, in order: women's suffrage; domestic policy during WWII; Henry Wallace's ouster as Roosevelt's VP nominee; Truman's presidency and the modern Democratic machine; Roger Stone and the Republicans' *deus ex machina*; and, finally, PAC money's causal relationship with all political auspices post-1975. Soon enough she was convinced that suffrage didn't truly exist, and neither did democracy.

Weeks passed. First winter break, then the public-school system's sugarcoated version of the Civil Rights movement. Julia's appetite fell into the black hole that was the world's malfeasance. She didn't want to see Shaz or even Liza. She couldn't even eat her mother's carbonara.

"*No one* gets it," she whined. "We're totally fucked as a species."

"Language at the dinner table," her mother warned.

"Call the UN. They should be home, watching genocides on TV."

"A little eggy."

"It's good," her father assured.

"Un-*fucking* believable."

"Julia!"

"What our daughter's suffering from right now is what's commonly known as a 'rude awakening.'"

"No, that would be if I dumped this pasta on your head and called you the terrorist when you got mad."

She'd remember nothing but his downstroke, catching the edge of his plate, launching creamy pink spatter across the wood floor. A noodled death-mess. The plate rattled still, somehow upright and unbroken.

"Who the fuck do you think you are?" As if reminding her who he was talking to, he pointed at her. "You're behaving as if we, without whom your welfare would be precarious and your existence non, are the main source of your problems."

"Dad," Julia said, tinged with plea.

"...Do you have any idea what we're going through right now?"

"No?" she said, eking relief.

Without hint of affectation, he drew himself up. "You will go to your room. You will not work on your site. You will not read. You will consider a broader perspective on things."

She'd almost smiled then, but now, curled on her bed, her father's words scraped away the plaquey buildup between her and Shaz. The world's infinite fucking blunder stung the nerve center of her small selfish universe—and other assorted teenage cutter lines. She could think it because she'd done it, just a few times, trying it on for size. Really, the volatility scared her more than the self-harm itself. The guilt upon succumbing to the urge to holler herself hoarse into her *Amélie* pillow.

Who *was* she to speak to her parents like that? Who *was* she to play the intelligence agency, everyone she knew a microdot of existential wisdom she could study?

If it was impossible to truly escape yourself, how could Shaz escape her father, her father his father, each meiotic division? How could she stay the world's hand from wringing her precocious sponge?

She got out her phone: Shazni, is you a down-ass bitch?

A quick reply lit her phone: Pick u up in twenty.

Certain wanton dot-coms solicited *Pussy Vitale* for ad space—a glib misunderstanding of the site's intent, but another sign that they'd broken ground on some expensive online real estate. Site traffic had increased such that Liza learned another language to free up flow. Trolls came out from under the bridgework, bearing the banner of schadenfreude. Mainly these men (sometimes boys) would queue up for Joanathan Stanzen only to bombard the live-streams with bigoted language. Though Liza programmed intervention tools, their vigilance had stretched to all hours.

Their trolls spewed the like:

On 1/17/2010 at 1:55 PM, Nomar Fucking Around said:

Fact: Men are physically superior. If we can recognize this openly as a society, why can't we recognize other facts, like how we're also more spatially adept, coordinated, and do better in STEM—i.e. logic-based—fields of work and study.

There's a conclusion here somewhere, but my male brain is having trouble with the logic...

On 1/21/2010 at 1:59 AM, As if said:

As if the most important contemporary challenges should—in fact—be resolved by savagely athletic means. It amuses us that you think institutionalized measures of logic are a reflection of objective capability, not to speak of said measures being under patriarchal control.

On 1/21/2010 at 2:00 AM, Nomar Fucking Around said:

I'm a woman.

On 1/21/2010 at 2:00 AM, As if said:

fucking quisling.

On 1/21/2010 at 4:15 PM, Forever Jung said:

Women don't take responsibility for putting themselves in dangerous situations. They walk home from bars drunk and alone wearing underboob tanktops and cutoffs I jokingly call slut wedgies.

On 1/21/2010 at 4:37 PM, As if said:

As if pussy is so vital.

On 1/23/2010 at 1:28 AM, Soggy Biscuit said:

More men are trafficked as laborers. Millions of men have died in wars, while women stayed back home knitting sweaters.

On 1/23/2010 at 6:37 AM, As if said:

As if there's no difference between a man melting down stolen rail ties and a woman getting fucked against her will.

On 1/23/2010 at 11:33 AM, Soggy Biscuit said:

My cock gets hard thinking of your responses.

On 1/23/2010 at 3:08 PM, Look What Fappened Here said:

I often have a higher opinion of females before I get to know them and fuck them.

KNIBB HIGH FOOTBALL RULES

I might be out of line here, but I think a lot of problems would go away if prostitution was legal. Look at Australia. Their divorce rate went down 8%. Numbers don't lie. And it takes women out of dangerous situations.

"*What?*" went Shaz, her squints furious in the rearview. "You're telling me you think it's okay to allow a man to violate a woman for fifty bucks?"

"I mean, it's a woman's choice," Julia said. "It's my body. Who's to say I should get thrown in jail for doing what I want with it?"

"Um. So should we make drugs legal?"

Julia let this irony pass like the blunt across the lacuna. Until she couldn't. "You're smoking weed right now."

"This is ridiculous."

"Your outrage isn't an argument."

"You're an idiot."

"Okay."

"…I can't be in the car with you right now."

Julia X'd out of *Pussy Vitale* and looked out the window. People in thick sweaters and wool caps braved the early evening bluster. Fog was forming over the Bay Bridge, shrouding its high girders. She didn't notice. She spent the remainder of the ride screening for guilt. Fucking Shaz, she'd condemn manmade climate change if only against the prefix. Just because she was mostly right didn't mean the teacher gave partial credit.

Shaz lurched to the curb. Her house was an Italianate blush of crimson bored with bay windows, its white porch like purity's invitation. She felt a bit sloshy as she slid out the door—a bit blazethed. She turned stiff and waved to Liza, but Shaz had thrust her body across Liza's lap and through her window. "Have fun reading *Daddy's Little Girl*. Or the one about Oedipus?"

"Have fun filing Chapter 11, Intellectual Bankruptcy," and she flipped the bird.

Julia muttered up the porch. Night was nigh and whatnot: a penumbra of pillars leaned along the wood, crossing things into gray polygons. She went inside—and stopped at sight of her mother. Sat at an island stool, Lucia Paolantonio looked all wrong. Elbows on marble, head in hands, hair a brambled doozy. Beyond her demitasse cup stood the moka pot, molten espresso congealed to its sides after so many successive boils. Dried bolls of tissue paper, dusted slate like skeletal roses, littered the island's counter. Only the stove light was on. Her phone's glow cast her streaked mascara an igneous black, as if volcanic plasma had erupted from her eyes.

Sicilian homes were synonymous with Sunday dinners, a foyer's crucifix or family shrine, the hawser-framed oil painting of the Amalfi Coast. And if home and hearth were their crown, the kitchen was its gleaming diadem. Whispered swishes to the fridge for a midnight snack, each creak of the floor's wood. At the cast-iron stove, grilleds cheesing, as her dad joked, when she'd dropped the tongs and, bending over, noticed dark archipelagos spotting her jammies—her Brit-Brits, navy with red trim, patterned by a thousand sparkling Spearses. A paisley of prima donna. "'Twas a tween they were trashed," her mother did in dangerously atrocious Irish, and Julia threw an agonized fit of hilarity. The ordeal had been less climactic than uncomfortable. This tableau of her weeping mother was impossibly juxtaposed with the one that joked about her sanguinary milestone. How had time gotten to them, too? Did this really happen to everyone? They just waited for this moment, when the bad thing happened.

"Julia, he—your," her mother faltered, collected herself, breathed. Her voice only warbled all the worse, "He didn't go to his meeting. He hasn't called. He always calls." Again, as if reprimanding the island counter, "He *always* calls."

By cloak of night they'd follow the dunes, worming trails of clay and dirt depressed by trod. Guided by glades of gibbous moonlight, the susurrus of their own moccasins, their shambling ambles weighted by fifty pounds of marijuana—or, in Peter's case, the steady thrum of his throttle.

Back when running for Rameen and Ravjeet, conscripts had waited at each end like pit-stop crews. But now, Peter muled the satchels 350 miles aggregate, not a soul either side of the border to give him cover. His gears rearing and bucking, he gut-estimated the embankment along the 5, that last eight-foot drop from raised forest edge onto man-made macadam. He'd hit the ground with his head turned back in sight of no one who'd seen him deep in the Pacific night, merging onto the highway, igniting his headlamp, seducing the nos tab, drawing thrusts of nuclear acceleration, and easing the throttle to save gas.

Peter left those circle-billed wood-rangers but a ribbed trace of his former presence. Each run was as if just that—a trial run, a course jog, a cinch, then he ripped off through brush and toward the embankment, burning under smoky wisps of altostratus that cauterized the moon.

Waiting in a storage unit in Bellingham, an hour and a half north of the city, was two months' on a slick studio. Of course, Peter was less imbued by the prospect of non-sequential bills and yuppie-pads than the satchels themselves, those labored-over leathers.

Heading up the 5 that night, Peter recalled a summer day long past. Quite young, he'd been wandering the scrubby yard, marveling at cumulus clouds, their enormity confusing their distance. He'd been a latchkey kid so blissfully bored with empty summer days, his time left so unfathomably long, it was effectively forever—and then Kaleigh had been born, and his mother had begun to visit his room, and bucking the trodden dunes, satchel's strap like a bandolier, he yearned for his as the pious pray for theirs.

The way it worked, Mr. K's guy dispatched his burner, and he did his job. That was all he thought of it. However Raciti had placated the cousins, whyever Julia had lured him into her moral amoeba—he no longer wished to know, regardless of whether he already did.

Mortar and pestle.

He'd made his first run on the third Thursday of December. The next two brought him closer still. To what, he knew not but instinctively, like how he redid his piece—unclipping, emptying, reloading, chambering, cocking, repeat. A paradox, in its appeasing his need to do, while providing him space to think. Julia knew about it, didn't like it, was complicit in its presence. Like his nine, they did not speak of the runs. Nor her granddad, Raciti, Johnny, whatever. Nor the drink. He got right for runs, not her, and his nights off were soaked terrors. She was always wearing scrubs. But he knew at skin-level it was over.

So he got right for runs—except before this one, when he got good and honest drunk. Locked up in his room, laying supine, laptop on pillow on lap, he watched twenty minutes of 9/11 hit shots. That Boeing 767 dipping gracefully into Tower 2's liquid steel and cookie-crumble concrete. Nipping at the Dickel, he watched Eric Harris turn his school library into a dice-kill.

Bzzzzzzzz... Bzzzzzzzz... Bzzzzzzzz—Johnny Raciti.

"Yeah."

"I need you to lose the stuff."

Peter spooned up some dry cereal, dusting bedcrops with rice and krispy. "Huh?"

"I need you. To lose. The stuff."

"Aight...So that's all? Leave it against the first tree?"

"Don't be a fuckin smartass."

"So you think I'm wasting both our time asking questions I already know the answers to?"

"I was taking down kings while you were in your fuckin diapers, kid."

Peter waited.

"Fake a little *force majeure*."

Peter crunched at the krispy.

"Get ridda the fuckin satchel, kid."

"Why?"

But Raciti hung up.

He delivered the satchel, because fuck him and the horse he fucked in on. As he had the first three, he made the drop at CubeSmart in Bellingham. Money marks the spot, four large rolled up. And a text from Raciti—to his personal phone:

Been a long time since I scrubbed a serial number.

He trudged down Denny—only to find O'Reilly locked in his office, on the phone with another patient.

"*Right... Uh-huh... And she stayed or left?... Right... Well, I'm sure that was quite difficult for you... The worst part about feeling the way you do about ah, ahem, about yourself, was your buying into the idea that this one thing defined—... Uh-huh... I understand... Well, Jed—now hold on, Jed. Hold on. She's not necessarily going to decide whether she likes you based—... No... No, that's not what I meant, you're focused on a word...*"

The negotiation lasted another ten minutes or so. Another minute of silence, then O'Reilly opened his door and, bathroom hanger jangling, started at the sight of Peter, sitting on the waiting area's the brocade couch, drinkless. O'Reilly corrected his expression with surprising ease, as though this were the first scenario clinicians were taught to prepare for.

"Peter. We didn't have an appointment, did we?"

"No."

"Ah," he said, nodding. "Come in."

He thought to refuse, but he was here. He followed O'Reilly, who sat with his legs crossed, fingers tented. Watching Peter's silence. He dug for it, but he couldn't express it. He muttered, "It's just gravity."

"What's that?" O'Reilly said.

He wanted to say that their personal galaxies did this dance, his and Julia's. One would inevitably swallow the other.

"Why bother."

"Peter, that's, ah…It's important to remember that we can affect change."

Peter looked up at the grated clock, similar to those he'd known in grade school.

"I want you to tell me—no bullshit—what's going on with me. Otherwise, I'm just here because I have to be, and I won't keep coming if that's the case."

O'Reilly was pleasantly taken aback. "I'm curious about this sudden, um, shift. From mocking this process to, well, I suppose, needing to understand its purpose. Can you, ah, talk a little more about that?"

Peter relaxed back in the armchair and parted his hoodie, adjusted his chinos, milking the exposed. The intended effect widened O'Reilly's eyes, his earlier start at Peter's sight pushed toward outright terror.

"Washington's open carry, but I'm hoping you can educate me about something," he drawled. "Am I allowed to carry crazy?"

"Ah, ahem, Pete—" he stammered, shifting, starched tattersall crackling. Body twisted as in a half-cower, correcting only his slipped glasses, his breath broke.

"Here's what's going to happen. You're going to tell me my"— and here Peter paused to consult his phone—"formulation. Then, you're going to sign off on the rest of our sessions, including the urinalysis. Urinalyses? Whatever. Point is, this will all save us a lot of time and effort, because I'm sick of coming in here and playing your intellectualized version of twenty questions."

"Okay," O'Reilly said, flat palms raised in defense or surrender or both. "Okay," he repeated, calmer now. "We'll go over your file."

"And?"

"And we'll sign off on the sessions…and the urinalysis."

In that twisted cower, hands still raised as if hoping to defend a quick draw, he shuffled to one of three stacks of plastic drawers like tupperware for files. It took him maybe ten seconds to pull his, and Peter felt a pang of remorse: he probably did care, but his science was pseudo and his unawareness of the fact Peter couldn't forgive.

O'Reilly sat, file open in lap, licking through session notes. His head hung throughout the ordeal, disclosing the clinical diagnoses, which had progressed throughout their process. Peter was impressed with the level of detail, considering how much time they wasted here. But what would stick with him was O'Reilly's frizzy orange ringlets, like tangled threads for an autumn sweater.

"So what happens now?" he asked. Though unable to look up, his tremble had settled.

Peter stood, pushed hands in his hoodie's pockets. "Nothing," he said. "Absolutely nothing."

Despite the fat stacks made running, Peter kept on as third shift security at Aspira. It helped pass the night, else he was liable to drink himself to shit.

One night, two young women in lurid gym garb hung by Aspira's entrance, grousing about their fortunate circumstances. Peter watched the younger woman, who did this often, loitered in the lobby post-lactic, all stretch pants and endorphinized chunter. Between glances Peter's way, flexing her calves on the façade's steel sill, she complained that climbing the nonprofit stepladder—composing grant applications; drumming up donations for monthly benefits; fulfilling insurance obligations for contracts in King County; and in general dealing with her boss's bipolar bullshit—meant doing her boss's job.

Peter hated himself for listening but couldn't tune out, his eardrums designed to heed the dulcet tones of what the voice of bravado blaring from his earbud dubbed a "dimepiece." (He also hated himself for listening to hip hop, that most vulgar chimera of American culture.)

His eyes went from her war-machine torso to the concierge log. Flipping through a notebook he hadn't opened in months—Matthew's elementary prose and lascivious drawings; Cammy's punctiliously petty script—he must've zoned. When he looked up, all trace of hunger games had vanished—except her phone case on the sill, pink, with pointless bunny ears. The concierge phone rang a few moments later.

"Yeah. Hi. I was down there like five minutes ago and I think I left my iPhone case? It's—"

"Pink?"

"Yes."

Her girlish giggle betrayed awareness of the case's absurdity. A few coquettish chuckles, and he'd forgiven her earlier mawkishness.

"Will you be at the desk in like, twenty? Just have a load to finish."

He envisaged her mouthing the phrase, the image, the act.

"I can bring it up," he heard himself say.

"Oh!" she chirped. "Thank you so much. I'm at 2107."

Rationale surged at pace with the elevator. Peter Fosch worked for Puget Property Management. Puget Property Management's corporate model subsumed resident satisfaction. The elevator halted and revealed a Persian rug, white molded walls, and, hung across the hall, above a vase of flowers, an ovaline mirror framed by gilded ivory. He stared at the embodiment of his choices.

Their exchange—phone case for an invitation to share lavender tea. "I'm Janice," she smiled. An objectionable amalgam of phonemes. Still in workout tights, her posture at the electric stove all pointed hips, hand hinging the kettle's lid so she could continue standing there like that as they spoke. It was both easier, interpersonally, and allowed him to gawk, which he didn't. He waited in a suede cream armchair, wondering how a nonprofit admin could afford a one bedroom in Aspira. He saw numbers. Leases. Pounds. Dollars. BACs. Numbers, by nature, provided order.

She brought him tea. "I've got chicken and spaghetti squash with a balsamic drizzle. It's a recipe from this paleo cookbook."

He declined, palm piping his hot tea in what he considered hoping was an expression of gratitude. He mustered a question about the paleolithic culinary arts. Watching her speak turned into listening to her speech. Its young-professionalness grated, inflection all privileged irony and bored cadence and a barrage of transitional "likes."

"Where you from?" he sort-of interrupted.

"Little Rock."

"Little Rock," he mused. "Lot of gang violence."

"I wouldn't know. What about you?"

"Catonsville. Ain't a girl I know that would open her door to a stranger with a gun."

Her regard drew manicured brows, which as a paradox amplified her perfection. "You're a security guard," she slashed. "For this complex."

"And?"

"And what?"

"And what would that mean to a psychopath?"

"And you're a psychopath?"

A flash of O'Reilly's trembling lips, mouth moving mute in his *memory...dysthymic presentation...repressed lability...superannuated survival mechanisms...post-traumatic stress...*

The charlatan's corrosive lies about Peter's mutated drives. That he'd survived by mental mortar and pestle, grinding his memories into grist that gave rise in the cauldron of his mind. And so the cook went to work again.

But what in dick's fuck did the charlatan know about grind? What did that charlatan fuck know about fat stacks? He could keep his reuptake inhibitors. Peter moved that which was packed in a baroquely embossed satchel at four large per clip. His grinds were through the Canadian pines. He chased dragons at checkpoints along the dunes, inhaling after a fellow mule's foil, catching the full moon's alloyed reflection as the skag smacked and, knocked prostrate, he howled to his insides. He'd started fights on occult impulse. He'd stumbled into traffic to hand out high-fives in an unfaithful fugue state. He knew what the fuck he was doing more than that charlatan cunt of a shrunk dick.

"Well," Janice sighed, and Peter's eyes jumped—just under her perceptive threshold. "It's getting late," he heard her say.

Her timbre's recoil. Her put-off posture. Prone corpse, bleeding out. *Lability.*

"No need to apologize for vanquished demons."

"What?" she said.

"My mom," he heard himself say. "…She tried mainlining pure grain, like heroin or something. She's…" Peter looked at his mug, set it down on the glass coffee table. He'd realized himself. "I'm sorry," he said, blinking, shaking his head.

"Oh, no, it's…" Janice let trail.

He couldn't slip out quick enough. Avoiding the ovaline mirror, he elevatored down and secured the perimeter as if fit to do so. He knew he'd lapsed back at Janice's, but for how long he didn't know, had never happened. He texted Dylan, who was in Des Moines, consulting with some rigging syndicate.

How's the blood of the earth?

Its a bitch out here so many subcontractors theyre layered like a bad paint job. What gives?

I haven't been telling Julia everything.

Another girl?

About a week later, he and Julia hit a jazz club in Ballard and caught a Coen brothers matinee at Big Picture on 1ˢᵗ Ave. Riding back to the Iliad, the balmy breeze swept west unsalted and Julia's arms wrapped around his waist. Nothing. Normal.

"*Fargo* still tops it," she said, her holler calibrated down as Peter slowed up Olive.

"Band was shit."

"Mediocre," she modified. "But that bassist's do-rag?"

"No eyebrows either."

"I saw that."

"Each note, a dollar toward leukemia."

"Peter," she scolded.

"Oh yeah, forgot to mention. I actually saw their album in this apartment the other day. *Songs in The Key of Peace*," he shook his head once. "Should've known."

"Whose apartment?"

Peter let a moment to think. "Some girl's," he then said, immediately regretting his choice of pronoun.

They got a green and Peter gassed. Tension stretched as if from his bike's fairing, pulled taut by the time they reached another red, awaiting their left onto Bellevue. Silence prevailed. Just City Market's green awning, jutting like a bruised upper lip in the breeze.

"I brought up her phone case," Peter blurted, not loud or anything, but impulsive nonetheless. "She invited me in for some tea, and then I left," he said, and his tone had succumbed to the idea that this was now a thing.

"And you didn't think to tell me about this."

"Hands on hips," he said, accelerating again, then shouted, "I'm telling you now," and, buzzing down Bellevue East, distracted, he realized the turn too late. Julia's arm hooked under his ribcage as the bike closed angle with the pavement, tread-braking, their bodies floating off-seat. He planted a hand on the smooth concrete and ploughed the bike upright, her helmet cracking off his in recoil. Rubber marks were fanned across the garage floor, the burn stinking, his wrist smarting.

"Peter, what in the actual fuck."

She ripped from him and blustered off, furious sashay toggling the back pockets of her white capris. Then she stopped and stamped back.

"So why the fuck did you even go up there? She's only like, an elevator ride away."

"Exactly."

She cut a caustic laugh.

"My apologies. I don't have videotape of this non-event."

"Because like my trust, it doesn't exist."

"I don't know what to say." Peter looked past her, toward twilight's peri-twinkle.

"If you don't say something, I'm going home."

"I'm not negotiating your emotional terrorism."

Their fights maintained a pattern. A day or three's silence, like some synesthetic staring contest, before one of them summoned the escape velocity needed to reach a conciliatory space.

After two days and a morning, Peter arrived unannounced at Comp 56's glass doors. He nursed his flask for two hours before she returned from a shift at the student co-op. Her dusted blue apron was a vaguely talented impressionist's cloud. Her crossed arms refused to talk, but her presence would listen.

"Look, I couldn't stop myself from going back," he said, eyes a saccade. "So I did…Just to make sure it was real—"

"Why in the actual fuck are you telling me this."

He revealed from behind his back Janice's copy of *Songs in the Key of Peace*—"Will you forgive me?"

Momentarily incredulous, relief then broke her dam of silence. "You are fucked up, Fosch."

"Not quite." He opened his other palm to reveal the tiniest gunnysack, that misnomer of color they called the eight-ball.

Halfway down the bag, Peter knew they'd keep doing this—listening to Milt Jackson and Wes Montgomery, scrolling Myriadal Mates (that mill of garrulous cunts), his finger shying the small of her back—despite there being nothing left for him here.

"Get it?"

She'd pulled up a photo of a Barbie doll laid prone across a grill, with skewered shrimp strewn the length of her body. He squinted, pushing round riddles into square puns.

"Shrimp on the Barbie? No?"

He chuffed, a coke-sparked laugh at his idiocy. He noticed Julia's floured apron hooked on some boutique coat rack.

"You'd miss that. So *cahm*plicated," she camped.

She was justifying his mystery. She truly believed there was substance behind his raffish mask. Its existence notwithstanding, that it was even worth reaching. She and the charlatan might know of his memories, but they'd never know them. It was shrouded in steam.

"Ready to work?" she said, opening Blackboard.

"Indeed," Peter said, cutting up another line.

"Yo," she admonished. "You really need to start applying for jobs before the rest of us do this summer."

"You know how they say work hard play hard?"

"Peter," she said in display of dismay.

"Well"—insufflation, sniffing, wiping once—"for some the adage implies simultaneous action."

"Peter,'" she groaned and closed her eyes, which he exploited by cadging her computer. "Peter, what are you doing."

He hot-keyed a new tab, googled "Motor Trend Peter Fosch," and turned the screen.

"So you're in to cars now?"

Peter's hand suggested she look closer.

"Oh."

"A competitive comparison between the Lexus RX and Acura MDX. Anyone wanna guess who wins? Spoiler alert: it's Lexus because they're paying me."

Later that night, Peter left the bathroom's drawer latch tucked and stepped into their dank shower. Slowly adjusting the knobs to a boil, he washed himself, a series of ritual ablutions that zoned on the erogenous. He shunted from shower to bath faucet, took up the head, and sat. Hot water rushed around his lotus. The shower's coil hung by the weight of its head, which he then whipped over shoulder, lashing his hide raw. Fresh licks burst sanguine down his back, flagellating older scars—the light splitting his room, her silhouette to follow, her bottle *thudding* the nightstand, her panted halitosis, her ketosic skin-rot. His father sneaking home late from the local hole, pulling off the kitchen's community bottle—Rikaloff on the

15th and Stoli on the 1st, their chasers of air either grimace or sigh. Then his feet worrying the wood along the short hall to Peter's door, pausing on a shifting creak, deciding, the same process each time, the certainty amplifying each time. But he had pussy on him and, in his head, the other option was to whup her, and he'd never done that. He'd make like a tree and fall at the foot of his mattress, springy squeaks like restive visions: her tugging at his limpness, her showing his hand where it was, her fucking his pale thigh, bedframe metaling the wall, springs squealing, maybe baby Kaleigh crying in her crib, and finally quivering atop him, moaning disembodied, *Yea-heh-eah… Tha's a gooooood boy.* Spittle at her lip, lifting away, leaving warm stick right for him to huff to sleep. His eyes tore open, gamma against the shower's mold-ridden tile. He choked up on the showerhead, bent over, and brought it behind him. As if presiding as midwife to an inverse breech, he delivered the shower's head into him, fetal in his feculence, swaddled by sepsis. He warbled, shunting from bath to shower and back, his arms synced like two ends of a seesaw. Pulling out, he ass-blasted the showerhead's brass, spurting the tile's grime and verdigris. Curled up with the showerhead, crotch shot with hot beads, he killed the water. His hand leapt up and lurched. He perched on the bath's lip, basking in the humidity before dripping to his room, where a clever crow cackle-cawed in his window.

> *A groundling gropes while his lover hopes*
> *that jokes are put to bed.*
> *When the locusts croaked,*
> *God gave hope,*
> *but dope took them instead.*

The Bargeman came from his captain's quarters as though he'd been glued to the CCTVs. Seamen bustled cubed pallets. The gristled contractors in tucked flannel, loosely circling the ramp, showed no regard. Peter could tell they were all privy or paid or both. The Bargeman slipped him the satchel and returned to his haunts. It was always that simple.

Now Peter yawed off the southbound freeway and hit the silk road, hard. Daylight was two hours. He could do the dunes in less than one.

The smell of pine thickened under gaining clouds. He raised his helmet's visor and felt a fat drop lick his lip. Incoming: no Sound-side mist, but a real banked-up soaker.

He set off again, slower now. He took less tread, drawing his brakes and rotations. Soon the rain fell hard, turning the trail turbid.

He idled once again on a mound's crest, engine hissing sibilant. Maybe it would pass. Unlikely. This was the east coast's equivalent of a stalled squall line: it couldn't pass over the mountains. He hadn't seen lightning since Maryland, two years ago, and now the cracks and booms reported from all over, as if closing in on Peter's position.

The laser jammer, like a fuse box with radar, had blipped and cut out a click south of here. He toggled it to no avail, snugged the satchel's strap, remounted, and forged ahead. He'd forgotten to bail his holster. He bucked against the slopes, muck-splash like crashing cymbals in the rain's roaring drumroll. Mud-yuck yipped at his hinds, a cold earthen lather that splashed around tight corners. His back wheel whined high, spewing half-foot holes and lurching forward, this time hurtling down upon a row of rustic continental duffel bags he discerned only as his front wheel hit the heavy packs and flipped him into a stunted cartwheel—the swashbuckler's famous last pose. He kept grip of his handlebars until the bike's weight ripped from under him, throwing him headlong and thrashing through wet brush and bramble. His bike slithered between pines as if witting to these woods, back wheel torqued, and ploughed to a sidelong stop. The engine gurgled.

Decumbent, Peter's head fell on his forearm. He took bodily inventory. Other than some mud-rash, he was intact. The satchel safely strapped, rawly he rose—and heard commotion. People. He remembered the duffels he'd hit—the purpose of his presentiment. He scrambled to a small outcrop and had begun cracking his burner against the striated bedrock when a gruff hand wrung his shoulder. "Hey—" was all he could manage before the other hand muffled his mouth.

Fuck me in the Nuck, Peter bemoaned: his captor was decked in the emancipation-era uniforms of the Royal Mounted Police, or Mounties for short.

His struggle was for show: though incapable of overcoming the Mountie's cornmilk strength—the sort of stodgy farmboy burl some men are born with—Peter wanted his perspective acknowledged. He writhed in his beefy vise, kicked his legs out from under him, bringing them both to their knees and taking a blow to the side for his unruliness. His bike's thrum dimmed with distance as he was dragged off, his burner's entrails left spread across slicked crag in a forensic technician's wet dream.

The rain relentless now, Peter let himself go limp, like an accomplice to his own sequestering. They rallied up muddy runnels, viscous slop flowing around their ruined shoes.

"What about my bike."

"Shut your fucking mouth."

Summitting the last slope, Peter was confounded by the scene below. A modest hand lamp wobbled in slop like a lighted buoy in a flooded river, revealing more Mounties—a standing five-strong squadron, each of their arms raised at a squadron of four serried on their knees, hands clasped behind their backs. One of these genuflected Mounties, head hung, moaned desperately over the deluge's backdrone. The rest knelt silent, spines erect, eyes gleaming, honoring their badge or crew.

"Who the fuck is that?" shot a voice pitched up to beat the band of heavy rain. This one's hat hugged his back, thin string strapped around his neck. The rain made a mâché of his forehead, commas of wet hair papering his high hairline. Gaunt depressions carved hollows in his cheeks like tumorous dimples, lending him a physiognomy of perseverated joy. His position among the rest—standing a few steps from the firing squad, weapon hung at his side—marked him the leader of those standing.

"I'm—"

Peter recoiled, fought for breath, and retched up a spot of blood before consciously registering his bludgeoned stomach.

In his watery periphery he caught his captor spinning his piece to regrip the handle that'd gatted his gut.

"I'm sorry, someone ask you something?" his captor growled.

"Must've been the wind," Peter strained, parsing the specifics of his pain series. Blood's iron tasted his gums. His stomach performed its plangent threnody. His wrists rung from having clung to the bike's handlebars, and he thought of Sundays long since, his father watching his Redskins, hollering after big hits, "That boy got his bell *rung.*"

"Not much space in that fancy bag you got there," said the leader of the standing. "Lotta miles for a couple pounds of grass."

The moaner's fits and sobs redoubled as if the question were addressed to him—as if his de facto dictator's every utterance screwed the final bolt in his fate. His stoic comrades paid him no mind. Hands cuffed, as opposed to clasped, Peter now realized. Chests puffed as if, pledged to uphold Canadian law, deeply contrite at having failed their allegiance.

Not that Peter had required further evidence, but no cop would've tried to tease out whether he muled marijuana for money. Cops asked direct questions, simple derivatives of the only one that mattered: "And what are we arresting you for today?" From the posture of those standing in pole position—as if fully prepared to unleash their enfilade—Peter had prefigured them fakes.

Whose leader now looked expectant, so Peter said, "Promise to rein in kid Guantanamo over here?"

His captor spun the gun, daring Peter's mouth, but the leader raised a hand.

"Let's put a moratorium on the hitting." Then, to Peter, he said, "Speak."

"Antinomíne," Peter started. "Central American plant embargoed in the States. It's nothing, some Guatemalan nostrum, but this old rich guy outside Bellingham thinks it's God's gift. Must have cancer or something."

"The fuck is a nostrum?" his captor grumbled.

"Think it's that plant everyone's been hyping these days," another fake Mountie quipped, unwinking eye trained along the barrel, his prey's glare unwavering. "Think it's weed they're calling it, eh? Pot. Bud. Mary Jane. Plenty o' names for you to choose from once you quit shitting us around."

"It's like you said," Peter doubled down. "Would I really be running for—what would this be?—ounces?"

"He said pounds. Two pounds," his captor insisted. "And if Liam says your fag-sack fits two pounds, it fits two fuckin pounds."

The leader—Liam—studied him for answers veiled by his responses. Peter mirrored his gaze, abdomen tightening around the blow to his stomach.

"I'd show you my burner if it didn't get busted when I crashed."

"Bullshit," claimed his captor. "He was breaking it on a rock when I showed up."

"Oh the satchel's worth a pretty penny. This much is obvious," said Liam. "But whether it's worth our while…"

Liam assessed his surroundings. His men alongside him, guns leveled like guillotine levers. Then Peter and his captor, still standing halfway up the slope. Peter could hear his bike's engine in the distance, humming under the rain. The chill had leaked underskin. Pressure dropping, colder layers seeping in—these mountains made things difficult for meteorologists, but this was a veritable storm they'd whiffed, the layfolk left holding the rainbucket.

Liam shifted his utility belt, wiped his wet mouth, and said, "Take it."

"Don't you have enough problems on your hands?" Peter pled as his captor unburdened him of the satchel.

Liam both ignored and addressed him, or at least included Peter in his thought process: "One of these fuckers got loose and they're not being as forthcoming about it as we'd hoped."

The moaner fell splat on his face, piteous groans churning in the mud. "I'll help you find him," he wailed. "Please, I swear to fucking Christ I'll help you find him and I'll never say a—"

"You'll shut your fucking mouth," one of his own snapped.

"They'll kill us," he sobbed.

"They'll kill us anyway. How do you think they got our uniforms?"

"Whaddya think boys?" Liam said. "Mark 'em and leave em?"

Mules weren't the onlys marauding the dunes. Disenchanted Mounties too, real ones looking for an unofficial bonus. Following a bust, they'd claim half the evidence and sell the other half back to the farmers who employed the mules they'd pinched. It'd gotten bad enough that, like corporate CEOs trying to capitalize on a bear market, farmers began anticipating the buybacks, ledgering them as operation costs. The more indignant farmers, though, had assembled their *own* Mountie units: imposture squads wearing uniforms recouped from stockpiles or dead cops. These fake Mounties hacked police transistor frequencies, waiting for a bust to ambush—like this one.

Retaliation was one thing: you take their shit, they take it back, and so on. But when regional outlets started spinning narrative's oldest trope—good versus evil—weed farmers were no longer satisfied with trading eyes. Local news stations spun up segments about heroic Mounties perishing at the hands of cartels and their cocaine-hollowed cores. To the farmers growing what they felt was floral succor—and certainly not yak—the media's hypocrisy justified heavy means: carving a corrupt C into a cop's be-forehead. "Mark 'em and leave 'em"—this was truer to those who trafficked in the *devil's lettuce.*

"We oughta," said one of the fakes. "One already got away."

"Which means it'd be moot," said another fake.

"Who gives a nutted fuck? Let's leave these sacks of shit in the mud."

"They know what we look like."

"It was just the mule," the moaning Mountie cut in. "Just him."

"Shut the fuck up, Olenik."

"Just the mule," the moaner—Olenik—babbled, flopped prostrate. "There's none of us out there. Please," he whimpered. Burrowed in the sludge, Peter could feel Olenik's toes curling within his boots. He felt for him, which itself had become an estranged feeling. Peter tracked his futile procession toward acceptance, this asymptote of life and death. Watched him writhe in the mud, working at something in his pants. He sprung up, eyes peeled like large lychees, pistol's beaded steel glinting off the lamplight—igniting the firefight.

Shots bloomed blue until the bodies stopped twitching. The sodden night overwhelmed the blood. No one would know—Peter had fled, having socked his captor and repossessed the satchel.

He skidded up and over scree rushed with mud. He put twenty yards' distance from the execution site when he stopped, choking on pants, and listened.

"*Fuhhh-kiiin* moron."

"He was drawn to kill, the fuck's I s'pose to do?"

Their voices warbled, breath ragged. Peter's clothes were all weight and water. He heaved beyond possibility, his pain profuse, but persevering nonetheless. He heard through the wet static, in wake of shots fired, a soft hum that could only be his bike's. Voices in the distance sounded nothing like the two that'd given chase. They'd pincer him. Condoning the sounds of his breathing, he hurled toward his bike's waterlogged rattle, which he found lying sidelong like a dying intelligence. If fate had felled it left, the starter fluid would've flooded. Finessing his bike upright, he slung the duffels of bud on each the fairing's cannula wings. When he sat the leather squelched like a sad whoopie cushion. Sodden footslaps rushed toward more muck, but with him in it. He gassed it straight to 70, engine screaming bloody murder, back wheel churning forest syrup, catching and lurching perfect upon the trail, all sounds of pursuit sucked into the soaked chasm become of the dunes.

Later, he'd tell Julia they were ruds: fuck-ups and fall-guys sent
to do moneymen's wet work. But he recognized them all too
well, his former captor's mullet where his Mountie hat had hung,
ripe bruise where he'd caught him during the execution, and
his fake Mountie friend, the one who'd been the first to suggest
they off and mark the cops. As they commandeered the pickup
game, the 'shrooms turned to shit, sheening the world in horror's
lucid hue—clear and uncolored, the illusion come undone, and
yet the charlatan's specter haunted him with one hope: that they
wouldn't notice Julia, which required his feigned ignorance, and
her tacit understanding.

"What's all this about?" said the dude donned in Knicks gear,
the orange headband and Sprewell jersey.

"We ain't playin no four-on-three," said the guy whose white
shirt was all sliced.

"Check the fucking ball," Peter drawled all casual, but his breath
caught in his numbed chest.

It was clear, as the mullet sidled up to guard him, that he'd
been savoring this moment. "Remember me?" he hissed at Peter,
who clapped half-assed for a pass, phoned in cuts to the basket.
Shadowing him along the baseline, he continued, hisses staggered
against small exertions, "Maybe not, it was a little dark."

Displaying unparalleled density, the dude in Sprewell gear
called a foul, drawing ire from the D-boys who were up to speed
on the proceedings. As they bickered, Peter's defender tilted his
mullet toward the park's entrance, "Your girl over there. Might
wanna give her a wave goodbye. Not sure if she mentioned it, but
she's going on a little trip with us."

The mullet's glance at the girl by the park's gate was like a
gun's mistaken discharge.

Peter had heard, whether from that dime-store charlatan, or
some armchair philosopher, that happiness was merely pain's alle-
viation. Relief turned Peter's body into a country home's breezeway

lined with bikes of every matte color. His beautiful wife working the garden, the plain's cloudless noon sky—and the muffled crack off the living room, the panicked rush inside, where a meretricious young woman lay mauled, phone still in hand. Standing over her was a pale boy with strawberry-blond hair, shocked eyes reckoning with what he'd done. Morals and metaphysics, both manmade, both an illusion, both in contradiction—and the boy turned the rifle on himself. Peter lurched but the boy vanished in his grasp. He turned back to his wife, also gone, along with the mutilated girl, the living room, the brace of bikes in the breezeway. The clear sky and fields of wheat had turned to haze and blight, far as he could see, save for a lone mule, neighing, kicking dust up in eddies. He recognized the mule, its natty peach coat, strawberry-blond mane, oxheart eyes. He recognized the pile of supplies under its undulating tail. He brushed the mule's mane, sensing an immense sadness, and loaded the supplies—saddling a second seat, doubling his provisions, preparing his mule for added weight.

"Understand what I'm saying to you?" the mullet seethed. "Or you too stoned on our fuckin product?"

Peter phased in with the mullet's sharp questions. Or perhaps his breath had brought him back, an acerbic rot that reminded him of his mother's. Sometimes, when passed out on the couch, he'd be woken by wafts of loud snores, lifting along his philtrum and filling his coke-cracked nostrils. For the first few moments, before his brain cells took their stations, he'd recognize his breath, his father's breath, the mullet's—the scent of inevitability.

Play resumed, and Peter demanded the ball, barreling toward the basket, bony shoulder ramming the mullet's gut to the ground. He flipped him a heartfelt fuck you as if calling upon true injustice, and perhaps he was, as it all is. Sneering, the mullet waved off his fake Mountie friend.

"Check the fuckin ball," he grumbled, wincing, walking off the hit. One of the D-Boys tarried up top, bickering with Sprewell's officious calls for an offensive foul, bickering with his obliviousness. The mullet leaned into Peter's ear, "Merchandise plus the juice at the same spot in the dunes at midnight, or your girlfriend floats down Green River," and called for the all-purpose Nike, which he chucked to the other end of the court, brandished his weapon as if wearing an inlaid vest of bombs, and backed to guard the entrance while his associate made off with the girl.

They'd gotten incorrect intelligence, or were simply incompetent—either way, they took the wrong girl. Only as they returned from the screeched-off van, tumbling with human laundry, could he see again.

Mounties were dead in the dunes. Peter had offed their bud to Rameen as cheap apology, and now, the wrong girl was paying the markup.

Julia might as well have been in that van.

Julia and her mother returned from the Bay Heights blood drive
to find the kitchen's bay window broken at the stays.

Julia hoped his homecoming, though unconventional, proved
he was still in there, somewhere, perfectly preserved within a
crystalgenic freeze. However, helping her mother pick through the
pilfer, the wreck left in wake of his recent presence struck her as
the stains of a bad dream, a leftover residue that only made it realer.

No, San Francisco wasn't what it was back in the '80s—but
back in the '80s, he'd been using in New York, and he'd left it back
there. After following him to 433 Lombard and eavesdropping on
his commitment speech, Julia had prodded her father for details.
At first reticent, over time he dropped little snippets, casually, and
only in context. But he never allowed access to primary resources:
the Polaroids of him at upstate biker bars; the track marks on his
ankles hidden by socks; his black book of sponsors and sponsees,
former and current, proving, if anything, that San Francisco carried the day for meth's target demographic.

Since he'd left—or gone back—she imagined him skulking
the Tenderloin, ripping narcotized lushes, diving for newspapers
and discarded blankets and squatting in the Haight. Alas, like
the morsels and crumbs she'd shaken from him, her imagination
couldn't recreate the feast of his firsthand experience.

But then, today, she saw with her own eyes what she'd so
lustily sought in his stories: his faint shoeprints leading from
the prized window; the pillaged drawers and ransacked closets;
the lockbox's busted emptiness. As witness to his ruin, Julia
realized that juicy details were just arid derivatives. She'd never
touch his darkness.

But could she be infected by it?

A few days later, she slipped into a black shift and carried her loden coat to the bus stop, willing away a mid-May chill. The streets were quiet. She put on her coat shortly after sitting. Legs swinging under the bench, whistling an improvised dirge, her black clutch suffered another seizure—just her phone's buzz.

Below his number read that simplest of palindromes: Dad.

She waffled—whether answering her phone, attending Al-Anon, existing, she was less sure than ever. She was behind on her summer reading. She was tired. She patched together this tarp of excuses and covered her contaminated pool of deeper beliefs: that the conversations, the meetings, the hope and worry, would all be for naught. Whether because of or despite this, she accepted the call.

"Julia?"

Another of the pool's contaminants: she'd never again be his Jules.

"Yeah Dad," she said, aware of her weary croak.

"Hi, how are you? I'm—How are you?"

If she were in the mood to play their game, she'd start here with *vacant*, which described both her affect and his awareness. At least he wasn't loaded.

"I'm…here, Dad."

"We're all here."

She lifted her face to what god that would. "Yeah."

"Fuck off!" he bellowed, abusing Julia's eardrum. "Sorry. I told these Mexicans they could use my phone for a ride over the bridge. Hey, so I gotta ask, were you there the other night? When I stopped by?"

"No," she said, looking down at her swinging feet. "You came at just the right time."

"Those were mine, Julia." His voice had dropped below recognition. "Did she tell you otherwise? Because *I* gave those to *her*."

"Those jewels were your mother's," she said, picking at a nail. "And you gave them to Mom."

"My father bought them and he is a tyrant, so what's the fucking difference," he snarled. "He is a cancer borne merrily by the system. His value systems are toxic. I won't have them in the house any longer, you understand me?"

"Okay—"

"What the fuck would you know about my father?"

Julia folded her body, forehead pressed against knees, and waited. He weaponized a tone he couldn't wield, hurling blunt obscenities that boomeranged back at his unwitting gut.

"Look, I'm sorry," he said somewhat softer, like a pillow poked through with feather stems. "I'm going to a meeting tonight. Out in Oakland. It's just a matter of time. I just need time. There's a couple of things I need to do and then I'll be home."

"You're in Oakland?"

"Like I said. I'm getting a ride."

All she could say was, "Okay."

"I have a friend out here."

"Who? The Mexicans? I thought you said you were going to a meeting."

"Your mother won't let me in the house."

"I wonder why."

"I wouldn't have to do that if I was treated like a normal person instead of some cretin."

"You emptied my fucking bank account!"

"Who opened that account? Huh?"

"I put my own money in there," she sobbed. "Money I earned from a website that my oh-so-feckless-friends helped build."

"Then it seems you two are getting along perfectly fine without me."

The line went dead.

Fellow Al-Anoners had given strongly competing advice about answering the phone. It was one of the program's many dogmas, neutered by the slightest critical pressure. Unhelpful, until she'd met a man near her father's age. He'd approached her outside the school cafeteria, where Al-Anoners smoked and drank burnt coffee after meetings.

"Julia, right?"

Under his mustard cardigan hung gray silk trousers, punctuated by smart dress shoes she couldn't yet name. A spendthrift's threads.

"Jeffery," he introduced himself. "I'm a professor as well. Nothing like your father, just basic American history at Santa Cruz. I'm truly sorry to hear about him."

Julia nodded, accepted his hand. He glossed over his daughter's struggle to stave the syringe. "Four years now. Anyway," he waved, "I didn't walk over here for commiseration. I find all the sob-swapping entirely cynical."

Julia smiled at this reminder of why she attended Al-Anon meetings. These gleaming nuggets of real connection were few among the coals of dogma and platitude. Whatever it was—awareness, intelligence, empathy—Jeffery had it.

"What I wanted to tell you is, your father is not your father right now. You can't expect him to take reasonable action, or action reasonable to sober eyes." Like his eyes, inset with patient wisdom, as if he'd memorized the Milky Way from the monastery's sole window. Julia had forgotten the eyes of hope and purpose. "Nothing," he went on, "but his own revelations—or hardship—will bring him back."

"Dad," she said now. "I'm sorry about what you're going through."

She walked back down the block, toward her house, which now hung precariously over the country's deep canyon of bank takeovers. Skipping Al-Anon added another contaminant: if she couldn't progress his recovery by proxy, how could he face it himself?

By the time Logan Chinni took her to see some rom-com in Presidio, Julia's father would be gone, her essay about it zipped up in a file among Myriadal's thousands of others ("It has been more than a year since my father leapt headlong off the edge, equipped only with the nostalgia of euphoria's phantom wings…"). The house's second mortgage would be thirding. Another school year would near its end.

But it wasn't until her last spring break at Bay Heights High that Julia climbed out of her hellhole and into Shaz's hooptie, headed for a free at B-Ray's.

"Okay, ladies," she announced, accepting the blunt—her first hit in months. "Shall we play some tonsil-hockey?"

Heavy subs. Like, *heavy*. The type of bass that shakes the nearest precinct. This was San Francisco's pastiche of an Oakland banger: flat-brimmed baseball caps; BroCal patois; and banana-boats of bud, mountains of marijuana, blunts stuffed like the Libyan refugee trucks they referenced with besotted sorrow.

For a girl like her, in a situation like this, all it took was eye contact. Each look shared a little longer, a little more longingly. Perched on a couch's pleather arm, repose all thrust and arch, Julia waited, caught his lolling eyes, returned hers shyly smitten. Patience. Boys were scaredy-cat sluts. Let him drink his weight in courage. Study his symptoms. Emulate them—fake it until making it.

Julia was privy to Logan's fall from grace. All the seniors were. Two years since the lax stud had graduated and, still, Logan lived at home. Still did spring break at B-Ray's. Still brandished his gilded beer steins and glass das boots, hardware as helpful as the state of his liver. He'd recently earned his second dewy, so at party's incipience announced his pretense to stick to beer. But, buzzed abreast his teammates, his turn as anchor ended by flipping home the winning cup, to many a cheer and much a chug, including a celebratory slap of the Franzia. He'd given the Heisman to the hard stuff for like, an hour. Now, he was waterfalling an opalescent cordial, its sumptuous runnels sneaking around the lip of his Solo and down his chin. Slamming the Solo on the ping-pong table, his gluey eyes took on a greedy twinkle: finally, he was proper fucked.

Within the hour they were hockeying their tonsils—until intoxication had him stumbling to and from the bathroom, face blanched of whatever blood had rushed to his poisoned stomach.

If kissing was a transaction, Julia had been ripped off. His saliva's lab numbers were well within the range of normal spit. She'd been told it was an illness, a disease, with genetic predispositions. Perhaps recessive, perhaps uncommunicable, either way, she still didn't get it.

That Tuesday, Logan took her to a movie near his parents' chalet in Presidio—took being a misnomer. More literally, she arrived forty minutes before him, the bulk of which she spent worrying that her Flaming Lips t-shirt, black jeans, and neon Nikes were too tepid.

But then he arrived. Glazed, gaunt, the hunky jock turned sad ectomorph. His longish blond crop hung in greasy curls, clung to his glistening forehead. Far more than the unmemorable romcom, for days after she'd think of his hand resting on her thigh, the ghastly talon of a craven predator. His breath reeked of rot-gut courage. She found him amusing, almost. Almost, but not quite. All too quickly had the Logan experiment turned into a poor distraction, the first of so many to fail her.

But who could blame her for trying? Not Shaz, certainly, yet her post-date texts were all told-you-so. She didn't respond. With two months until summer, reasons to keep kith with Shaz were nominal at best.

Her mother found work hosting for Acqua Al Firenze, an Italian fusion joint in the Mission. The job paid a pittance and tested her restraint. "If I have to lean over one more prick with a wine list who's staring down my shirt, I'm gonna kill someone."

Insolvency loomed. After the funeral expenses (for the few who'd showed up) and loan repayments, she could barely afford the low-cut blouses she begrudged her boss. Apparently, insurance policies and wills were for accepting capitalists. Upon marrying, her mother had traded business acumen for homemaking. But Julia's inheritance hadn't fallen victim to the perils of gender roles so much as their estrangement from the family's grifted largesse. Soon after April Fools', Shaz texted, rekindling their ramshackle friendship.

Saw your moms while on a date.

Who's the lucky guy?

Freshperson at Berkeley. Super cute. You'd like him.

Before Julia could think of a response, Shaz texted again:

Most of the Berkeley dudes play this social justice version of soggy biscuit. Like a circle of ethnocentric high schoolers busting their sociopolitical loads onto a Guardian article used to fact check someone's claims to a decrease in sex trafficking, and the loser has to swallow everyone's seedy conjecture.

Shaz worked as a bar-back at a Castro dive. On her 18th birthday she'd moved into a veritable cupboard in the basement of a seven-bedroom rowhome in Oakland. The house's ten residents seemed synced in time and space. Common area-confab would transition, without cue, into solitary activities, as if observing a shared ritual or faith in the confines of their respective cupboards.

Despite the size of her room, Shaz's walls were imposing. Their cinder whiffed of incarceration. But the posters helped. Billie Holiday, Mary Daly, Martin Short, Amy Sedaris, Toni Morrison, James Baldwin, Aretha Franklin—all shape and stagger of the 2-D American idol seemed to earn representation on her otherwise drab cloister of walls. The furniture consisted precisely of one pale wood dresser along the wall opposite her bed, and the bed itself.

As the laptop crackled Flume and Madeon, she absorbed Shaz's comparisons between Logan and her new beau (still referred to as "the guy who goes to Berkley").

"I mean, he's not my boyfriend."

"I mean, you've been on two dates. The ring be blingin," she sang, fingers aflutter.

"We made out at a party and went to a movie."

"And you're still talking to him," Shaz said, pulling a plaited pigtail.

"I'm not gonna ignore him just cause I don't want to date him."

"But wasn't I supposed to just ignore Kyrie, and Jamaal, and David?"

"I mean, they were toxic." Julia remembered now: the direct correlation between the volume of 'I means' and the hostility of their conversations.

"Whatever dude." Shaz flopped back on the bed, her orange thong a phosphorescent strip from her skirt's dark cove.

"So lemme get this straight. You're *telling* me he's my boyfriend?"

"Who else have you fucked?"

"Um, no one? Including him?" Julia scoffed.

"So sucking face is the bar, which you've done with him."

"Shaz, I made out with him because I'm depressed. You're supposed to be the one telling me this."

Shaz sat up, propped on elbows. "Which is like, *exactly* what you told me not to do."

"Okay, except you're pushing your arbitrary relationship levels on me, just because I got to second base with some burnout."

"We're doing bases? What are you, twelve?"

"Really Shaz?"

"Are you seeing him again?"

"I don't know."

Eyes hooded, Shaz pressed, "*Are* you seeing him again."

"Why do I have to answer that?"

Hugging her pillow to chest, lashes aflutter, Shaz entreated the ceiling: "Oh Shaz, are you still Facebook friends with David? Shaz, you're going to block Kyrie's number—*right?* Shaz, listen to me

Shaz, do what I say Shaz." She dropped her head and peered up like a girl possessed. "Like, f'real hon. None of those guys were half as scrubby as Logan."

"Okay, I get what you're saying? And I'm sorry? But I'm just asking you to understand that I'm dealing with some shit right now—you know, with my dad *dying* and all?—and to maybe not put this boyfriend shit on me?"

"Do you know how often I felt the same way?" Shaz shot back. "*So* many times I thought to myself, wow, *your* perspective of *my* world sure *sounds* good, but you don't actually live in it. You live over there. I mean, I get it. There's a feeling you get when you're forced to be near someone else's pain. You want to run away from it, but you can't, so you try to get them to stop talking about it. It's easier."

Julia blinked, broke breath—couldn't summon a single counterpoint. Which said something, having played the dead-dad card. Said that her *skepticism*, whose etiology led back to her first day of junior high, had yet to bed rock bottom.

"I think you should go." Emptied of fight, Shaz's defiant eyes fixed on the linty antigens in her fingers.

With a few hours until shutter time at Acqua Al Firenze, rather than home and alone, Julia wandered. She took vista from some steeple, the rolling pastel houses. Her windows were her eyes, her wipers the heels of her hands. Things had become funnier as they'd gotten worse, but now, she was visiting with her new friend grief, whom she couldn't have left tied up. She couldn't feed it gruel forever, mustard and Wonder Bread sandwiches, Hershey's bars with peanut butter, brussels sprouts when she also felt like shit. Oh, and she definitely couldn't keep switching out the shit bucket. So she wended toward water, sat pylon at pier, and completed the irrigation project she'd begun back when the hospital had called— driving back from a meeting, her mother's first, during whose free association exercise Julia had admitted to an instinctive notion that he was soon on the upswing.

"An embolus," the attending explained quietly: their privacy was silhouetted paper for curtains, "is an air bubble in his blood, which shares comorbidity with intravenous drug use—"

Because she was not born circa yesterday, her mother hefted heavy moans. Julia wanted to tell her that morbid wasn't being used that way, but it was, or would be, soon. She and the attending soothed her with hush and gentle hands. That she so freely caressed her mother's back, shared hands with them both—yet wasn't abashed. Nor ashamed. In fact, she felt quite little at all. And to this feeling, maybe the velleity of surprise, if anything at all? She raised a hand to the neurosurgeon, incredible tall and dark and thin, whose earnest nod lit thick nonchalance, a silent explosion, a supernova in space—the nothing-rush of diazepine, which she'd swiped from her mother's medicine cabinet before driving stunned, still in motion, a hovering bee's thousand flutters-per-second, to the Oakland Medical Center. Benzo, donezo, numbzo. She questioned free will—no pun on her father's clause to pull the plug should he be about this nap life. She almost *laughed*. She'd heard of paradoxical reactions to grief, but this had to be the drugs. How else would her father have made the time to submit a living will, if not under the auspices of high-grade ice? Julia had never taken amphetamine, let alone mainlined meth, but her curiosity was certainly piqued.

"In some cases it's fatal," said the attending to a calmer crowd, "and in your husband's case, Mr. Raciti's, it's left him in a coma he's unlikely to come out of…"

Seated on a pylon, Julia wept deep and warped, bending the Bay's waterline. Gulls got dipped into optical gulches. Refracted diamonds sparkled where the sun met tears. She'd forever equate her father's death with chemical indifference. She'd forever remember naming the neurosurgeon Manute Bol, MD. She'd forever botched her chance at feeling her father's conscious limbo, which was just another drug, one that sucked.

A boy—a man—fuck it, she couldn't see. The male presence took up the pylon adjacent hers, connected by sagging chain links.

"Warm as fuck today."

"Huh?" she wiped her eyes.

"The weather. Oh, my bad. Was something wrong?"

Incredulous, Julia felt her scowl relax upon recognizing the irony in his expression. "Indian summer," she shrugged, chuckling at the absurdity.

Now his expression faded as he said, "I won't ask the rhetorical question."

"What's that."

"What's wrong."

Julia laughed harder now, cleared her cheeks. He was right: everything was wrong. "You wouldn't want to hear it anyway."

"Then we're in agreement. Nip of the Dickel?"

She hesitated but accepted the flask. Fuck it.

"Have at it," he said, leaning and extending the flask.

She assessed the human spindle beside her. Dusk became him, enhanced his pallor into something saintly. For some reason Julia decided she'd give her night to his wanderings as if through sheer nearness she'd transmigrate into his life, any life that wasn't hers. Or, as if another fuck it.

Throughout the evening—his last in San Francisco—she braced herself for stock condolences, packaged clichés about life and death, despite his earlier *via negativa*. But he never faltered. He even made her laugh. In his bee-like bike jacket, he squired her first to Amoeba Records. Next, touristy bars she'd normally sneer at, but whose bouncers he correctly predicted would assume her of age.

As she gulped bourbonized corn syrup, Julia countenanced the idea that ideas were like the world, rounded, cyclical. Perspectives connected like democracy and communism across the Bering Strait. Or maybe liquor made it seem that way. She offered this idea as he returned from the bathroom.

"See that girl at the bar's kitty corner?" he said.

The girl, her platinum blonde wave and heavy eye shadow, avoided Julia's eyes as they found her.

"She's been whoring out eye-fucks all night, but I doubt she thinks about it," he said. "We aren't round or square or any shape. We're fucking random."

Julia nodded, dazed and unhearing. Jesus, his eyes. Big and gooey and canine, chemically lowered to shining crescents. From his parted jacked leaked cool dark spaces not filled by his trim frame, and she craved to become those spaces. He'd struck conversation with a neighbor about "real" metal versus "glam" or "post" or "*nu*" metal.

"Hey," she said into her drink. "I should go soon."

"It is a school night," he ceded.

"Actually, it's spring break for me. So you're just not getting lucky."

"The arrogance of this one," he drawled.

Julia smiled. She was not buzzed, but properly varnished. Another drink and she'd see double.

"I'm on break too." He signaled to the bartender. "I go to UW."

"Oh!" She covered her mouth as if embarrassed by her outburst. "I'm gonna be at Myriadal next year."

"Yuppiiieeee."

"Ha. I see what you did there," she swirled her dregs. "Their psych program is like, tops."

"Only reason I didn't apply was trimesters," he said. "Can't go to a school that cops a pregnant woman's timeline," he said, and after a shifty pause added, "I kid."

I am but a young goat.

"Oh. No. Sorry," she waved, coughing on her drink.

"You aight?"

Through a complex of tears she saw his smile.

"Here." He handed her a napkin from the bar caddy.

"Thanks."

"Pleasure's mine," he said, and watched as she composed herself.

"Soooo," she said, face stretched, allowing for a deeper rub around her naked eyes, "thanks for the drinks—that you're about to pay for—because I have no money on me—or in general—because my dad sorta stole it all."

His laugh shot from the side of his smile, more shape than sound.

"Sounds like we got a lot in common," he said.

Outside, hands in his pockets, hers in hoodie's pouch, they considered closing statements.

"Hey, so, we still live a million miles away, but when you get in town…"

"Sure," she shrugged, taking his phone and its tacit request for information.

"Okay, well maybe I'll see you."

"Yeah."

Shoving a stray lock inside her hood, she stepped back to accommodate a gaggle of young guys that flooded the space between them. A scuffle broke out among them. Difficult to tell whether the joust was in jest, but either way, within a few seconds there was no question. Men poured in to separate the offending parties. Julia bobbed about the melee like a hesitating halfback, unable to choose a hole, and even after the area began clearing, he was nowhere findable.

The next day, she received a Facebook notification: **PF Flyers** had requested her digital friendship. She'd lied to him last night: they could no longer afford Myriadal. She'd needed the night, and the needed night required its consonant ending.

Shaz and Liza had been mum on money since her father's death, which Julia took as the final sign of their tacit breakup. Nothing said we're through like sacrificing paychecks for the sake of expedience, Julia thought. Justifying her certainty that Shaz was to blame, Julia noted that nothing said privilege like throwing money at a problem, and opportunity cost counted as money. Then again, nothing said mutual fault like justification and certainty. If nothing else, her last hangout with Shaz proved that she'd expressed her resentment unawares, which, if nothing else, justified the power of the unconscious, her decision to major in psychology, and the resentment's very existence as proof of viable grievance—and around she went.

So she threw a coup on *Pussy Vitale*. True, Liza had written the code and Shaz had patented the name. But it'd been Julia, from the backseat of what had until then been but another boring blunt ride, who breathed the site into life and, most importantly, who handled the money. She wired Domain Gator the requisite $10/ month, set up the ads and sponsorships for both the site and its live events, and—most importantly—cut the checks. The new password would send a cold yet necessary message that they'd outlasted her, and would perhaps, she thought, outlast everyone else in their lives. In truth, Julia would miss Liza, but not enough to sustain a sideshow friendship.

Freed from the triune's obligatory blunt-rides, long hours lost to the haze in Shaz's ticking hooptie, she had tracts of time to work on the site. School days seemed shorter. Afternoons were a montage of hastily discarded backpacks, cracked knuckles, and spidey-fingers. The sun kept time as she typed well into each night with renewed fervor.

Other than in bated passing, Julia neither saw nor heard from them. Buzzed on espresso one weekend morning, she posted to Betch Banksy a photo of them all wearing football helmets stolen from the gym's equipment shed, mean-mugging among a football field misted in moonlight. New plan: leave the fate of their friendship to a passive-aggressive post.

For her mother's birthday she got a makeover—for herself. She called her hair into ornate knots. She braided it over one shoulder. Outfits that Julia wore only when fortified at frees now poured over her in the colors of those spirits and cordials: sheath dresses like luminous blue Hpnotiq; midnight slips like tumblers of Black Russian; sexy smocks and form-fitting scoop-necks; even a chambray chemise with a black leather waist-belt that did in fact turn too many heads for her liking. In the mirror, her face a canvas, her cosmetics the brush-and-palette of a minimalist master. *Maybe she's born with it.* Yeah, right. A little Maybelline, and even tourist dads jockeyed for trolley seats that offered a good view. Julia liked to catch them leering, glance at their wives and back, and relish not in their shame, but the power she wielded. She liked this power—except when they weren't dads. When, whether socially obstinate or unaware, they kept leering despite her clear lack of consent. When she'd grow so uncomfortable, she'd relocate seats or even disembark, whether to wait for the next trolley or walk the remaining distance. When she'd consider calling Muni or the cops, whether to complain or file an official complaint, whether to tell her mother or tell her mother a story—the warren of worries that, thriving underground and therefore unseen by mankind, keep women quiet, and she'd remind herself that the makeover project wasn't for them, but her mother.

Modeling a new number in the armoire's mirror, she caught her mother glancing up from some celebrity rag.

"Okay, Jules, look," she sighed, setting aside her magazine, "you can't have your stripes and eat them."

"But they're barely even showing," she said, bending like a ballerina to look at her Kate Spade booties. Though only $40 at Nordstrom Rack (whose tagline should've proudly read: *where the rich go to thrift*), the purchase, along with the dozen-odd swipes at various consignment shops and retailers, broke her poor little bank statement. But with the money for Myriadal all but gone, she justified the steal for its own sake. (Once aware of it, she really took to this rationalization thing.) "Plus," she continued reasoning, "it's like, *rebellious*."

"No. This is day-one stuff. And seriously," she said, standing behind Julia in the mirror, "that schoolgirl shit is too hipster. You want to cover your legs? Stockings. Though I suggest shaving and lotioning every day instead."

"So much effort," Julia lamented all campy.

"Rule number one: if you're going to dress as sexy as you are, don't half-ass it. I don't care what your friends say. There are things that men like, and things they don't like."

"Tell me about it," she said, eyes dropped to her booties. "It feels weird. The looks."

Her mother squinted, emboldening her crow's feet. "Whiffs of a Shazism."

Julia exhaled. She was both right and wrong. Right that Shaz would say something of the sort, but wrong about everything else. While her father was outspoken on subject Shaz, her mother's propriety masked a far deeper disdain. Julia thought of those English women who'd railed against their own right to vote. Her mother had modern motes in her eye. So? Who didn't?

She admitted, "I uh…I actually don't really see her anymore. We've hung out like twice since—you know."

His presence passed in the mirror. Julia swore she could've seen her mother start too.

"Here, come, sit."

She went to the couch, where Julia, suffering effeminate growing pains, pulled the hem of her dress and joined her.

"This is something I should've told you but…I'm a mess, Jules," she broke, her face a sudden clusterfuck of functions. "The bank's denying the second loan and—" she sniffled, pursed, preparing her own admissions. "We're gonna lose the house."

"Oh, Mom."

"I'm so sorry. I'm just so fucking upset, *all* the *time*. I can't *function*."

"I know," Julia squeezed. "I've never seen you wear sweats when not sick."

Her guff garnered a couple good guffaws.

"I really don't know how to say this…Your granddad, as you know, lives in Seattle."

"You mean Dad's dad?"

Lucia nodded, breathed, "He's offered to put you up for the summer, before school."

Julia's hand retracted before she'd processed the words. Her head turned as if to petition a specter. And yet, in looking, she projected his response to her protest. She saw that droll tilt of his head, the one that said, *Come on, Jules. Use your imagination*, and all at once she realized: "So Johnny offered to pay for school."

Lucia looked down and nodded.

"Why? I mean, why now?"

Lucia shrugged, sniffled, bent over and back and pulled her cheeks into a frightening stretch of skin gone raw from such rubs. Julia checked the armchair.

"I mean," she blinked, shaking her head subtly, "He could've done this before Dad went off the fucking deep end."

Arms folded, body rocking, Lucia nodded, sobs redoubled. "The irony is not lost on me."

"Nor him, I assume," Julia said, proud of her rueful aptitude.

"Oh boy."

"I *know*. I know," she said again, this time with a semblance of equanimity. "I know he's—*UGGGHHHH*. I know he's rubbing it in our faces," she said and rubbed her face, her voice a rasp of rage and despair, all moan and groan, a good shriek from ripping to shreds. "My theory's that he'd been hoping for this all along. That he even *planned* it. But I—*we*—must refuse to let this stop you from getting what you wanted. So you will enroll at Myriadal, you will do your psychology major, you will find whatever part of the brain responsible for the bullshit men put us through, and you will fix them all, every last one."

Julia deserved a slice of *something*.

"Julia," Lucia pled with her, genuflecting, rubbing her hands so hard it hurt, "I just want this to end. Do you trust that this is what I want? Because I know that this—everything that's happened in the last year—seems like the exact opposite of that. But I need you to trust me, because I'm having a hard time trusting myself."

Benison was having a day. He'd ripped from his new piece, purchased at Pike Place Market, the blown glass packed to the brim
with Jonesy's ripe bud, and—a world ablaze, a world in weed's luster.
Time to play some *videojuegos*—but for a text from his mother:

> Benison, I need u to cme home tmrw. The lawyer will b here.
> We ned to discuss the plan moving forward. Can u b here in
> the AM? Xoxo

Before Benison could process his mother's words, she texted
him again:

> This is vry important. We need to talk about ur father's hearing
> tmrw. I dont want to keep u out of the loop.

Benison ignored her and played nine spiteful games of FIFA
'13. By the start of the tenth, his high had all but vanished, head
ringed by a hazy halo. The virtual pitch eclipsed reality, and the
corona left him blind. When a ref brandished a red card, he threw
a fit into his headset, "What are these, Jim Crow laws? Balotelli's
getting penalized for fucking existing over here."

Marijuana was the myth of Sisyphus in reverse: with green
ichor flowing through his veins, he surged to the summit of his
moods, only to labor back down to his basecamp.

Ten games were nine more than necessary, so he switched
inputs and surfed the muted TV, stopping on *SportsCenter*. NBA
highlights, but a backdrop for rumination. By then his mother
had texted him twice more, pleading for a response. He resigned
himself to attending (but would wait several hours to confirm
such with his mother).

Back in November, he'd catch an occasional comment, a sidelong glance, but for the most part people seemed indifferent. But

then there were some kids. They'd confront him with profound
directness, as if they'd earned this right to initiate, then distill their
worldviews through the prism of his father's arrest.

He'd expected outrage windward of his father's fraudulence,
his by association. After all, the majority of Myriadal students had
matriculated for the Michelin star education and its attendant
moral instruction. But to these confrontational types, cosmic
forces had cut off his father's fifth finger of sense as if punishing him for a crime he couldn't have possibly committed before
birth (and Benison sort of saw it this way in this head because as
a kid his father had told him how the Saudis cut off the fingers
of thieves). Some of the savvier students taking the sole Deaf
Studies elective even railed against the dearth of Deaf rights as
some round-a-merry argument for absolving his father. On its
surface, Benison was utterly bewildered: his father had stolen
Deaf access subsidies, which were not only the pillar of Deaf
rights, but were also a bill footed by taxpayers –the Thatlady
Janes and Everyman Joes. Beneath this, however, awaited the
true question: da fuck would these social canvassers know about
his father?

Last week, some dude standing behind him in line for deli
sandwiches arrogated his attention. From under a straight-billed
Mariners hat, hologram purchase-sticker winking off the heat
lamps, he said, "Yo, Behrenreich."

"Yeah?"

"Just wanted to say. Your dad's a certified G."

He accepted daps from the future brogrammer—but now
he wanted to pull it in for the shoulder bump? He caved to an
awkward brush with the bro's clavicle. Over his shoulder Benison
saw a rankled rucksack slapped with stickers and stitched patches.
Most prominent was a geometric memento mori, the slate gray
sticker markered over with "TABS" in bleeding script.

The Commissary band slammed on a closing note and thanked
the students for lending their ears. Like they had a choice in the
matter. Benison and the bro stood and shuffled in silence until
ordering their sandwiches and thanking their lucky separations.

Growing up, his father hadn't reserved words for the plight of the Deaf population. A card-carrying Republican, he criticized the government's neglect of said plight amid hot-button issues of race and identity and oppression. He charged social justice warriors with selective hearing. Thought that hammer-and-sickle radicals were people with poorly sublimated personal problems. People too often unrepresentative of the causes they so vehemently supported. People too often representative of the demographics they so vehemently censured.

As he got older, Benison grew weary of his father's (or anyone's) claim to *a fortiori* political insight. But by then the facts and figures of Deaf oppression were burned into his brain. At well over 50%, Deaf employment was still hostage to the lack of access (ADA legislation had dragged it down from 75). They were a people that opened newspapers to scathing op-eds headlined: WHEN IT COMES TO THE CALL OF JUSTICE, SCALIA DEAF AND DUMB. They were refused service. Before Google, Deaf folks often deployed the sentence, *I'll have to check with a hearing friend about that.* The Deaf were an unwelcome people, an inconvenience, included by neither God nor government—God either didn't care or cared with clever malice, and the government heeded only that which was heard.

Wikipedia defined audism as "…a set of beliefs that include: hearing people are superior to Deaf people; Deaf people should be pitied for having futile and miserable lives; Deaf people should become like hearing people as far [sic] as possible; and shunning of sign languages." But the article's inchoate definition covered only half of audism's complexity. The most profound aspects of audism's prejudice were to be found *within* Deaf culture or coming *from* the Deaf. Certain Deaf sects deplored oral culture—Deaf folks who spoke or mouthed words while signing. Certain Deaf sects prohibited interaction with hearing culture. Certain Deaf sects despised hearing people, going so far as to claim that, should a cure for deafness arise, they'd never *dream* of making an appointment. Certain sects of Deaf culture believed they were *superior* to hearing people.

To Benison's father, who spared seldom a thought for plebian quibbles, audism was simple: the gaping contingency in American egalitarianism. So why give a fuck what one does or doesn't do?

In "normal" school, Marc made grades by dint of intellect, period. Forced to heed lectures he couldn't understand, he skimmed the texts after class and doodled during, acting as if they were sedulous notes.

One day, his ninth-grade English class was free-writing when Ms. DeLillo's proctoring amble stopped at sight of Marc's notebook. He'd never know for how long she'd watched him put the finishing touches on a raunchy caricature of herself, legs wrapped around a fantasy of Marc Behrenreich-cum-mesomorph, plying his engorged penis like a deeply pleasurable punishment. Curved *whooshes* denoted the power of his thrust as he managed her ballooned breasts. A product of passion over talent, her presence went unnoticed—after all, he was Deaf—until the bodice of her frond-printed dress inched into his periphery.

Marc looked at Ms. DeLillo, who couldn't stop looking at the caricature. Watched the rise and fall of her bosom, this rhythmic ode to impassioned breath and perfect breasts. Raising his gaze, he saw in her witch hazel eyes the wrong sort of passion. She ripped the page from his binder and clacked down the aisle. Thrill rolled through his stomach.

Later that night, the Behrenreichs sat to a dining table dressed in white cloth, its corners embroidered with lace and doily, and strewn with foil baking trays whose steam wafted ambrosia's salty savor. Marc watched the food he ate for five-odd minutes, when two seismic stomps pulled him back through the portal to Noshia, his mouth the magic wardrobe.

"You like this rubber?"

Forkful of delicious brisket hovering over his plateful of staples—the brisket, knish, and kugel—Marc nodded and shrugged, a frown to split the difference.

The Judeo-Christian God was an angry prig, His Testament an overwrought manual for henceforth demagogues who'd rise behind illusory veils of power and mystery. His father, Irving, tried to imitate this old testament vengeance toward the very creatures he'd created. Each night his family worshipped his silence, chewing, vigilant of wraths untold. In panning his mother's culinary work, Marc had laid at the foot of his altar this sacrificial brisket, thus staying his righteous temper.

"Brisket's too tough, Harriet," he said, his mild tone rewarding Marc's offering.

"Sorry hon. Can I make you something else?"

"It's eight-thirty," he scowled. "What, you're gonna go back to the deli? Christ, Harriet. Use your goddamn pea-brain. Pass me the knish."

"Here Daddy," chirruped Marc's kid sister, Jessica, as she handed the tray of perfect triangles of burnished pastry stuffed with luscious potato.

"Marc, your mother got a call from school today," he announced. "You understand me?"

Marc nodded.

"Then acknowledge your father when he speaks to you."

"Yes sir."

"Well," he said, dusting off the debris of his latest detonation, "your English teacher had some nice things to say about you."

"She said that—"

"HARRIET," he roared. "Am I finished talking?"

"Go ahead," she said with meek sheesh.

His lip trembled, ashine in oil. Thinning comb-over like day-old snow, a dusting to an inch from the center of his pate on outward. His overvalued self warred with the underwhelming world, the winner to reign over the void that awaited them both. Trenches dug below his eyes, attrition written into his wizened visage, wattle sagging like a mass body bag for dead cells.

"Seems she agrees with you. That you should try the Deaf school."

"Yes sir."

"You're not like your brother," he said, the elder object of his sentence oblivious to all but his brisket, "and yet you tell me you can't understand your teachers."

"You understand how to speak to me, sir."

"That's right," Irving enjoyed without expressional evidence. "But you're also smart, Marc. Smart enough to manipulate people. Look at your brother." They did, and Jessica nudged Joseph's elbow as if his attention were not only desired but optimal. "Nineteen-year-old janitor," Irving sighed, eyes piercing Marc's intentions, ignoring Joseph's confusion. Then he took up his utensils and said, "Your mother will bring you tomorrow."

"Irving."

"Harriet?" he threatened.

"He's not *Deaf*."

"Then how come he can't hear good! Huh? Use your goddamn pea-brain."

"Marc, honey," pled Harriet, "if you'd just wear the hearing aid properly, like Dr. Heim says—"

"Enough," Irving commanded. "You think that thing helps Joseph find a good job? Makes him look mentally disabled. Marc needs to adjust. That job at the market, it's good for a kid, but I don't want him behind a cash register three years from now."

After school, Allen Kaufman walked with him to K Street Market. A few minutes early, they sat along the curb out front and watched Queens' swirl of rickety beaters ticking along rundown blocks, the Hangul signs hung above neighboring grocers and food stalls. His father used Flushing as a verb for Korean immigration.

"How are you supposed to meet a girl," Marc said to Allen, "with that thing attached to your fucking ear?"

"Huh?"

"And it doesn't even work." He flicked Allen's hearing aid.

"What? Come on. Tell me."

Marc yanked the earmold by its wire.

"Hey!"

Can't you just try *and look normal?* Marc signed.

We can't all afford the new kind.

Allen tried to flick Marc's sleek hearing aid prototype, hooked discretely behind his ear. He missed, and Marc yanked Allen's again.

Do you mind? I'm Deaf, Allen scowled, tapping his index finger chin to ear.

"And dumb," Marc muttered and shook his head.

"I'm not dumb."

Then why'd you get kicked out of PS 47? Marc taunted.

At least my parents don't still think I'm hearing, lapping a horizontal finger up his lips.

He faced across the street as Allen made a show of readjusting his hearing aid's case and wire. He plucked his cigarette from the curb, brought it to lip, peering through the twirl of smoldering tobacco. Heat bored through the blue sky as if the sun were a spoked aperture into hell. His white t-shirt moistened under his K Street apron. A spackle-red Firebird rumbled past their perch on the curb, its crew-cut pilot glistening with coolant, some spacey Zeppelin jam decaying the moment it met Marc's ear. He'd trained himself to recognize the bands, if not math of music. In wake of the classic Trans-Am, Allen caught Marc gazing after Martinelli Heirlooms, the jewelry and antiques shop across the street.

"Women only like man with money."

"And that can speak English. *Have you ever even kissed a girl?*"

Sure, Allen drew an index from chin.

Your sister doesn't count.

"*Fuck you.*"

Did you do the math homework? Marc knocked fists.

I just joined your class.

But you did it.

How would you know?

Because you're a nerd.

Allen narrowed his eyes. *Two dollars.*

One, a twisting peace sign.

Two.

No, Marc snapped his fingers.

Yankees suck.

Dodgers suck.

Two dollars.

One.

Their gazes formed an obtuse angle, Allen's line pointed at the garage down the block, grease monkeys in gray jumpsuits working on a motley line of American-made vehicles. Marc indulged the shop window, seeking her silhouette, its sigmoid curves. He glimpsed her emerging from the back, bending over the glass display to check a price or cross-reference their inventory. He took a drag, imagining the ring of her dreams and buying it for her.

He fished out two singles and handed them over without looking. The tear of loose-leaf from Allen's binder sounded like scratching his own head, the page placed in Marc's lap just in time to catch fallen ash.

"Hey!"

"*Relax,*" Marc grimaced, brushing a comet-tail of char across the fifth problem.

"Give back," Allen reached, but Marc held it away.

"Lookit these little squirts."

Marc sensed Allen following his sightline—the Deaf's indirect optical latency—until arriving at Mr. Raciti's looming form, the pits of his black cardigan over a white button-up.

"Your mother told me you got tossed from the deaf school," Mr. Raciti said to Allen. Marc vaguely recognized the croak in his voice. "The hell you doin throwing a TV out the window?"

Marc used his hands to caulk the gaps in Mr. Raciti's words, and Allen turned from him to Mr. Raciti and said, "I did' throw. I push."

"We got a wise guy here. Go get you some sodas. Or a titty rag," he winked, brandishing a couple bills.

They took the Lincolns and watched Mr. Raciti disappear in the shadow of K Street Market's awning, its aluminum freckled by oxidation, and push through the dusty glass door.

A truckload of narcotics in back and all he can spare is a couple fivers?

"What the fuck did I tell you about that keeping that stuff quiet?"
Marc snapped.

So they know sign language too? Allen sneered.

Marc got up and flicked his butt, sparks sent sputtering around the rim of the garbage can beside a maildrop.

"Bring homework to game tonight," Allen called after him.

Marc curled around checkered tile, green and white, and took his position behind the cash register. His eyes adjusted to the sunlight slanting in striated rays through the glass façade. His ears to the added barriers, hearing muffled car engines, Mr. Raciti's murmur from the back, and jangling bells as a lady in leopard print entered and perused the newsstand bookending middle aisles.

"Hey, Mrs. Pierlo." His volume informed those in the back. More than a cashier, Marc served as point man for unsuspecting "customers" who saw only the mold and metal twisting his ears. He did as told, without question. This was how trust was built in this business, by not questioning the business being built. His mesomorphic fantasy pulling her dye-red waves as he took her from behind, he asked in the friendliest tone his ear could tune, "How are you today, Mrs. Pierlo?"

Door-to-door was his mother's defiance.

Wordless as the black welcome mat outside their second-floor walkup, Harriet maintained her vow of silence all the way to the health room at PS 47. She barely acknowledged the resident audiologist as he adumbrated the forthcoming battery of tests. An ungainly man with horn-rimmed glasses, the audiologist strapped Marc with headphones that dinged in series of varying quantity.

"And how many this time?" he'd ask. "Long or short?"

The audiologist wrote in a manila dossier. Marc couldn't figure whether he'd done well, or what well meant, an ambivalence that seemed to somehow permeate the results.

"Whadya mean they won't let him in?" said his father at dinner.

"Debicel loss of 70 required," Harriet shrugged.

"Decibel, Ma," Jessica corrected.

"Tomato, tomahto," she waved. "He got a 65."

"Out of a hundred?" asked Irving, as if it were a weighted grade.

"The hell does that mean, Harriet?"

"I told you already: he's not Deaf!"

Marc wanted to correct her to the contrary. They made it difficult to decide whether the idiot made the foible or the foible the idiot, a question of free will whose answer would've helped him decide whether they were worth the resentment.

He wanted more than what this life could give him.

It was as Mrs. Pierlo was leaving with her daily pack of Parliaments when a man held the door, entered through her wake, and hooked down the center aisle. Marc watched his shit-brown coat recede into the bodega's depths until he was a fedora hovering above the shelves.

"Can I help you with anything today, sir?" he called.

He approached the chipped pane, behind which Marc stood resolute. Irises the color of egg yolk, razor-pocked cheeks, Sephardic skin tone.

"Who's in charge here," he said, hands clasped over his crotch.

"Mr. K," Marc called to the office. "Visitor."

"Thank you."

The visitor busied himself with the bodega's boroughly wares. Soon enough Mr. K materialized beside Marc, flat smile underlining a blank expression but for eyes that beheld a wonder hidden from all others.

The visitor's trench coat fell open, revealing a holstered .45.

"I'm calling the cops," Marc said, as if disappointed in his etiquette.

"I *am* the cops, kid," said the visitor, who then produced a casing. "Found this little beauty kicked under a dumpster, near the body," speaking to Mr. K. "Picked up your friend, oh, say"—bringing watch to eye—"yesterday. Hit him with acting in concert. Being processed in parts right now, but I'm sure you already know all that. You really oughta instill a little prudence in your men. That is," he chuckled mean, "if you plan on subcontracting all your dirty work."

"Do you private dicks have an office number?" Mr. K lilted. "Or should I assume it's your personal line listed in the Pages."

"They brought me back. Special delivery, just for you."

"Unless you've come to collect some form of statement, Mr...I apologize—" and there was his *x*-axis smile—"but I simply cannot seem to recall."

"*Detective*, Lansky. Now why don't you excuse your deaf and dumb grunt over here so we can have a little private conversation."

Mr. K came around the pane, only fluid air between him and Lansky's .45. Paused in profile, Marc could see him speak.

"And here I'd thought the NYPD's stance was for progress."

"What you call progress I call evil."

"Evil?" Mr. K delighted. "Ah. Yes. That old word." Mr. K removed his hand from pocket as if not brandishing a butterfly knife before a stated detective, who stood transfixed by the move. Studying the knife, turning it over, he said, "This pains me to hear..."

From his body language Marc finished the thought: ...*that you'd worship these moral holographs through which my hand passes without resistance.*

"Considering the limited budget over at the ever-progressive Department," Mr. K smiled, playing the knife like a baton, "you'd think a fellow cop such as yourself would find virtue in their supplementary income."

"I'll never take a dime," Lansky seethed, fingers longing for his holster.

Marc steeled himself, ready to rip the piece taped to the counter's underside.

Mr. K caressed the knife's sharp side, ignoring jumpy hands.

"Murder is evil." Lansky trembled. "That's a damn fact—"

"Oh you can go fuck off with your facts," Mr. K cut in cold. "I find the imagination to be of far greater service. If, for example, I were to give the chief a call over at the precinct—he's a good

friend of mine—I wager he'd corroborate the serial number on
a .45 missing from the cache. Tell me, *Mr.* Lansky. Is that a *fact?*"
Marc's hand crept along the underside. He envisaged the .22
under its layers of glaucous tape, shunting his life onto this irreversible track. Time had turned into an asymptote, accelerating as
it approached Lansky's errant draw, firing wild into the ceiling as
a plastic bag enveloped his head, cutting his breath, the skintight
polythene mask like a waxen bust of mortal struggle. Marc awed
at Lansky, who clawed at the stranglehold as if deathbitten leeches
had stuck there rather than Mr. Raciti's hands, their knuckles
white. Lansky jerked and twisted and writhed, silent but for the
squeak of rubber sole across tile, miming death in its very moment.
He slipped out from under his flailing legs and slid down to his
killer's paunch as if tucking into his death bed. His end would
meet no equal and opposite reaction, no outward ripple of life
force—Lansky was going to die, simply and plainly. No ciphers, no
karmic recompense, until Mr. K ordered Mr. Raciti to release him.
    "AH?" Mr. Raciti grunted.
    "Do it."
    He released Lansky to the floor.
    "Close the blinds," Mr. K instructed.
    Mr. Raciti hesitated, panted in his perplexity. The freed Lansky
made undignified noises, *smacking* the tile between breaths like a
jet's sound-streak. His need harried his very recovery. His hacks
and wheezes sprinkled blood on the tile. Mr. K looked down with
vague interest on Lansky's respiratory troubles. "Marc," he said,
meaning for him to come around the pane.
    "Bring the gun."
    Now it was Marc who hesitated. Dusk's blood orange squeezed
through the blinds, dust motes ascendant in this weak light. He
ripped the six-shooter from its sticky moorings and came around.
He glared at Lansky as he stalked the tile and, three feet from his
subject, raised the piece and pulled.
    Click
    Click
    Click

Click
Click
Click

Lansky writhed, gasping, oblivious to his bonus time, to everything he was about to lose, and Marc looked on in disbelief. Mr. K, chuckling, dipped a hand into his apron's pocket and revealed a shining silver casing. He took the revolver from Marc's limp hand.

"It's good to know your heart, my boy. There's a thing about loyalty, you see. It's a choice."—spinning the chamber and slapping it locked—"The trick is to choose the right side."

He pointed the piece and Marc's ears ruptured. He opened his eyes and, as if the asymptote had hit axis, time lost meaning. It could've been seconds, minutes, hours before Mr. Raciti returned with supplies, and perhaps it was then, as Mr. Raciti began sawing, then bleaching, then mopping, that Marc had proclaimed Lansky dead.

"He was a cop," Marc seemed to only now realize, along with the acerbic scent festering in coolers stuffed with body-parts.

"*Detective*," Mr. Raciti chuckled over burning flesh.

"A pig," Mr. K said, "trapped in his pen. Where there's nothing but mud, and other stinking pigs."

Marc looked at the coolers and wondered, to his incredulity, whether Lansky had volunteered as an organ donor. "Won't they come around?" he asked.

Pulling a kerchief from his breast pocket to wipe down the .22, Mr. K penned tomorrow's frontpage headline: "A former detective, suspended twice and eventually fired for erratic behavior, turns vigilante with stolen NYPD .45. I suspect," said Mr. K in his natural tone, "the only way we'll hear about poor old Lansky here is from a missing persons report."

Mr. K carried his flat cheer toward his office. Marc watched his apron's knot shrink, lose its intricacy, and diminish to a uniform dot on the small of his back. His heel-clicks were distant, separated by not only time but something else, too. He heard a voice.

"I said you're done for the day," Mr. Raciti flicked a hand towards the door. "Gotta dump this pig fuck in the marsh."

"I don't understand," Marc said.

"It was a setup, kid." Mr. Raciti wiped his hands on a cloth and faced Marc. "A cop he trusts gives him an anonymous tip: every day, at between so-and-so in the evening, Mr. K's here alone before they close up K Street. Erratic behavior," Mr. Raciti giggled. "Shoulda known what's good for him."

"But Mrs. Pierlo," Marc said, not feeling real, as if he were the one saying these words. "Or anyone else who might have seen him come in."

"You remind me of my son," Mr. Raciti said. His laughter scratched at the surface of Marc's daze, irritating its translucent skin. "Mrs. Pierlo don't come in for the paper. Her and her husband run storage for us." Returning to the coolers, he muttered, "Now scram."

Marc shuffled home like a bad surveillance craft, oblivious to all but the sidewalk's stony stipples, weeds sprouting in the cracks. To everyone else around him: a workday turned twilight; air so temperate you couldn't feel it; or, he'd released the biological equivalent of emotional novocaine.

Once home, he went to his room, sat on the floor, leaned against his bedframe, and stared at the wall. Negatives of Lansky's exsanguinating neck scudded across his skull. How the .22's hollow tip had mangled that waxen bust beyond all hope for restoration.

A tap at his shoulder.

He looked up.

Her hip jutted, in one hand the rotary, the other proffering the phone.

"F'you."

Dazed, Marc held it to ear. Heard breathing. His own.

"Welcome to the pantheon."

Click.

His mother dropped him off at the library. Rather than changing into his basketball clothes and sneaking off to his game, he struck toward the back, behind the stacks, where a big Webster's was bolted to a wood lectern. He relished its onion skin pages, their gilded edges, scrolling the words beginning with Pa…

Pantheon / panTHē̩än,-THēən / n.   1   a temple dedicated to all the gods 2 the gods of a people

Marc had attended three classes, seen the first of the Gallaudet football Bison's obstinacy of victories, and consumed five Miller High Lifes, a shot of grain, and popped his bud on a bowl's greens, and chucked at Tanya Jackson's dorm party. Then he bussed back to New York for a funeral.

A balloon had burst in one of Mr. K's mules. Standing in line at airport security, the mistaken suppository delivered $100,000 worth of pure powder of the poppy. She'd noodled to the floor in a boneless heap. Her wake near the Marcy Projects, the embalmed body, talking about who else had left them that year.

Frank Gerdin.

Larry Epstein.

Jorge de la Rosa.

Alberto Domani.

Mr. K brushing her burnished cheek.

He manned the door at Johnny's in Southeast DC. Not exactly an eclectic crowd. Every fortnight, a few rooskies brazed by Cyrillic played a few hands, were congenial if brusque, and left with everyone paid up. Marc couldn't cut the translations, so these were general impressions.

Mainly, the stone igloo saw wops that moved tar.

Standard shit. Baize tables dappled about. Johnny hobnobbing as his brother did vigs in a black moleskin. Behind polished walnut, Larry Cortina wiped tall glasses in his impeccable waistcoat—Marc would tip his head, Cortina in kind. The made ones

gave him a right tit for money on their way out. That sort of thing.
But Ellen hated it. It bewildered him, how she could unhand
him with words. She swung truncheons, "*I can't* bring *people into
my* life, *Marc—I don't know what to tell them.*"
But the money, was his reply. *If you'd just stick to the signing,* was not.
O, the money. The twenties stuffed into his blazer's pocket like
refuse in a receptacle. Those shoebox banks he managed back in
Queens? Baseball cards. Here at Johnny's, Marc made *money.* The
kind you spend cautiously. The kind politicians stage left couldn't
seize and poorly redistribute.
   Two more months, he avowed, *and my trucks will be on the road.*

```
Kid,

The banana sundae was sorry to hear about
your losing the delivery contract. The banana
sundae has your best interests in mind, but the
banana sundae keeps its best interests in mind.
Unfortunately, it seems our interests have come
into conflict, and no one wants conflict. The
banana sundae would like you to consider the
deafies suffering because of this conflict next
time you file a W9.
```

Marc crumpled the note into a sharp ball. "Fuck."
What's wrong? Ellen asked, a backward *y* bounced off her chin.
Nothing. Life is great.
   "Mah."
   A sound like that from a woman that pretty, he mused. *Did
you call the guy?*
   I had a paper due today.
   We can't shower.
   I had a paper, she scowled, really slapping up some *paper* this time.
   A hand's splat upon the oak table explained Marc's exhaus-
tion. The place had cleaned up good since moving in prior to
senior year. In the living room lay a rustication of rugs and tawny

leather, dry-rubbed sandalwood, antique box lamps like cliffside miradors. Potted cacti cornered the squelch-brown stucco walls. Sure, it looked like they'd retired to the red hills of New Mexico, but that *was* the dream, if not the state. Next, Ellen wanted to do the kitchenette. Marc had told her they'd as likely move a couple years after graduation—the preretirement dream being IBM, the state that of Washington, or wherever they'd place him out West. *It'll raise value*—and he was unhanded.

Spanish tile might've been all the vogue, but what about the trend of his finances? The trucks had cost him $20k a pop but would salvage at five if he was lucky. He owed a last round of paychecks at about $1,500 altogether—though Guillermo hadn't even made his last drop-offs. Just left his truck on Georgia Avenue, hazards flashing, outside a classmate's apartment. In fairness to Guillermo, he'd not heard word one about Gallaudet's recent ruling—that current students could no longer form business contracts with the University; and all such standing contracts would henceforth be void—before the classmate, who'd received a box marked FRAGILE, delivered the University's *fait accompli.* The classmate—Punjab Velanki, which Marc could now disclose in lieu of the courier's obligation to confidentiality—had called and explained Guillermo's crisis of confidence in Behrenreich Courier Services for which Punjab felt responsible despite having only been the messenger.

Marc didn't know what angered him more, Guillermo's consummate indifference to all but *número uno,* or GU's profound hypocrisy. Thoughts of driving the abandoned truck into Guillermo's split-level apartment phased with NBC's local broadcast, which was on the Zenith set bevel in living room's corner. Too far to read the closed captioning, Marc took stance near the TV, hovering over it with his arms crossed.

In a stroke of serendipity, NBC was running a segment on the Deaf President Now protests. Field reporter Bill Sayers, a spry little man in his late fifties, stood in front of the Gate House entrance off Florida Ave, his mic held peacock-out, underlined by the network's call letters:

"... *Students are writing letters, using TTY relay to reach school board members directly, walking out on classes and demonstrating in the streets of campus. For the students at Gallaudet University, it's simple: Harvey Corson is Deaf. King Jordan, the favorite, is, more importantly, Deaf. Elisabeth Zinser, however, is hearing. Stoking student outrage were last night's comments from GU board member, Jane Bassett Spilman, who said, and I quote, 'The Deaf are not yet ready to function in the hearing world.' But many think otherwise, including national leaders such as Vice President Bush and a group of US senators. With their support, it might only be a matter of time before the students get their way...*"

The rain's percussive drone, the wind rattling the windowsill's potted plants, the quivering basil, the trembling rosemary—his mind matched their vibrato, tremoloing an idea-note, and there was a music to this moment of metacognition. He stood, his mouth parted slightly, and saw the sliver of his perspective spectrum rip open like a wormhole into *color.*

Where are you going? Ellen wagged an index.

Marc pivoted a cursory *L, I'll be back later.*

Mere minutes later and he was pounding away at Allen Kaufman's dorm room with force enough for idle hearing aids. His Armani blazer all but ruined, his meticulously authored mane in wet disarray, Marc let their conversation wring itself out across his doorframe's threshold.

Dressed down in pinstriped pajamas, Allen squinted against glasses out of reach. One peek at his desk and Marc saw that Allen was poring over stats from the last GU basketball game. His bulbous curls were matted from running thoughtful fingers through it, his scent a covalence of scotch and sweat. He asked what about *his* room at *this* time inspired Marc to suffer a weakening tropical storm.

Deaf President Now.

What about it? Allen twittered impatiently.

I know how to get what we want.

Take a number, Allen signed. *We've got forty people working on the next press release alone, and they all have an opinion.*

Good, we need their opinions. Whether for Harvey or King.

Who else would there be?

Elisabeth, Marc supplied with a slashing index.

"What?" Allen grinned, blinking, incredulous.

"*Think about what's happening now. Then think about what* would *happen if she were the Board's choice.*"

Allen's impatience shut off as if remote controlled. He signed, *We'll walk out.*

"*Then,* Marc thumbed, *we get* everything *we want. Not just a Deaf president, but no curfew, no permission to visit girl's dorms or go on dates.*"

Hand running through his matted bulbs, he asked his desk, "But how we do that?" Then he looked at Marc...*No.*

"Allen"—an avuncular hand placed on Allen's shoulder—"*Johnny's good at what he does.*"

Raised in Jersey, Ellen Russo wasn't *deaf* and *dumb.* Not in their neighborhood. Not in front of the Russos' friends. Her sisters had crowned her Princess Eleanor—for her royal needs. Her family didn't deign to her "selective hearing," which only enabled her reluctance to pay attention and untenable need to understand.

So Marc found himself in a bind when, two months after quitting his perfectly fine job at IBM, he still hadn't told a chosen soul, let alone a goy such as his wife. This would change at dinner, he determined. After Benison asked how his day at work had gone, he announced into his napkin that it hadn't. That he'd quit—to start his own company.

"You quit?" Benison's eyes bulged. *Dad's starting his own company!* he broadcast over a brainy pile of Bolognese. His son turned back, eager to hear exactly what this meant, but Marc was occupied with the object across the table nearing critical mass. Her expression read betrayal, while her eyes said they'd tuck in their little citizen before debating matters of state.

"*There's an opportunity,*" which he did with an upflung *p*—the infamous finger all in his eyes. "*So I took it.*"

Thus commenced the protest. She wouldn't look at him. Wouldn't sleep with him, whether next to him or with him inside her. Didn't let him sit for dinner. Made a show of organizing their valuables on the table, prepared to pawn her way out of poverty. It was a controlled rage. Unannounced departures, bedroom residency, kicking him to the couch without signing so much as its suggestion. It was mean. It was scary. She meant to break Marc, to make him regress into a helpless little boy that beseeched and wheedled. She'd point to the TTY on the counter, loaded with phone, ringing for Ileana Eshescu, Accounts Management, eleventh floor.

After dinner one night, the little citizen asleep, she slipped. *Then what's the opportunity? Huh?* She exuded a savage capitalist rage, the kind that ends marriages.

But Marc had sharpened his sword of grievance, to which she'd now left her midsection vulnerable. He set his fried chicken on the coffee table. Rather than detail the opportunity, he diagnosed her anger as if it were a textbook response to unrelated traumas: that it was rooted in jealousy of his past successes; that this *opportunity* would be another of them; that she'd used their son as a shield against marital strife.

So ensued screaming matches of a particular incoherency. Spittle flying from gyrating mouths, spraying pops off non-manual *p*'s, the wet clicking of throats, and Ellen's operatic bellow, indistinguishable from that of a surfaced blue whale (even Deaf people had the Discovery Channel).

Those BIS fights turned dynastic. They revealed to Benison their every bruise and welt, each gloss of scar tissue: Marc's alleged affairs (the Deaf world is a very small one); the $15,000 tapestry Ellen had bought a year into their marriage; that Benison wasn't exactly planned. They revealed to themselves their union's original sin: that he'd never satisfy her lifestyle standard; but that her anxiety (hint: her jealousy) prevented him from risking for more; and around they went. He saw it on his son's face: being an adult seemed dumb.

It was true that Marc had located an opportunity.

The geniuses on the twelfth floor had built a patch for the NOAA's Global Forecast Model, and IBM's management had called Marc's number. He and his deskmate, Jerry, prepared to pitch the new mainframe to the NOAA's Technical Supervisor, Katherine Doyle, and her small cluster of computers people.

Marc and Jerry's pitch hinged on the developers' delicate translations. The gist was that their patch represented the NOAA's best shot at topping the ECMFW, or King Euro, the weather world's leading supercomputer.

Pitching from the prow of the pearl-slick conference table, Marc did his thing, working the stark contrast between his voice and its eloquence. After interviewing for an engineering position, IBM's hiring squad had crapped on Marc's preferred salary range—they'd double it, if he'd work high-level sales instead. They'd heard what he couldn't: how his throttled voice would press his pitches into precious persuasions, which his wits would then cut into the settable crystal of a comprehensive business plan. Marc was, among the Deaf, a linguistic anomaly. He didn't feel exploited so much as the wrong kind of lucky. He'd liked coding. He'd hate sales.

Following the pitch, Jerry and the rest of NOAA's reps took their leave, allowing Marc and Katherine some room to schmooze. As Katherine cut acute arcs in her swivel chair, Marc took inventory. The mock-ups loaded in the wood presentation easel, charts delineating memory enhancement, fiscal proofs befitting the government's thrift. The slides he'd referenced while demoing the product (which he had enjoyed deeply, as its preparation required learning the program). The last slide, left projected upon the blackout cloth, depicting the ease with which users could toggle between 850mb height anomalies and QPF forecasts. The detritus of a victory he didn't believe—not for want of a better product, but the way he'd sold it, the way they'd bought it. From him. From his handicap—ten strokes off his game. Bleeding heart delusionals would claim the Deaf weren't handicapped. He'd viewed such sentiments as semantics in service of the new socioeconomic census to come, the public's myopic attempt to uplift that would only separate people into competing factions of demographic suffering. But this desire to play without a mulligan made him wonder otherwise.

Reposed in her swivel, Katherine hinted that Marc too might indulge a closed deal. "It's Friday."

Her hair's high twist was like a coif of soft-serve orange sherbet. Her pugnacious nose anchored shrewd black eyes. Composed, deliberate, nothing her corpulence suggested. When she asked what was his story, he saw a darkly sparkled desire to know things about him.

He related the terse version: computer science/math double major at Gallaudet; class treasurer, then class president, a race run and won on the strength of his work for GU's first Deaf President Now campaign; statistics graduate at RIT and member of its flagship NTID program; hired by his business stats professor as a statistician at the Census Bureau. "Those red lights along DC's metros? That was my idea."

"But you weren't rewarded for it," Katherine averred.

"No. And I'd studied to be an engineer."

"But these guys," her quickly canted head indicating this corporate monolith, "they want FDR with the wheelchair and blanket. I'd say that's a lateral move at best, but that'd be too simple a geometrical description."

Marc pressed his lips and peered in keen frustration. Katherine understood. Not only that he hadn't, but why. She repeated a condensed version, enunciating, "The job pays, but so do a lot of jobs that you're qualified for."

"Better than Noah," he said, referring to NOAA by its colloquial term.

"But I think you hate it here, and I've got an idea."

Marc was seduced by her ability to read subtle cues. Most took him for his surface malaise. Katherine, however, saw past his crotchety crust, through his covetous mantle. What he wanted had no origin, no core truth, galactic desires exploded from emptiness. Unlike those to whom he pitched—geeks jaded by their anachronistic genius—Katherine saw in Marc what he saw in himself: pure unmitigated ambition.

"Do you know Orange?"

"John Neau owns Orange," Marc said.

"Have you heard how much he sucks?"

He smirked and looked at his lap. "I heard he cheats at cards."

"Our contract with Orange is about to expire."

"Expire? Or…"

"We're opting out," she admitted. "Why don't you look over the new solicitation and see if you can't muster up the work?"

Marc had to smile at that. "I have no experience."

"You worked on original ADA legislation," she said, referring to the metro lights. "You're a former class president. You *must* have contacts. And these hearing-owned companies, they don't know dick from cunt about Deaf culture. Their interpreters suck. Their quality control sucks. Listen," she leaned in, and Marc fought a glance as her bosom was tabled. "Why don't you just peruse through the Registry for interpreter rates and availability, and I'll personally walk you through any questions regarding the RFP."

Katherine's proposition came with misgivings. Feeling marooned here, Katherine was his desperately thatched raft. But what if he pushed off the Isle of IBM only to float along the free market's desolate chain, bailing his pathetic boat, his flare gun only good for illuminating where he was:

Which was out of his fucking mind with boredom. So absolutely riddled with ennui that his mirror reflected actual hollows of disinterest—rutted cheeks, undereye divots, morning dewlaps. He was sick of clockwatching, passing time playing minesweeper, flicking paper footballs, logging the minutes, staring at Elsa Rodriguez's tits. Tired of traffic jams. Of 2PM's raw desperation, the spiritual fatigue behind his eyes, his brain dialing his ocular nerve-line just to remind him that *Your life is this.* He hated his colleagues. He hated how they spoke to him until a hearing colleague came along. He deplored the most creative aspects of his work—thus was beyond through with the menial labor, like poring over client-assign memos against all apathy save for the prospect of pitching to companies with systems compatibility issues, which could really fuck his week. He spent the first half of each day slogging through this procedural work. Then, he resigned himself to taking mental snapshots of Elsa Rodriguez's tits, cotton-bound and pearl-buttoned, perched above her keyboard with ergonomic thrust that sent him to the loo to finish the job. Each day, his desk-neighbor, Jerry, returned from Mamma Lucia's with a trite quip about his post-lunch shit. He hated Jerry. He hated Jerry's kids, who wouldn't stop smiling at him from within that frame that read 'Family' around its borders. He hated his cubicle, a cage to share with Jerry—always more Jerry, mother*fucking* Jerry. Days passed toward nothing, no end. He spent pent energy on E*Trade, trading until late and rotting him by morning, when he crawled back into the incubator. He was sick of this claustral icebox of a conference room. Sick of following a formula that won business for a shadow boss. Sick of willing through this work for the quarterly opportunities to pitch the Noahs of the market's ark.

Sign language interpreting companies were swindlers. They were back-alley dealers in trench coats, leering over upturned lapels, slinging bad coke cut with titrates not safe for consumption. Not only Noah, but entire collections of government sectors were dissatisfied with the swindlers they'd contracted for sign language interpreting services they were now required by the Americans with Disabilities Act to provide. Meanwhile, Marc wallowed with a corporation that'd sooner promote him than provide him an interpreter.

Yet ideals alone wouldn't spur him. Marc needed to defeat boredom, the barely conscious cousin of death. He needed to know he wouldn't end up painfully aware that he was behind another desk. Assessing the thatched coracle that Katherine had thrown him—the 54-page RFP and seven procedural attachments—he'd never know.

They worked two dogged weeks putting a proposal together. Despite a few charged meetings, he didn't fuck Katherine Doyle during what they spun as a magnanimous collusion, though he would once she announced the award without hitch.

"Now, just so you know, I can't make guarantees," she said. "I can't control who else bids and for how much. I can't control the other judges and their biases and hang-ups."

The soft soles of her flats whispered to his ankle, his knee, his thigh, belying her frank disclosure, unfazed by his alarm. He'd quit his job. He'd betrayed his wife's trust. If Katherine welched now, he'd either kill her or marry her.

"But as the contracting officer, I select the judges, and I have sole access to proposals before the bid opening. Which means I can control which company offers the lowest bid. So," she sang, soft sole massaging his crotch in the corner of Capitol Hill's draftiest café, "you just get to hiring the hands."

At breakfast, Benison's mother asked him if he would brush his teeth before leaving for school. His head hung over his plate, its rim a frieze of fall leaves, its texture a varnish that made it look like earthenware, like rustic yellow clay straight off the wheel. He stared at this celebration of scrambled eggs and rye toast, obdurate, but she fussed after him until he acknowledged her.

I could smell your breath when waking you up.

Still hangdog over his eggs, with venom in his voice he muttered that she could go fuck herself.

She squinted, jabbing her lips, *What did you say?*

Rolling his eyes, he whined, "Never mind," and left his plate for Angelica.

Never, to his mother, was he to utter that phrase.

At the bus stop, Benison secured the perimeter of social creatures awaiting their ride to a socially restrictive destination. *Compulsory,* came a word-thought. *Like my mom's OCD. Like an autistic kid when you take their cartoons.* His gait assumed speed and drew eyes.

Bristling, he imagined walking back home. Imagined finding

her on the sunporch, or in her sewing room. Imagined conjuring his contrition, raising his linguistic wands, and, slowly, deliberately, signing, *I was thinking on the way to the bus and…on second thought*—and here he'd hold his hands in limbo, where his mother's hope was frozen on her stupid face—*you know what? never mind.* "Bye," he said aloud now.

The social creatures stared. Moments later the bus pulled along the lipped curb, and they lined up for their ride to Bellevue High.

After school, he walked into an ambush. They'd staked out the living room, which came straight off the foyer. He'd no choice but to join them, taking a far seat on the brocade couch, the appliqued paisley like fractal black tears.

"Look at your mother."

His hand twitched like a caged bull, lusting to leap forth and buck, and so it did: glaring at the TV's black reflection, he thrust his arm and flung the finger and held it there, trembling.

With incoherent caterwauls she appealed to his father, who coaxed her into their bedroom. Little grief went with them (until it would). His father returned a minute later, reclaimed the couch's cousin, an armchair whose paisley pattern and base cloth were black and white, respectively, reciprocating the couch's. She redecorated yearly. Sitting ankle-over-knee, his father's practiced repose was Benison's portrait of vanity.

"Your mother is sensitive."

Shrug.

"You're a man now."

Jesús Cristobel, the bar mitzvah card, a full year after the fact. Somehow, time lent the trump its spades.

"You need to take responsibility for how you make her feel."

Benison smiled. A smile that said, *This, coming from you. That's rich.*

"Your mother's time was much more difficult for Deaf children. Still, she helped build this life for you."

"Yeah, yeah," Benison sighed wearily. "I'm a piece of shit."

His father's sigh was different, reproachful, yet ashamed. He started telling the story. How Benison's grandmother, Myrna Russo, had pretended she could hear, as if Deafness were merely an impudence that could be corrected through strict discipline—like mixing her martinis at ten in the morning. He loved to tell this story, and Benison knew why: because it wasn't his story. So Benison buckled in for the long boring drive to Pennington, New Jersey, where—but had his father just used first-person in reference to his past?

"I left home at sixteen," he said. Caught between curiosity and appearances, Benison's head hung in his lap, turned so slightly, a sneak view of the narrator. "I was arguing with my father in the doorway—we lived in a second-floor walkup, so this put us right at the top of the stairs. He didn't say anything I hadn't heard. But something snapped. Maybe he said them one too many times, but I clocked him in the gut and he tumbled down the stairs...."

Did either of them know that *Nevermind* was a Nirvana record? That it could mean something outside themselves?

His father brushed his pants and looked there. "Did you remember when I started my company?"

"No."

"You were very excited."

"That and when Barney came on."

"...Your mother was furious with me. She was so sure I'd fail. And we'd go broke."

The grandfather clock chimed the hour. For some reason isolated noises reminded Benison of his size.

"Can I go now?" he said with screws, standing, waiting, "Sounds good."

To his room, direct for his desktop computer. He woke the monitor. Undrawered the tube of Eucerin hand cream he'd borrowed permanently from the bathroom. Surveyed the floor for the nearest load-bearing article of clothing: the pair of threadbare briefs he plucked from under his chair's wheel. He noted the wheel's impression—a nice mitt. Desire trussed disgust up like a chicken and shoved a bit in its beak. He searched an old favorite: sports bra titty fuck

Dressed in his obligatory birthday suit—beige slacks and a pastel-blue button-down—Benison watched his parents fuss in the hallway mirror. *Don't worry if you're not hungry. We won't eat for another two hours. Okay.*

"I wouldn't worry, period," Benison muttered, and his father's eyes angled off the glass.

Palace Kitchen checked all the boxes. His father's unfamiliarity kept him from inspecting the kitchen (though not from enlightening the waiter to his goose allergy). His mother's pretentious palette would be tested by Tom Douglas (though not by the *medium* burger: meat temperature being the straightest line from "unexamined need to complain" to "complaining").

The host led them through the restaurant's patchwork of families Benison envied for not being his. A tap at his shoulder and his mother signing, *Can you ask her to sit closer to the middle? I need more light.*

Benison begrudged her in service of his birthday wish: that everyone just get through the night. The unfortunately pretty host, elegant in the uniform black dress, smiled at her ne'er-do-wrong customers, snapped up the menus. Benison fell in love as she escorted them into a private room—where a roundtable burned under a max-bright chandelier dropped low's she goes. He tipped and doffed his phantom hat, and she stifled a stiff chortle or two, skittering back out.

Squinting, jabbing the chin, *What did you say?*

If she wanted to get a drink later.

She smiled wry.

A good start.

His father could read French yet still asked about the foie gras for the express purpose of reminding the waiter of his fucking goose allergy. His haughty rejection of the wine: "This is corked. Here, see? Where it cracked? Now smell this."

His mother sent the burger back till it burnt and, abject, Benison interpreted her substitute order. "New York Strip…medium…*He heard me*…medium, yes medium…no butter or salt…side of—Do you have steamed broccoli?"

"Sure."

"So steamed broccoli…and that's it." *Mom, stop*, he popped, then screwed an index into his chin, *I'm serious.*

A Tom Douglas restaurant observed modern nonchalance. Noses turned up to leather and prunella. But his mother didn't even understand the Internet, and his father was already clipping his Centurion card into the billfold when out came the crème brûlée, candle-stuck and all. Benison was sat in setting cement, watching waiters encircle him like Jacobins in monkey suits. Their rendition's casual perfection was frightening. A shred of decency: they drowned out his parents' drone, jeroboam bellows for a happy birthday. Remembering last year, singing alone, together, just for him, just before Pink Door's Tuesday cabaret—he blew the flame from the record, the singing switched to clapping, their grins quivering against a truth desperate to surface.

Spoons wielded, they cracked what looked like the congealed skin of a peach. Benison hit another hard layer beneath—chocolate ganache base.

Bottom of the brûlée? his father signed with his free hand and raised brows.

His mother slipped the crust and pushed, rising from her seat for leverage, the plunging neckline of her black dress hung clear from her cleavage. She plied her spoon like an earthmover, lifting gelatinous shards that jiggled giggling into her hot red mouth. Splitting the chocolate, still bent over the table, she said what she'd have signed as, *It's so hard!*

Adolescent angst, far from liminal, was the hazy dawn of his becoming. At night he slipped out of bed to check his backpack, making sure all his books and binders were there. He made it a baker's dozen.

Do you want me to call Dr. Phan?

"So he can pump me with meds?"

She squinted, jabbed her chin.

"Never mind," he enunciated.

She couldn't come back with word one. Not after the incident.

He celebrated his middle school graduation by brooding in his room, masturbating and watching TV, his legs too long for the bunk bed. Most days that summer he bussed to the center for teens, downtown, where Denny Way began ramping up the Hill—where he smoked cowboy killers, drank from paper bags, basked in his mud-green ringlets. He'd take the last bus back, smelling like he-don't-care. He kept on like this into his freshman year at Bellevue High—until he met Ricky, who caught him watching an after-school scrimmage in the main gym. He'd gone to Bellevue High's sibling school, Bellevue Middle, so knew more kids than Benison, who'd gotten redistricted. One look at him and Ricky said, "Yo you play?"

"I can dribble aight," Benison shrugged.

"Got gear?"

"Nah," Benison said, looking down at his baggy blue jeans and too-loose button-up.

"You got sneakers on," Ricky observed, which seemed to settle it.

They played Mondays and Wednesdays after school, squeezing as many scrimmages as possible before the volleyball girls trotted out, scarifying the court. Ricky lived in Magnolia, too far for after-school hangouts, and they hadn't broached the subject of information exchange, which required an invitation, which required a modicum of vulnerability, which though they both contained in great volumes, they'd also bonded over basketball, whose culture bred tough exteriors, superficial values, and, mostly, masculine manners of relating.

He couldn't help but beam out the window during the bus ride home. *Varsity,* he thought on rotation and, despite December's chill, luxuriated along the road's lipped curb, strolled down his steep drive, stood in the foyer and just appreciated the day.

He grabbed Oreos from the pantry and flipped the TV to *106 & Park*. He watched a continuous shot of Lil Wayne strutting the set for the video he was in, admiring Weezy for attaining this level of fame before his cerebral membrane had finished its formative molting (which happened in your mid-20s according to some article based off a study whose findings they'd probably cherry-picked). He felt great admiration and appreciation. He'd been pulled up to varsity.

During commercials he flipped to dumb dating shows on MTV. Angelica dislodged her cleaning gear from the closet off the foyer, and Benison slumped deeper into the brocade cushions, deeper into fugue states of fame and fortune, his features sunken by sugary confections and glory, fallen into this bliss-coma.

His mother took stance behind the couch's back, watching the "A Milli" music video as if piggybacking a neighbor's Wi-Fi.

Benison savored his secrets, tended to them, let them ferment before pouring them out like libations for a potlach of grievance.

Varsity.

He was ready to disburse his most valuable secret, spend it in the only way he ever wanted: to feel the fury he unleashed for forty minutes between buzzers, between baselines, between brawls for loose balls, his bottled rabidity foaming all over the court, bullying opponents to the rim, stalking them on defense, talking shit in their ear until he felt sorry for them.

He was ready for the family détente.

His mother came around to sit. Her weight squished the remote between cushions and changed the channel. A meteorologist stood before a busy weather map, calling for all hell and brimsnow to stall against the Cascades. Tomorrow's game—their anxiously-awaited second against Hebron; his first with the *varsity* squad—would be canceled. As if forewarned of the reverse-intervention, his father came home early, funereal in his black-on-less-black suit.

They'd lied to him—no, they'd deceived him. They'd deceived others, and belated confessions only magnified the enormity of their deeds. Leaning over, elbows on knees, his father unveiled the company's summary scheme, and it occurred to Benison what he—what anyone—might be capable of. What they were weak to. What they inevitably were and weren't.

Var—

Just remember—the thought like a vandal in his body's boiler room—*they could've gotten you killed.*

"*So what, I just forgive you now? now that I finally know why you're pieces of shit?*" he sneered and, turning to his mother, signed, *You don't know about that day. You never asked and s-o you'll never know.*

Sleet started salting the porch. He felt his father watching him. *What was it like?* she frowned. *Please. Tell me.*

His silence was his refrain, had *been* his refrain, during the last year-and-a-half of justified irreverence.

"Benison," his father said with soft command on his tongue.

Benison obliged, but steeled himself. Against what, he couldn't name. Whatever his father said now would be dipped in bullshit. But what that bullshit was, he'd never know. He couldn't know, not consciously. If he did—if he saw it or heard it or felt it—it would cease to be bullshit. It would cease to be anything but the smoke shrouding his mirror.

"*I make no excuses,*" his father signed and spoke. "*I never have. But we didn't choose this, and we're doing our best to get out…*"

His office blinds were drawn. Within, Dolores Whitmire, Marc's stalwart CPA, detailed exactly how much overhead required overboarding to stay afloat—indeed, they were drowning.

After two years of marriage, the Internal Revenue Service's ADA compliance officer had claimed irreconcilable differences, and with them had walked an exulted divorcee's percentage of revenue.

He didn't need a shrink to pick up the parallels. (If only for Benison…)

The IRS's main complaint: the handjobs were shit. Fair enough. Upon winning the contract, Behrenreich Interpreting Services had

thirty days to prepare for a 250% spike in volume. Marc rushed
new hires through training programs and certification exams. He
flailed to file state licensure exemptions. He dipped into personal
funds and took out a loan to defray an array of required insurances
(cyber security insurance's sticker shock had conducted voltage
reminiscent of the Milgram experiments). He blasted emails out
to potential subcontractors in Andover and Philadelphia—and
forgot the blind part of bcc'ing agency owners and managers and
coordinators, all of whom now knew BIS's playbook. With all these
hoops to jump through, he was bound to catch fire.

Somehow, he made it through—until the complaints, which
rolled like a tidal wave, a deceptively rapid rise of ire that, by
the end of the first option year, had flooded coordination's inbox.
Somehow, however, he made it through the second year—until
the Contracting Specialist had caught enough shit from the
Contracting Officer, and on up the Treasury's bureaucratic lines.
Just days before the third option year would take effect, BIS received official notice that the IRS was opting out.

Even a week later, Marc found himself rereading the contract's
terms and conditions for any fireless loopholes through which he
could leap back into labor hours—but the clause on page 24 lit
flame to all the loops:

F.4.1 Stop Work

The Contractor shall not be in default because of any failure to perform this
contract under its terms only if the failure arises from causes beyond the
control and without the fault or negligence of the Contractor. Examples of
causes beyond the control of the Contractor include acts of God or of the
public enemy, acts of the Government in either its sovereign or contractual
capacity, fire, floods, epidemics, quarantine restrictions, or strikes. If the
Contractor believes there is an IRS-caused potential or actual delay in completing the tasks and deliverables stated herein, the CO and COR are to be
notified immediately verbally and in writing via e-mail. All delays that the
Contractor believes are caused by the IRS shall be sufficiently documented
so as to provide adequate proof of the cause of delay (e.g., dates, subjects).

God didn't exist—or didn't care.

The IRS *was* the Public's Enemy.

The Contracting Officer had made not a one damn misstep in their contractual capacity.

The only thing that'd caught fire were his fucking loopholes.

The only epidemic was that of his sickly sign language interpreting service.

Therefore the only people who needed quarantining were his interpreters.

And the closest thing to a strike would've been a government shutdown.

Of the hands Marc had hired, most were 1099ers he could rid with a winnow of the office's drab carpet. Still, another $190,000 would have to be hewn, meaning admins, and maybe even his office space in Tacoma, along with its drab carpet.

Marc watched Dolores flipbook her ledger as though the money might appear should she search a little longer and harder. He rubbed his face and turned to his office window—and saw a man in a fine Italian suit, engaging BIS's coordinator, Sheila Hackenburg. Marc remembered this man, who twined a lock of Sheila's black curls around his finger. Marc's breath kept as Sheila pulled back, smile strained, pointing, and the man leaned and looked along her aim.

Marc stacked his copy of the ledger, slid it northeast, rattling the rolodex near desk's edge, and woke his desktop.

"*We'll talk later,*" he said to Dolores, pivoting an L against his other hand.

She fluttered a hand for his attention. *There's one more option I'd like to—*

"Dolores."

Doleful Dolores, she nodded once and made for the door only to find a human barrier.

Johnny's jacket was edged at the shoulders, a captain's epaulettes. His hair slicked back like finished silver. His wide face sagged, each fatty deposit making a mask of the man's mood and manner.

"Johnny Raciti," he articulated.

"Dolorous," she requited.

Raciti smiled, as one would to a woman unwitting to such consonant disclosures of sadness. A grin that said, *I want you to feel full and powerful, like I do. But I don't care if you don't.*

Dolores slipped by and shut the door behind her. Johnny spent a few moments admiring Marc's office, drab as the carpet. Smug as ever, he tilted a title from the modest bookshelf along the left wall. Marc recognized its cover, its optical play at steel corrugation denoting themes of imprisonment and bondage: *Deaf President Now,* the 15-year anniversary anthology of the first Deaf president elect at Gallaudet University. For any other, Marc would pleasure his guest with his part played in that campaign.

Johnny replaced the anthology and sat opposite Marc. He rubbed the tawny leather chair's arms, dappled with twin rows of gold buttons. "Busy?"

"Always," Marc replied, knee jostling under his desk.

"You did well, kid," Johnny nodded, appraising the office. "Most deafies I see are selling ABC cards for a buck."

Marc could've rebuked him there, whether citing the IRS pull or Johnny's relegation of the Deaf, but such polarities had their place, and Johnny hadn't come for dialectics. Glancing eyes filled the next few seconds, Marc's dread a multiple of these moments. He adjusted his hearing aid, its clipped bleats like a tiny klaxon.

You're old, Johnny signed, milking his chin's phantom udder and pointing. Breaking the silence with more silence.

"You here to talk business or to learn ASL?" Marc quipped.

"Remember what you used to say to me? 'You couldn't make a *stop* sign with a post and sheet of aluminum.' Those were some days."

Marc forced a casual smile.

"Americans," Johnny said. "Right to the chase."

"Since when are you not a citizen?"

"Since I offed Janorg in '81."

This look of Johnny's said, *Yes, we have problems, but they will be taken care of, or you will.*

"Okay kid. You're a businessman, on a schedule, I get it. I'm here about Video Relay Service. What you know about it?"

Marc's dread redoubled, moisture pushing up through his pores. "I know about it."

"*I* know about it. I know everyone's making a killing."

"You want to run minutes."

Marc had witnessed a VRS call center for himself when back East for a big interpreters' conference. John Neau, whom he'd beat out for the NOAA contract, had opened one just outside DC. In each booth an interpreter, wired in, wearing neutral colors, took calls. But these terps weren't translating conversations with doctors or lawyers or hearing relatives. Rather they idled before a monitor depicting another idler, as if in idler's solidarity, or holding vigil for what no one could name, each minute passed another $17.50 invoiced to the Federal Communications Commission. Marc, ostensibly disgusted, had signed to Neau, *You're not even bothering to connect to a third party?* He knew Neau's ostentation and gave him a year before the FCC either tightened regulations or rang the Feds with a friendly lead on a fraud scheme. Well, that year had passed, and Marc yellowed in envy.

"We'll hide in a forest of money," Johnny said. "Our tree among a thousand others."

"I have no interest."

"We had guys running trucks of gear. DC to Queens. Marc," Johnny leaned in and tapped his desk, "their cabs were nicer than this dump."

"To run VRS you need a platform. A platform requires certification with the FCC. I'll be ruined by the time I hear back from those moonwalkers. Not to mention the equipment and software call tracking."

To which Johnny replied, "Behrenreich Interpreting Services Video Relay Service provided by VisiTech Platforms."

"A bit long in the tooth," Marc smirked.

"Look, it knows normal jokes," Johnny smiled. "Marc. I know it's been a long time, but you know how it is."

Marc looked out his window, sighing as if longing for Sheila's long-withheld requital. "How did you find me," he said.

"You think I don't know you got that Kaufman kid over at the FCC now? That you're not five moves ahead of this ramshack? Look," Johnny adjusted the slop-knot of his gaudy purple tie. "This is what we do. We've done our homework."

"I don't have the interpreters. I don't have the money."

"Kid—"

"I'm not kidding, Johnny. I just got my legs blown off by the IRS. We're on prosthetics."

Grin going on angry, Johnny released a short breath out his nose. "The jetlag must still be fucking with your memory. We did a good deal for you back in those DC days. And your severance package came with stipulations, stipulations you agreed to." His smile contracting, Johnny continued, "You seem to forget: I don't deal in metaphors, and I don't aim for no fuckin legs. Now, we're not asking for you to front nothin. You work for the house, you play with house money."

He studied Johnny, calmer now, as if he got off on bare facts equipped with fetters. "Is this your baby or what?" he asked, sinking an inch into his chair and clasping his hands over belt.

Smiling again, Johnny shook his head. "Just 'cause I don't want my name on the cap table don't mean it's not my idea."

"How?"

"How?" Johnny sneered. "How what? How do cows make milk? You squeeze their fucking tits."

"I mean so who's going to handle the fucking money Johnny?"

Now this—*this* was a statement of risk.

"You lookin for leverage or a death sentence?" Johnny grimaced, shifting, his patience waning.

"Tell me," Marc said, leaning on elbows, a single bead rolling down his cold stomach, "who is going to handle the startup money. Just give me the name."

Marc was wielding his only weapon and Johnny knew it. His

rostrum twitched below his glower. He looked away and back, much like Marc had earlier. "Mr. K," he conceded. The truth was, he'd enjoy it. They'd put Allen on the payroll, their rapport slippery, thick as thieves. Allen approved invoices from VisiTech, whose checks went to those on the dole: nonprofit shell companies whose charity could be written off. The philanthropic sector teemed with these looney goons, degenerates in loose suits dragging ass to some prefab office off the Turnpike where they sat sinecure all the live-long day. As regional managers of payday shacks, they understood their role about as well as their paychecks' FICO deductions. They took their taste and left the rest for the brain trust: Johnny running the platform (VisiTech); Marc the call center (BIS); and all of it remunerated by Allen's loose pen at the FCC. The difference between Marc and Allen was simple: only one of them consented. The other got off on playing the submissive.

Years would pass before they'd see each other again. Not only were they coast opposite, but traveling left a paper trail, and paper trails were an investigator's civet, their pet that shat energizing evidence. All the same Allen offered to fly out and buy dinner at Marc's favorite spot, El Gaucho, on 1st Ave. It struck him odd, Allen's willingness to suffer El Gaucho's *snobbery*, which he'd deliver with droll brows. No matter, he was simply wrong about the place, as Michelle was wrong about Pink Door. He didn't understand, never would, that Marc didn't come for the scrumptiously scummy escargot, the fine drapery, certainly not the flapper band. But he did come for a music, if not the music. A rhythm, really. Tapping to the silent pulse of second, another hour, another day, another 200 terps doing 420 minutes times $10.50 ($882,000 a day on VRS alone). An exercised option on their five-year $8.4 million contract with Procurement (the NSA's nom de guerre for the marketplace). Another deal done under his LLC, Stuart Irving Estates, off a tip from Rabbi Yizhak Friedman to go in on a $43 million Renton property with 84 units and a $25 million outstanding loan on which he earned an 8% yearly dividend reflected upon his $13 million investment ($1,040,000 before taxes) plus a 30/70 split between the underwriters (Woodhill Realty) and other investors on profits left over after payments on the loan's interest and principal and operating expenses (management fees, BGE, water, trash removal, leasing fees, etc.). Another day up 5.6% in the market (a disciple of Graham, he bought heavy into the Vanguard 500 Index and spared a few million to play the slots on TD Ameritrade).

Another day making money meant another night spending time with his money, which sometimes meant sitting amid El Gaucho's unapologetic decadence. The steakhouse on 1st reflected the human experience, less a taste than a metaphor for taste. Raising tumblers like commemorations to Art Deco, he and Allen toasted to struck gold, to Michelle in a red-laced underthing, to records broken, hands thrown up like fluttering field goal posts in silent applause, cue the streamers and confetti...

Through the open door of his father's study he heard fingers flicking, mouths clicking, and the susurrus, the *whish* and sigh, of American Sign Language. Bent over his cereal, following a maze on the back of the box, Benison absorbed this background noise—until his father's voice boomed, and his mother looked up from her celebrity rag, forehead slung with isobars of concern. His father crossed from the living room's parquet to the kitchen's Spanish tile. His peremptory stride had eyes for the liquor cupboard. Tumbler pinched as he teethed off the top to the crystal, bourbon going *glug glug glug glug* from the mouth of the glass, and those dollops he gulped up for another.

Holding his navy pajama robe, initials monogrammed on the breast, he finished off a third glass as Benison's mother wailed, failed, and stomped to get his attention.

What the hell are you doing?

We're flying East this weekend.

The contractor is coming on Saturday.

Then cancel it! he X'd and glared, leaning over the dinette. *Benison has to come. We can't have anyone at the house.*

There went Benison's spring break. Prior to the family détente, Benison would've summoned his most sardonic signs and
threatened to stay home with Angelica (which had raised hackles
upon his father's past attempts to coerce him into a family trip).
But now that he wasn't need-to-know, he simply wanted to know:
why the urgency? Either way, he wouldn't complain: any excuse
to miss his calc midterm. (Maybe they'd even pull him down
from the AP class.)

And the truth was, he liked flying East. East was home to the
Hayses and Aiellos and Kaufmans. Their kids—Benison's CODA
comrades—were kindred recombinants of his lot in life, like
fraternal twins estranged from some common ancestor.

They never—*never*—flew Southwest, but emergency required
triage, and not even his father's gestalt could delay their trip for
JetBlue's mid-morning flight to BWI.

The din of coach, a baby's ears going pyrotechnic, a corpulent
man complaining about leg space—Benison's folks were freed by
an easy stroke of the hearing aid, a click of his mother's cochlear,
and audible murk was sucked into the void. Embroiled in sound,
Benison skipped his iPod and book (Bill Simmons's *The Book of
Basketball*) and watched Seattle fall away, shorn stratus banking
against browning mountains to the east, peaks gripped in ice. He
lost himself in miniaturized landscapes until the seatbelt sign
dinged on again. A couple rumbles was all that forewarned the
flight deck's abrupt dip, bodies rising from seats, their viscera suspended along with them. Oxygen masks dropped and dangled like
jellyfish robots. An elder woman behind him grumbled, "Hell if we
ain't gonna go now it'll be later." Benison groaned and tightened,
others gasped or yelped, sensing the beyond from which there is
no return—from which time turns into a dog awaiting its family's
return. Pasted to his seat, Benison focused on the window, where
clouds like wool boats reflected off quicksilver sunglasses, off a
chrome Glock with steel plating, off the tinted windows of the

GMC Suburban idling along a quiet side street, and there built in Benison a phantasmagoric panic that passed into breathy relief as the 727 banked up against wuthering currents.

"…Oh darling, come here. *Sh-sh-sh-sh-sh*…"

"…Well that'll put a spring in your step…"

"…Yer fucking kiddin me. Just a dang air pocket. Hell I was just about ready."

"Captain speaking. We'd like to give our apologies for the turbulence. Hit an air pocket turning out over the mountains, ("Toldja.") *seems we lost cabin pressure. Nothing to be afraid of here folks, systems are all running fine, but unfortunately we're going to have to land the plane to check out why we lost pressure. The crew should be around to help clean up shortly."*

The collective groan rang discordant considering their recently imminent death-by-freefall. Scattered crap, a couple books, broken black heel, apple core in crumpled shrink-wrap, an uncased iPhone. A whole row wore wet brown coffee spots on their pants. Flight attendants filled the aisles, were glared at as if they'd held foreknowledge of the plane's geodesic dive. With time, however, spread calm, if not the reconciliation of delayed arrivals.

Wow! Benison's mother looked up at him, juddering a claw over her shocked snarl. *That was scary!*

The plane's gears whined beneath the belly, wheels cantilevered to landing formation. A quick rumble retched a few gasps from the more traumatized passengers, but his parents didn't seem to notice.

The Kaufmans lived in a quaint suburb of Baltimore. In a rental Mercedes E-class, Benison's father took to roads winding along farmland and baseball fields and white bungalows not like theirs, but smaller, older, poorer. Benison felt like he could trace the local colonial history. The oldest buildings in Seattle were all on the Hill, where, during the year-and-a-half of justified irreverence, he'd marauded with local wastoids, hopped backyards between schist houses, smoked cigarettes outside bars along Pine. Downtown Seattle was modern, high glass buildings and affluent satellite developments such as

Bellevue itself. His father accelerated at the light, crossing into Centennial Manor, where antique ranches became boutique brick, bigger, better, moated by lawns you could run full-squad whiffle-ball games on.

Mrs. Kaufman waited on the stoop with their dog, Dodger, who was tied to a long leash tied to a few cinderblocks stacked on the porch. She seemed a child, Mrs. Kaufman did, even up close. Mr. Kaufman came out grinning, and they carried on inside with their bags, under an upstairs overpass, and into a two-level family room, all polygonal and capacious. Benison sat at the end of a stiff cloth couch the color of fancy mustard, embroidered with barely brightened fleurs-de-lis. Too big to blend in, Benison watched them silently: the Deaf aristocracy greeting in this picture of Dorian's parlor.

...*I* love *what you've done with this pool...*

"...How was the flight in..."

...*We're so happy for Sam. He's doing what he wants to do and that's all we ever wanted for him...*

"...The plane lost *c-a-b-i-n p-r-e-s-s-u-r-e*, a pretty bad drop..."

...*That's wonderful...*

"...Benison was *calm...*"

...*He's a very talented basketball player...*

"...With Joan new job, my turn to interview *security clearance...*"

...*How about Robert? Where is he?* "Allen...Allen!" Mrs. Kaufman stomped her little legs, her arms waving like slight boughs in a breeze. *When will Robert be home?*

"Sorry," Mr. Kaufman grinned, an odd energy stoking his manner, as if his affability masked something dreadful. He adjusted his hearing aids to a high quick tune. "Rob be home"—twisting his wristwatch into view—"*Ten minutes,*" he flung up a thumb. "Then we have *dinner,*" tapping a *d* against his chin.

Robert arrived late, setting his backpack down as Mrs. Kaufman did the pasta. In dowdy jeans and a loose white t-shirt he drew a wake of vernalized spring air, chilly and sporous. The East was cold in a way temperature couldn't measure, subatomic, as though central heating's molecular warmth were a band-aid for the quarkish cold.

"*Sorry I'm late*," Robert wagged a downturned hand. "*Had to take a makeup test.*"

He leaned in for greetings before sitting beside Benison. The adults returned to silent conversation, Benison's parents not much for quizzing the kiddies (they preferred the parents' perspective).

"Sup man," Robert said, panting from the brisk walk back.

"Just hangin with the unheard."

"Hear that."

They chuckled. Benison looked down at a salad of romaine, Italian plums, balsamic, and fresh parmesan, searching for more words to say. "How's tricks?"

"SAT prep."

"Girlfriend?"

"Keeping my incredibly limited options open."

"I hear that," Benison said, thankful for the self-deprecation.

"You must be *buried* in strange. I hear you already had a scout come to a game."

"My dad likes to exaggerate to your dad."

"This is true."

"Speaking of strange, how's your bro?"

Robert smirked. "Miserable, as always."

"Isn't he doing a college circuit?"

"He could be Louis CK and it wouldn't matter. Comedians," he shrugged.

"Yeah," Benison agreed, stuffing down a desire to commiserate, but no one could know about his little hip hop hobby.

"So what's with the surprise visit? I was looking forward to my spring break. Had it all set up. New graphics card on the laptop, fresh tub of lube…"

Benison snorted to stop up a laugh. Grinning, Robert's beady eyes ricocheted between Benison and the adults.

"So what do you get into around these parts, besides donning the cock-sock?"

"I dunno. Regular shit," he shrugged. "Usually just dick off with my best friend, Peter," at which Robert seemed to darken a bit. "This isn't exactly the most exciting place in the world."

"Bellevue ain't either."

As was Kaufman family custom, the kids did dishes, the women drank tea in the window room, and the men descended into the basement for cocktails. Robert washed, Benison dried. The chamfered window at the corner sink had long since blackened, battered by cold specters. They switched their assembly, since Robert knew where everything went.

Sensing Robert's mental recess, Benison ventured, "You aight?"

"Huh?" he said, startled. "Yeah. I mean…"

He no-looked a dish to Robert, who took a dry towel hung on the Heartland cooker's handle. Shuttling the dish across the kitchen, Robert nearly impaled his head on a rustic chandelier's spikes

"Try not to kill yourself." Benison said. Robert's laugh was like a pacific fog descended upon them, a sound of safety. He ventured, "Do you know what they're doing down there?"

Robert's glance was all sarcasm. A glance that said, *Um, drinking scotch?* A glance that said to fuck off with this phatic fodder, for the birds. A glance that was disproportionately harsh, so Robert said, "He's always down there. Your dad's just an easier excuse."

Finished with the dishes, Benison rested his butt on the Heartland's handlebar. He'd noticed Mr. Kaufman's penchant for an evening scotch, but his father drank too. From a vague and impulsive sense of duty to reciprocate family problematics, Benison said, "You know they're cooperating, right?"

Robert squinted and shook his head a little. "Like, they were in a fight or something?" his voice pitched.

"No, I mean. They work to*gether*."

His head canted, Robert peered deeper into the unknown. "You mean like…huh?"

"Yes. I mean—Yes but—" Benison rubbed his forehead. He didn't quite know why he was doing this. "My dad provides VRS… Your dad oversees VRS shit…"

Benison must've hit one of the Heartland's buttons—heat on his buttocks. He didn't want to say it aloud. Despite its enormity, the information he possessed was delicate, dependent on perfect phrasing—the unwitting result of his futility in communicating with his parents. Only anger could burst his futility, which he coopted from Robert's oblivious sneer. Looking down, he saw hot air roiling below the handlebar, quicksilver, like sunglasses reflecting a perfect blue sky.

"They're ripping off the government, dude."

"…Um—what?"

"My dad runs VRS minutes—like, fake phone calls. Your dad signs off on those minutes, pays my dad, and gets a kickback for being a good little soldier."

"Wait—*What?*" Robert said, his words blunted by utter bewilderment.

"Are you deaf?" Benison sneered, possessed now by ghosts of anger's past. "They're fucking criminals."

Robert stammered, halted by Benison's caustic tone. "Are you— Are you fucking with me right now?"

Benison's stolidity—his tacit affirmation—sent Robert stomping to the foyer. Benison heard him strap a leash to Dodger's collar and slam the door behind him. The aftershock brought forth the families, Robert's mother the last to appear at the front door.

What's wrong? Mrs. Kaufman asked, bouncing a *y* off her chin.

Standing at distance along the hallway, Benison raged, *You'd better go see about your son.*

His father came upon him. "What did you tell him." He placed his drink on an end table, stepped closer. "Benison," he urged.

He didn't attempt to hide it. He'd spent this secret twice: a cheater should understand. Mr. Kaufman turned the hallway's corner. After a momentary survey, he moaned, "Jeez' fucky Christ."

He ran out to find his son.

"You done yet?" his father said, and then began doing something quite strange: turning, slowly, as if appealing to whatever cosmic force that'd bequeathed him his Benison. Finishing his slow pirouette, fallen arms slapping his sides, "You'll be happy to know, they dropped us. So come on. Give me your best shot. Soon enough, I won't be around for you to get them in."

Benison had never seen him like this—unhinged, a desperation so raw, Benison recognized it immediately as his own. They both wanted nothing more than to achieve, but this precept was helplessly vague and mercurial, so dependent on opportunity and circumstance and opinion, even their own. The difference between them would also be the difference between Benison and the Big Three: the depth of that desire, the arrangement of its planes and coordinates—he'd never know.

Only now, for the first time, had his father's dog whistle dipped into Benison's rhetorical register: the Feds had dropped him and Mr. Kaufman as cooperative witnesses, leaving them open to the full force of the law.

Benison and his father bookended an abutment of tables kitchen and dining, respectively, all of it awash in yiddishly white lace and untreated silver (bought from an auction for stored artifacts at Yad Vashem—invite only). White porcelain plates like rounded Israeli flags, Stars David in their centers, rims dipped in perfect Israeli blue—smothered in Passover staples the likes of matzoh, haroset, gefilte fish, kugel, brisket, haroset on matzoh, horseradish and haroset on matzoh, and perhaps a small pile of greens here and there.

The CODAs sat with Benison at the slender end (his mother had set a seating chart). Their parents down the way were wealthy as well. Having Sundayed with the Ken Burns WWII documentary—at the expense of *Rocky*—Benison went so far as to joke that their parents were like the Deaf's Vichy government. It was all a racket. He could close his eyes and spin and land on someone who was getting greased for something. His father's six-figure endowment earned the good rabbi's praise for Ellen's feast—but his tips on popup massage parlors cut him in on slam dunk real estate deals. Jerry Gerschwitz was here to kiss the ring for his free pass into the CART business. BIS didn't need Communication Access Real-time Translation—or Over-the-Phone Interpreting (OPI); or document translation; or Video Remote Interpreting (sign or spoken language); or Deaf access consulting—because BIS made nearly a mil a day on VRS alone. His father did onsite sign language so his accountant, Dolores, could better fudge the budget, Benison knew. Benison knew these things not because of any pledge to transparency following the family détente a few years back, but because it was remarkably easy to eavesdrop on Deaf people, which he did to leverage his folks into greater transparency.

Yarmulkes were stuffed in a plastic bag in the middle of the table. The CODAs continued their conversational pissing contest. Jerry Gerschwitz would not stop calling Passover "Pesach," replete with fricative rabbinics. Because like, really? Were they not in America? Was this not the second night? Who was this Ashkenaz with his shiksa wife to favor the holy word? Angelica zipped around the table collecting plates. "*Grathia,*" Benison said as she took his plate. Spanish's proper pronunciation was the peak of pretension, was what Benison's body suspected.

Walled in by chest-thumping capitalists, Benison grieved in silence over cold beer and *Rocky*s *I-V*. He could only sit and stare into the middle distance, which by the grace of Freud happened to be directed toward Vanessa Schafer. Vanessa was signing with Janet Weisenberger and his mother about the trend toward online retail and subscriptions (the optical eavesdrop: so easy, you might not even notice yourself doing it). At $75.00 an hour, his father had hired Vanessa to translate that which he could've signed himself if not for his shameless exhibitionism. Vanessa's presence, Benison knew, said, *Our enormous revenue affords us many employees. Some of whom are bound to be quite attractive, such as this one.* On the contrary, her presence was a travesty. Vanessa galvanized his rigid need, whose paradox of pain and pleasure was particularly desperate during these late stages of adolescence.

His size—in all present senses—kept him from making a move. He stared at the candle until it went away. He then mumbled something about the bathroom and absconded to his room. No one stopped him, less seemed to care.

Taking to his bed, unbuckling, he imagined her knocking on the door to this examination room. Imagined her in nothing but a parted doctor's coat, him laid on the patient's mat. Imagined her using her hand to draw him. Imagined her every pump shuddering her bust, his every blink a stereoscopic snapshot. Imagined her leaning to his ear and whispering, in a cosmopolitan British accent, the sensuous words, "Where do you wish to deposit yourself, Big Ben?"

It was imperative that he maintain the fetish. Dress slacks trussing his ankles, he searched his room. Within seconds he saw the brown plastic cup on his nightstand, warming under the gooseneck lamp. Very clinical. Very embryonic. He shuffled over and chugged above his pumping fist, the chafe worse than the tepid orange juice whose receptacle he lowered quickly to catch his nacreous sap.

Prophesy fulfilled, he splashed into his bedcovers, flipped his 35" flat screen to TBS, muted. No way would he return to the Seder. Instead he weighed texting Enid or Ricky, Ricky or Enid, earnest or sardonic, lovesick or sick of love. Weird truths were refracted in his ejaculate. He had two intimates and a sport, and everything else sucked, mainly because he could lose all three come fall if Coach Williams didn't call. He wouldn't call. Not tonight. Not until well after Benison's mother came knocking, first to scold him for abandoning his duty as sole representative of the Behrenreich brood, and second, to deliver his summons to appear at his father's study.

Blistering in his Audi. His father's Audi. The FCC's. The American public's. On hundreds of millions of phone bills was a tiny tax apportioned for VRS subsidies—the slush fund his father siphoned like a Saudi oil magnate.

Ricky lived in a Magnolia cottage. Benison parked along the curb, their driveway packed with a black pickup and a dark blue sedan, both Fords, both washed as they were each Sunday morning. Ricky's mother answered the door, her hair in a state, as if she'd been scrounging the bathroom sink for crumbs of coke. She was wearing the spandex pants and leotard that she wore until she went to the gym again, which was to say almost always.

"Hey Ben," she smiled. "Rick was bummed not to watch boxing with y'all today."

"Yeah." He didn't mean to talk down to her, but he was all the way up here. "He here?"

"The men are in the room," she sang, slinking off to the kitchen.

Ricky lay shirtless along the L-couch, plaid boxers frothing over his baseball pants, watching TV along the length of his body. His mother reengaged in debate with his sister in the kitchen, and Benison felt bad about the cleft palate thing. Ricky's father, the former verger, verged on comatose in his tattered recliner. The smell of casserole clung to the air—air rife with release, with noise and temper and laughter. Benison would've traded everything for it, without knowing quite what it was or what it meant.

"Everyone bailed," Ricky said. "Fuckin bull, dude."

"Language," said his dad, who shut his eye again.

They gaped at *Rocky V*.

"Sorry," Benison said, eyes on the TV.

Ricky said, "Yeah."

Benison wondered whether Ricky would've accepted his dull apology had his mother not paid for their European jamboree—the only topic buoying their friendship. Regardless, they muttered at *Rocky V*, made stupid jokes. Benison snuck texts to Enid. Mere minutes after the movie ended he hit the road, headed for Alki Beach.

The smell of the Puget, the shells and sharp twigs and dappled black sky. He heard Enid's blue pickup pull into a spot. Watched her approach the shore, occult in the pier's relief, until she resolved into the same old hoodie, the same old jeans.

"Hey."

Strands fluttered from her hoodie like live black tendrils. Benison patted the beached log and she obliged.

"You look nice."

"You too," he requited.

"Only the best cotton," Enid plucked at her hoodie and smirked.

Benison pinched his charcoal dress shirt, its silk of undeserving, and shifted a bit.

"You okay?"

"Same shit different day," he replied.

"What'd he do this time?"

A flash of panic: did her droll tone imply boredom? He wagered a glance—earnest or sardonic—which wiped such fears. Sardonic could be earnest. Was everyone this pedantic?

"What should I start with," he looked off, hoping she hadn't caught his glance, its concern, so petty and misplaced from the moment. Of course, she had. She saw everything he felt and thought, or wanted to think and feel, or wanted not to think and feel, and though this last thought consoled him, he worried he'd spoken all this aloud. Or worse: that she couldn't see him at all. He felt his body flicker like an electron under a powerful microscope. Pinpointing the incipience of these slips would've been like identifying World War I's singular cause. Or the difference between the fresh recruit's romanticized vision of glorious battle and the reality of his horrid experience. These charges across mental no-man's land, rushing into the chaos between what he sensed and what he imagined, though ordered by his sergeant's whistle, were impelled by the pistol held to his gut should he choose not to cross. An anachronistic sergeant, wearing modern black slacks and aviators glaring under a strong afternoon sun. An anachronistic gun, chrome Glock glinting. An anachronistic memory—one recurring yet stuck in times before his, which could only be now, and now, and now.

Enid waited as he stared along the shoreline. He'd lost the thread—later on, during his second trimester at Myriadal, it wouldn't necessarily be the weed, but, like the sergeant, the weed would be easier to blame, if less accurate.

"I guess with the part where he smacked me in the fucking jaw. He just—"

With great patience Enid watched his words smash the churner like eggy dough. But the silence was an invisible flay. It raked his skin back and revealed the truth in his tubework, in his sinew and gristle. He wouldn't say it though. He'd get angry, act out, fart, lick his nipple, masturbate, despair. Except with Enid.

"Oh Ben."

He shook his head and shrugged.

"Well, shit," Enid said, a bit choked. "I was—I mean I don't want to hijack the conversation."

"No," Benison assured. "Please. I need the distraction."

"I uh—I got in."

"Enid," he heaved. "That's awesome."

"But now I am hijacking the conversation."

"No, seriously."

Her face's matrix of emotion reminded him of their incident. Their incident was why they hadn't touched each other since their incident. Art school across the Atlantic was why they'd never touch each other again. Already Benison felt himself reaching into his future, grasping at her absence, the thought of her surfacing in a swarm like the life cycle of the cicadas, their carcasses littering his memories every few months, then years, then now.

His father understood happiness through an economic lens: that it could be found at the nexus of supply (how we can feel) and demand (how we want to feel). But it wasn't a simple straight-line equation. For one, hope and expectation pulled that nexus point all over the place, the equation along with it. And what his father failed to countenance was that happiness took on the dimension of others, required their happiness, was not a zero-sum game.

But did it matter? Whether happy or sad, angry or indifferent, moods were an abstraction. You could never be inside a feeling, an idea, an orgasm. They all passed into palimpsest, a memory ever overwritten by proceeding moments and their memories. Experience was a metaphor for experience. There was no answer, would never be one. Only hope, for better ways to be.

"He did something about Myriadal," he blurted.

Was this a better option than kissing her? Or did he have to say this to kiss her again? As if the last time they tried, it was his disingenuousness that'd rendered him impotent.

Flicking a bitten fingernail, he said, "He spoke with the AD there. I don't know what he did but I know it was categorically fucked. He also said I needed to start doing shit for myself because he might not always be around, though he's said that plenty of times bef—"

"Wait, slow down," Enid shook her head. "What did he do about Myriadal? And why won't he be around?"

"So you know he owns an interpreting company."

"Okay?"

"And you know he makes a lot of money with VRS."

"I'm aware."

"But it's…not exactly legal. What he does. He runs minutes. Like, he hires people to make bullshit calls so he can bill the FCC for it. And he does this to the nth degree, you know?"

"Jesus," she whispered.

"He tried to get out. A few times. But the people who want this to happen…there's a history."

"What people?"

Benison rubbed his face. He was telling her things he didn't bother telling himself. "Bad people. Very bad people."

"Is he in danger?" Then, to Benison's deepened regret, she quickly added, "Are *you* in danger?"

"Considering things that have happened…" Benison groaned between his knees.

"What things?" Enid pled with him. "Benison, is this serious?"

He came back up for air, staring out over the water, which winked with moonlight.

"Benison."

"I don't know what's going to happen."

His chest tightened. The world bent in on him like the walls of Yad Vashem. Whorls warped the ophidian roots braiding the log he'd sat on but now saw at the wrong angle, lying sidelong, Enid's voice trailing down a lengthening tunnel of sensory access.

Sitting on the hood of Enid's truck, sipping stale water from a Nalgene, Benison pulled the roughhewn wool blanket over his shoulders. Enid respected his silence. It was easier to be passive, to accept that ruined people were passive in all the wrong ways. His father's affiliations, the danger they'd put them in, the Feds' betrayal—they'd settle under additional layers of experiential sediment, sinking, compressing into his core.

He'd passed out midst a panic attack.

He realized how rattled he was when backing from the lot. He'd see her again, over the summer, here at Alki, on nights like this. He hoped. Her truck peeled off opposite as if they'd split the loot and agreed to bunker until the heat cooled. He envisioned them together in that truck, whose braille of rust had exhausted the belly's oxides, coarse sepia creeping up the powder blue paint job. Spitting rhymes to her old country songs. Being with her.

Benison strolled along the flagstone leading up to the porch of their ministerial house (his parents' house; the FCC's; the American public's…). He found his father waiting in the living room's brocade armchair. No light but the TV's.

"Sit," he said, his hand working within a lampshade. "Please."

"That light's out."

In a manner akin to obeisance, Benison sat in the same place he had a few years prior, when they'd held the family détente. This correlation between unpleasant admissions and intimacy made him wonder whether people were worth the struggle. Made him think he'd be better off crawling into the hills, withdrawing into his carapace, living amid his reek, his rot, his semen congealing the corner he ejaculated in. The child of a Deaf god.

Fingers tented beneath his chin, his father said, "I want to apologize. You know I want what's best for you."

Looking at leery angle, Benison shrugged. "Okay."

Fox News flashed the room. If only Benison could toggle his existence as light did its, with instantaneous ease.

"There's something else we need to talk about. With…what's about to happen. I can't have the money in my name." Was decency his father's pause? No, the moment enforced absorption, acceptance, surrender. The same man as pre-apology. "I've taken care of that. Your mother will control the accounts…But your name will be on them too. You're eighteen. The lawyers will help you with all of this, particularly the municipal bonds."

"Okay."

"I'm trusting you, Ben, not to fuck me on this."

Benison stood. "Can I go now?"

"Can I trust you," his father said, eyes closed, "with my entire life's work."

Benison watched his father, whose lids flittered as if he'd fallen straight into REM. He did look tired. He waited longer, the pundits engaged in pointless debate, coruscated flashes screening them in sharp shades of blue. Finally, his father opened his eyes, and Benison confirmed his suspicions: that, more than fatigued, he was vulnerable.

"Yeah, sure," he said. "Whatever."

Benison's empty gaze and mental blear floated open roads. Somewhere along the 520, safe from camouflaged cop cars, he elbowed the wheel and lit a roach off which he got a couple good hits. Drawing within mortaring distance of his neighborhood, he glimpsed the delicious cut of blue lake sandwiched between two green slices of ponderosa hills, the city stuck atop like a decorative holding pick. Soon after, he turned into their sloped drive lined with boxed hedges.

Locking his mobile greenhouse, he debated the ethics of caring before spraying a spot of Old Spice through which he walked.

She was in the kitchen, sitting with coffee and his father's attorney, all hoar and paunch, though the thousand-dollar suit kept him looking hale. A quick slurp cleared his vocal musket, and Aryn Kalb introduced himself as such. His *thudded* mug and toothless smile appealed to but did not placate Benison. His mother got up to check on breakfast.

As she flipped sizzling starches and organic eggs, Mr. Kalb's patience guised real hope. Benison slouched all splayed, legs bullying a wider berth, not unlike his masturbatory repose, and threw up his hood. The potatoes screamed that they were done but she just stood there and smoothed her sweater, which looked to Benison like a big Brillo pad fashioned into some dystopic prison jumper. (Although the straw cloche hat did work, especially its maroon sash bow.)

So the potatoes screamed, and they waited until she brought the food and sat, whereupon Mr. Kalb could say the thing he'd come to say. Scrolling *The Myriadal Gazette,* Benison wielded his phone like a wand of indifference, clicking into and scanning an article with an unretentive glare. He'd woven a suspect web of pages by the time his mother set the skillets on cloth mats the color of her cloche's bow. Through the ides of steam Mr. Kalb said, "As you—" but then broke off, allowing the chimes to finish.

What's going on? his mother managed to say merely through matchmade brows. Benison pointed to the living room, where the recently-fixed grandfather clock tipped the hour.

"As you know," Mr. Kalb restarted, "your father's on remand for his own safety, while the District sorts out a pretty complicated series of evidence hearings."

"I could be learning more in class."

Taken aback, Mr. Kalb looked along the arm that Benison raised to snap *No* at his mother's falsetto demands that he interpret. He let her wave and stomp, her heel too effete a tool, her hand too familiar to imbue him with frenetics.

"Your mother is trying to say something to you."

"I am just absolutely floored by these facts."

"I'm gonna give you two a moment," he nearly hollered. Standing and tucking his chair, he pointed behind him, "I'll get some air on your lovely patio."

Benison watched him walk away, determined to make his mother work for his attention—or go corporal.

"What in the fuck," Benison bellowed, holding the ear on which she'd given a good hard tug.

What's wrong with you? she managed with one bounce of a *y* off her chin.

What's wrong with me? Benison signed with furious deliberation, each word delineated in linear English. *How about this. I ask you what we're here to discuss, and you answer with the knowledge that I already know the answer.*

His mother could understand sarcasm, but he couldn't convey it well. The meanings got muddled in translation. But the thing was, Benison relied on futility. It both fed the feedback loop of failure and made him feel alive, like a cancer patient doing chemo: futility begot frustration; frustration begot anger; anger lifted the fog of futility; and he could finally see, clear and wide. Benison may not have liked his cage, which came equipped with nothing but the futility lever, but he was comfortable—far more than he'd ever countenance.

We're discussing this with you now.

Too late.

Benison. "*Think of your father.*"

"We're just talking here," came Mr. Kalb's voice from the banister dividing the kitchen and family room.

"You keep saying *us* and *we* like there's no *I*, or like *you'll also* be in a desert shack with a changed last name. *I'm not stupid*," he said, knuckles knocking his head before thumbing his chin. "*I know these evidence hearings are bullshit. I know he's just going to leverage those municipal bonds against them all, and I know he'll get his way.*"

Whose side are you on?

Why did you call me here?

"What's she saying? What are you saying?"

Because your father and I want you to know what's going on.

Great, flat palms shoving the sign into her face. *So let's hear it.* "*My mom says she wants me to know what's going on,*" he translated for Mr. Kalb. "*But what's funny—to me at least—is that I don't think you know what the fuck is going on.*" *Anything else you want to add?* Benison signed and, with thumbs like binary stars, signed, *You can tell Dad next time you visit him: I won't be associating with you anymore.*

Six hours of justified fury. Six hours since he'd handed his mother his walking papers.

Six hours of lifted fog

He saw the fear for his livelihood and his life. He saw the catharsis that came with seeing. He saw, sans all the debilitating self-consciousness that otherwise came with watching himself.

He saw that he still loved Enid. Still felt he could win her on the basketball court (or a hot beat). Was still in love with this futility.

Benison saw how he approached the axis of his existential ideal like a platonic asymptote—just like his old man. Sometimes, when the fog lifted like this, he got so close he could smell it, so close he could taste it, hear it, *see* it. But however close he got, he couldn't ever *be* it.

And now, Benison tracked napalm over glistening tarmac. Approaching something he could touch—albeit something that truly fucking sucked.

He busted through the Balloon's doors and stalked its cold corridors, duffel beating his thigh like it stole something. He dressed as if under threat of imminent attack, grim and rapid, and hustled out to hit the hardwood.

Persona non grata had graced the premises. So conspicuous was his absence that his presence pressed pause on practice. No one was a no-show at this level, not incommunicado. The squad's prevailing silence permitted the staff's banter, the air units' industrial hum, tennis rackets' *pops*, their wielders' heaves, to carry clean across the Balloon's expanse.

"Behrenreich," Coach Williams called over the generators. "Nice of you to join us today. Do a few on the bike."

Benison heard him. Rather than oblige, he slunk out onto the court.

"'The fuck you doing?" said Eddy Dominguez.

Benison took his man and said, "You gonna step across the sideline so I can sub in?"

The squad was still as a diorama, transfixed by Dominguez's eyes like optical buckshot. Benison dared him: either step, or duly relieve himself to the sidelines. Whether condoning the fractious atmosphere as a teachable moment or tolerating the team's unteachables, Coach stood there, straddling the hash mark, arms crossed—so Bouman assumed the former and said, "Yo we in two. Right D?" which implied that Dominguez should sub out.

"*Sssss*," Dominguez sibilated and begrudged the sideline. Coach Wyles tossed him a towel that clung to his shoulder like a pet dove.

"Yo that was cold, bruh," snickered Del, and then Gabe Griffin started cackling—and Coach went ancient Egypt on them.

"HEY," he roared at the ten-headed warhorse he rode, audible whip at his side. "HOW MANY SPARTANS ARE LAUGHING NOW…" he bellowed, weaving through that diorama of petrified athletes. "AT THIS VERY MOMENT THEY PREPARE FOR WAR, WHILE Y'ALL GIGGLE LIKE *FUCKING*

SCHOOLGIRLS...THIS *ISN'T. FUCKING. CUTTING IT.* THIS IS TOM IZZO, AND THE 400 ARMIES HE'S MOWN TO PIECES...YOU THINK THAT TWENTY-HUNDRED MILES FROM HERE, THEY'RE *LAUGHING* RIGHT NOW?"—descending to demonic register—"THEY'RE PREPARING TO MUTILATE YOU, TAKE YOUR BIOPSY, AND STUDY HOW A FORMERLY UNDEFEATED TEAM FUNCTIONED, SO THEY CAN BEAT US *AGAIN, AND AGAIN, AND AGAIN, DO YOU UNDERSTAND ME? NOW YOU'RE GONNA RUN IT UNTIL YOU CAN'T STAND. BLUE.*"

Screech.

PART THREE

PART THREE

Sir Heimlich and his squire had perhaps saved Mr. Lillard's life in that artery-clog of a Northside Diner. As though a single if most significant motive could seize control of the human body, Jason's greater purpose, more than Jason himself, broke across checker tile to hump up some hoagie, and with deft thrift at that: he counted three long beats between humps, knowing each one would test the elder baron's ribcage. Mr. Lillard's entourage, in their antebellum regalia, sunny pastels better fit for the races, effused genuine praise for Jason's performance. He tipped his cap like Paul O'Neill, as if he lived to serve without joy, and ducked toward his cooling counter stool—until Mr. Lillard called him back to their table.

"Guess I ought to thank you for that," said Mr. Lillard, still blushing and a bit embarrassed.

"Oh," Jason waved, "proves luck."

"Takes skill *and* luck," said Mr. Lillard. "You know who I am?"

"I do."

"So? You were just gonna waddle on back, tail between your legs?"

Mortification struck as he remembered his Marian Catholic windbreaker, deep blue and bearing the school's crest. "Well that's an icebreaker," he laughed.

Thomas Lillard III was frowsier in person. Heftier too. Last year's Twitter campaign—#taketomtotask—must've killed his sleep numbers. (Jason was studied up on the escort scandal at UA.) He tipped a bit of tincture down the President's bile-scorched throat before applying for a spot in the old boys' club.

"Got to admit," Jason said, "I'm kinda glad that chunk of club sandwich got lodged in your throat."

And the President quite liked that. "Be happy to buy a drink for the man who ripped me from the maws of Hell. That is, long's there's no spiel about the inverse correlation between bite volume and chewing factor. Get enough of that from Dr. Bachelowski."

They were on hard round stools speckled red. Soda jerks slung them malted milks. At times, before he spoke, Mr. Lillard's throat cleared years of macronutritional accretion.

"People are pussies," he spat. "They *want* to hear what you're really thinking, cause they're thinking the same thing, but they'll kill you for saying it." He turned back to his entourage at the round table. "What do you see there?"

Jason thought a moment. "Pitiless sharks who extorted their way into your inner circle."

"Also known as?"

"Businessmen."

"Right. And what is a businessman's top priority?"

"With all due respect, Mr. Lillard, you don't want to be the Ken Lay of college basketball."

"Now that's one hell of a statement, son. In this economy?"

"I apologize if it sounds that way—"

"Don't give me that apologetic shit. You were doing well for a moment there. And how could a schlub like you even begin to understand our books?"

"I'll show you," said Jason, raising a finger to a soda jerk for pen and paper.

Mr. Lillard ripped from his bendy straw as the fruits of Jason's business degree from Autodidact U (he'd earned an undergrad degree in sports management from Northwestern) spilled in cheap blue ink on a scrap of server pad. Using the 2003 Syracuse Orangemen as example, Jason applied his formula, which cooked student-athlete salaries into revenues generated by player reten- tion, to a hypothetical: what if Carmelo Anthony had stayed three or four years (two footballers went pro in '03 as well, but David Tyree and Chris Davis were both seniors).

He proposed player salaries that graduated with each year of schooling completed. Said salaries would accrue in untouchable trusts to be liquidated only upon graduation or departure for professional application (bearing proof of either). Graduated salaries could be stimulated by interest incentives and bonuses to encourage yearly retention.

"How many times was Melo on ESPN? Not just for games, but *on* ESPN, *promoting* the Syracuse brand, the then-Big-10 brand, the NCAA brand. Now double that. Then imagine bonuses for degrees, joint contracts with the NBA, who we could get to buy up our debts."

Mr. Lillard roared up the rest of his malted milk, shoved it toward the soda jerk, pulled out his wallet. Jason watched his best shot count out the small bills he'd be relegated to for the rest of his life, along with the D-level dramas that developed at Marian Catholic.

"Well this sure is something," Mr. Lillard said, as though speaking to someone he thought crazy enough not to vocally disagree with. "Look, I like to surround myself with people who think. If anything, it keeps my mind sharp. But I'm more interested in what you have to say about PR. I want you to read a book, *Iron Jaw*. It's by a Soviet propagandist who expatriated here in the early '80s." Mr. Lillard stood and, breath labored, hand indicating the abstruse scrawl, said, "Remember, these are just teenagers. You don't buy your kid a new convertible. You teach him to earn what you got."

Mr. Lillard got him an interview for his first college gig, at the fancy liberal arts school in Westchester. The NCAA flew him out for the formality, but Jason never used the return ticket. He stayed at a Ramada off I-87 until he received official notice. Despite the fairly significant pay cut, now, in New York, Jason could continue his apprenticeship closer to Mr. Lillard and, more importantly, meet the bigwigs—the backers, the sponsors, the money people.

It was strangely difficult to sip Yamazaki 12 in an oaky parlor drenched in power and return to the squalor of his Yonkers apartment, reminiscent of Jewish diasporas and inherited sadness. He schemed ways to short his rent (he rented illegally from a co-op whose "landlord" lived in Romania). His laundry card broke within weeks. He parked on the street. At the college, he slogged long hours in a cramped office whose window overlooked a truncated pool used by film students more than lettering swimmers.

Thursday evenings, he'd do happy hour at the Irish pub down River Road. On one such occasion, he found himself arguing with a grad student over the efficacy of safe spaces and trigger warnings. Jason knew better than to think this insulated liberal would perform a realpolitik about-face if made privy to the world's brutality. But beer was liquid polemic. Over time, however, the grad student's excitement revealed itself as more carnal than combative. She began kneading rebuttals into his hand, slapping the silliness from his knees, which was how he found himself inviting her back to his apartment, where she read her spiritually reckless memoir thesis from her phone in his kitchenette. Regret flushed up like acid reflux, burning his esophageal lining, his words. He experienced the exact opposite of priapism, quite literally shrinking before the narcissistic angst through which her naïve assumptions about the world were distilled. He'd hit rock bottom.

"Mr. Lillard," he said into his cell later that night. "I apologize for the hour."

"So it's you behind the clock face?" he croaked. "Slow the damn thing down then, you treacherous bastard."

Jason was comfortable enough with the NCAA President to simply smirk.

"What is it?"

"Look, I know I'm young. But I can't spend another year accidentally fucking these socialist doughnut holes."

"How's that?"

"Give me a real job."

The line popped.

"Why were you there that afternoon. In Chicago."

"It was my spot," Jason said, his tone affected. "To cool off after long days."

"Hm."

"…I'm sorry, is there something I'm not following here?"

"What kind of high school AD frequents a ritzy diner at three in the afternoon? You think we didn't notice you, days prior?"

Jason's sigh broke like his purpose had across waxed checker tile. "What do you want me to say?"

"What the plan was. Go from the guppy tank to Sea World; slave's food to slave? That what you want?"

"No."

"Then how do I know I can trust you?"

"Because I've been loyal from the moment we met."

"You mean after you got your photo op of fucking that sandwich out of me."

Regret redoubled, or was it actual acid refluxing up from his gut? Then Jason realized: Mr. Lillard had possessed these suspicions from the moment they'd met—no, before then even, from the moment he'd noticed Jason lurking at the counter all those afternoons, struggling to find an opening. He *wanted* Jason to give him reason to trust him.

"I'll give you everything. Who sent me, when, and why."

"...And?"

"Eric Dodd." The ease with which he betrayed a multibillionaire whose greatest aim was nothing short of centralizing data under Azalai's servers—it frightened him more than the betrayal itself. No, *thrilled* him was more accurate. "His work with Myriadal's just the beginning. He's throwing a protracted coup on the board, installing guys one-by-one who aren't hamstrung by personal incentives."

"Well that explains Rick Hammond," he grumbled. "But why?"

"Because he wants to assert himself. Because he's bored. Who knows why genius billionaires do what they do. But my guess? He'd use the NCAA presidency for compensation reform. Perfect launching pad for a political run."

"Ah," breathed Mr. Lillard. "Hence your little spiel."

"Just looking out for you," Jason winced.

"I'm still having trouble understanding the motive here. Isn't Dodd a walking Super-PAC as it is? Why waste his time stroking off to college athletics?"

"One, he distracts the commoners from the KeyArena boondoggle, legislated under his direction. Two, he distances himself from his public narrative: that he's a digital-age robber baron. Can you imagine him in the House or the Senate?"

"He'd own both Boardwalk and the Monopoly board."

"Pretty much."

"So what did he offer you?"

"To tag you?" Jason said, his voice chipped by shame. "Enough that he's probably got twenty other dickless Sherlocks roaming the city."

"What, he hopes to catch me belting at the top of my lungs that I tampered with the UA investigation?" Mr. Lillard chuckled with notes of compunction. "King for a fucking day."

"I swear to Christ, Mr. Lillard. The day we met, I cut all contact with the guy who put me on. I never spoke to anyone else," he said. Mr. Lillard breathed, waiting. "Look, my suspicions about Dodd being behind the UA smear campaign are just suspicions. But Mr. Lillard," Jason exhorted, "I'd be happy to find out for sure."

"Well, son," Mr. Lillard said, the smile back in his voice, "that's all I ever needed to hear."

Rapping twice at his office door, Jason relished in the one moment of unmitigated disgust afforded the old ball coach before he corrected his frown.

"Came by to check on Jonesy."

"Doubtful."

Jason nodded. His gambit to catch Gary before his second coffee was still out for jury. Allotting for this, his let his eyes fall and linger on the lineup card, as if waiting for the listed names to transpose to his liking. "Dominguez isn't a shooter. Behrenreich's our backup two. He should get the call."

Gary peered over his desk's strategic clutter, through his office's ascetic dimness. "We just had one of our players assaulted on campus, this one drugged. And you're coming to me about this?"

"Gary—"

"Jesus," Gary wiped his mouth. "What happened to your apprehensions about Behrenreich last spring? Not that it matters, but I thought we'd settled this, Jason. This is my team. Either I run it, or your administrative duties will henceforth include finding yourself another head ball coach."

Impertinent heat washed his chest. He had Mr. Lillard. No one could fuck with him.

"You know, Gary, all this principled posturing? It's middle class. It's mediocrity costumed by an ethics that doesn't actually do anything but fill some vacancy of personal meaning. What it is, Gary, is selfish." Jason replaced the stress-ball on Gary's desk. "This isn't Xavier. You're coaching a five-star team, and I'm making sure you act like it."

Stadium dark, hushed as 17,500 humans could be—just in time for lineup introductions, Jason took his seat four rows behind Myriadal's bench. He held fast to his phone, prepared to transmit the contradictions between Coach Gary Williams's expense reports and his visitation logs. In any other circumstance, the NCAA board would eschew in bad humor such an insignificant transgression. But Mr. Lillard didn't like Gary, his Amish purity, his philanthropic pretexts. He'd said so himself over dim sum last month.

For his godson emeritus, he'd hike up his moral standards—but to ensure that Marc Behrenreich held those renovation bonds until prices bottomed out, he'd do anything. Sure, Marc owned his own motive to horde hundreds of millions in municipal debt notes: such a stranglehold on city funds influenced all branches of government, including the judicial. Nonetheless, it was in Jason's best interests to stoke this motive, and amended agreements went a long way toward doing so.

"*You have a collect call from*—Marc Behrenreich—*an inmate at a Washington State Correctional Facility. To accept the charges for this call press three, if you do not wish to pay for this call please hang up. If you no longer wish to accept calls from a correctional facility press*—"

Glancing at his office's door, which hung just ajar, a yellow slice between wood and frame Jason had hit three.

"*Your call is being transferred*...Jason," came Marc's voice. "Don't bother responding. I won't be able to understand you. I got your note. I'll do it. Prices should start to level out when the council sets a meeting to refinance the project. Give me a signal and I'll sell off."

And he'd hung up.

And now, as the jumbotron began strobing, intimidation beats blaring, there was an elasticized moment following Gabe Griffin's introduction—a moment stretched taut—until Jason heard the name boom from the rafters, and Benison glided low through a tunnel of teammates extending their arms as if to consecrate his place among them.

Jason stood in the doorway to KeyArena's media room, where Myriadal's chosen four sat at mics, behind them a blue backdrop cookied by NCAA insignias. He finished the last of his protein bar, wrapped the wrapper in tissue paper, stuffed it in his back pocket.

Some people change upon getting money. Jason, he still ate on a schedule (clinging to that mesquite sub as though it were his only vice). Still called his mother once a week. Still slept in red waffled pajamas, like a kid on Christmas morning. Still watched the news each morning over plain Cheerios gone soggy before he dumped the milklogged rafts down the disposal. Still appraised his players like the kids he'd recruited back in Chicago, at Marion— still somewhat scared, of his power and pay in comparison to his implicitly incentivized players.

Being shrewdly attuned to his six-figure contract was one thing, but watching Marc's son now, he sensed a reckoning. He couldn't trust the kid. Not at all. Not with a freshman blacked out on vodka and stilettos, much less with replying to a room full of reporters scribbling each of his brainless syllables. These vermin broadcast the Messiah's belated word, an Iversonian outburst, and everything in between. They revolved around star power like Pluto, minor designations that hoped in vain to one day become real players. These fucking people. Worst was, Jason needed them and their sniveling sniff for a story. They kept things attached to the world, did the dirty work that allowed people like him to reap real benefits. "Your first significant minutes came against a top five team. What were you thinking during the first TV timeout after you'd missed your first four shots?"

Jason watched Benison worry his water bottle while saying, "I was aiming it. You can't shoot with your head."

The postgame proctor selected another hand near the front row.

"This for Benison as well. Do you think your fall early in the game took the pressure off you?"

Benison had surprised the defense by taking a hard dribble by his man early in the shot clock. The painted area clear, he torqued for a dunk as a Spartans defender lurched and hit him on his rise, sending him cartwheeling like a spacecraft knocked off its trajectory. The crowd's collective "OOOOOOHHH" pitched them out of their seats to better see the players shoving and jawing, both Gary and Tom Izzo taking verbal shots, arms spread to the effect of yellow tape. The fracas debriefed, and all eyes trained on Benison, who waved off team trainer, Dave Kelly. The zebras pointed to each bench in official warning. Jason's box seat was close enough to overhear.

"Dominguez," Coach said, "get Ben."

"Nah I'm good," Benison sniffed, favoring his leg along the sideline near the coach's box.

"Get Behrenreich."

"I said I'm good."

Jason watched him walk it off. The game was adjourned long enough that calcified sweat started caking his forehead, rimming his eyes.

"We gotta get the game going," said one of the refs. "You good?"

"I'm good."

"He's good," the ref slapped the scorer's booth.

His fall had knocked the needless from him, was what Benison said presently, in so many words. The proctor picked another hand.

"Rick Harper with *Yahoo! Sports*. Benison, how are you, physically, after the fall?"

"Butt-hurt."

Obligatory chuckles, the wheedling scum. Another sycophant's hand, holding pen and paper. Some had laptops. All with press passes strung around their necks.

"Josie Salt with *FS1*. Benison, how has it been for you so far this season, living in the shadow of the Big Three and playing behind Mike Jones? Was a night like tonight necessary to help you feel like a contributor?"

"Absolutely, it's been tough. They're such great talents and, you know, being on the floor with them, you just want to feel like you're contributing."

"One more for you, Benison. How has your father's recent hearings and upcoming trial affected you on the court?"

Only now did Benison seem to recognize Josie's first question for the platitudinous softball it'd been. "*Inherently, the spotlight seeks darkness,*" went *Iron Jaw*.

But, again, there was no hint of the squeamish kid they'd recruited last spring. Up there on the dais, Benison's eyes had fallen below concern's poverty line. His tongue glossed his red lips. He shrugged, and answered Josie Salt's question, "They haven't."

The vermin kept spreading their questions across the podium like rodential feces across a countertop. Watching him, his preened patina, Jason lent the kid some circumstantial credit: that he too might sift out the superfluity if his life had suddenly erupted on November 5th. Another hand selected:

"This is a two-parter: what's the timetable for Jonesy's return; and is there any suspect linked to the incident involving him and a former employee from his apartment complex over New Years?"

Back at the office to pick up materials for a call that night, Jason had time to reflect. The process began well enough. Memories and thoughts eddied in rational harmony, running fluidly downstream—until hitting a repressive dam, which in this case took the form of a *Times* article he now found spread across his desk. Left there by someone with access, it functioned now as that whisper in Fredo's ear.

He'd stayed clean during his stint in Westchester. Yet at Myriadal, pressure to persuade recruits came from rival ADs who trafficked more talent across state borders than Lucky Luciano. He'd no choice but to keep pace, though caution was advised. Even under President Lillard's aegis, mere rumors amid NCAA higher-ups could've cut him down. As delineated in *Iron Jaw*:

> Nothing threatens a man like his past. Necessary actions that in the public eye will appear contrary to the ideals of his future goals must be well-documented so as to remain indemnified. However, unless his acts are particularly brazen, scandals will most often come to light from within. Thus it is as important as indemnification that relationships within the organization be maintained with great care.

Jason trialed by fire. He learned how recruits put their demands on the wire. He rationalized: he was only engaging in a form of subsidy he believed should be legalized; he was far more Robin Hood than Ken Lay. He'd hardly been coronated by Myriadal's movers and shakers, who resented his youth, much less his fiscal ideas, so he bullshat the bullshitters, collected useful people, and grit his perfect pearls into receivers he was alone with in the car, where he took most of his meetings.

He created a failsafe method: a) He never involved the coaches themselves; b) Never paid off in liquid; c) Had a trusted third party make anonymous purchases of house deeds or vehicle pink slips or whatever appreciable or at least salvageable asset that would suit your recruit's desires; and d) Never, *ever* mentioned to the recruit or their family who that third party was, so help him God—

But *accepting* bribes? This was venal hinterland. If greatest strengths were in fact weaknesses, Jason's brand of progressive economics included a "subsidized" XLS. That Marc had never fulfilled the bigger part of the bargain—well, Jason repurposed this welching as a risk-free investment, a free shot at getting what he really wanted: to be the youngest (ever) NCAA board member.

Except it couldn't be just that.

Jason stared at the lead story's photo under the headline: "MA'AM'S LABYRINTH" (*The Seattle Times*, as reported by Reuters). Cunning, aquiline eyes, silk of obsidian mane that shone through the crosshatched print, as if Edward Gorey had tried his hand at photojournalism. According to the caption, Michelle was shaking hands with the president of the Registry of Interpreters for the Deaf (RID) at some industry function or another mere days after Behrenreich Interpreting Services (BIS) had suffered their subpoena back in April.

He imagined her now, hiding out in some Indonesian hovel, or perhaps some villa on the French countryside. But from there his fantasy differed from popular opinion—or rather, inculcated opinion.

Sometime during his reverie, someone had walked into his office without an appointment. Had been standing in his office for an unknowable amount of time now. Had been the one, Jason realized, to leave this newspaper, feature-up, on his desk before entering again without an appointment. Jason watched Benison put up his Rapiers hoodie, close the door behind him, and face his desk. He sniffled once and said, "Whatever he was paying you, he's not going to anymore. So…do what you gotta do."

Jason allowed him time to consider his words, his actions, now that they'd manifested before his own eyes. "Your dad knows what he's doing."

Benison flashed an angry smile. "Does he?"

"So what now? You fire sale the bonds? Leak them to some provincial Assange wannabe? What's your move here, Benison?"

"Why do you care?"

"Because whatever you do, you better think it through, or you'll end up a lot worse off than you are now."

"I'm not here to fuck you over, or fuck my dad over, or fuck anyone over. I'm done. I want nothing to do with any of it. And if you try to touch me again, I'll fucking kill you."

Jason's snide chuckle was a show of force: the kid could make him a suspected accomplice to assault with three strokes of his thumb. "I'm flattered that you think of me when we're apart, but why the hell do you think I would do something like that?"

Benison left without answering.

What gall. To leave his door ajar like that. To traipse in rather low-eyed, cooled to his capable movements, and say what he'd said. Mere weeks ago he'd been a faltering wreck at the lowest loom of a father figure—a juddering jack-in-the-box at first whiff of events with moderate stakes. A kid on a Top-10 team with issues completing bounce passes into the fucking post. A kid who wouldn't have started tonight if not for Jason's urging.

A kid who could ruin his life with a few strokes of his thumb.

Starting his seven-month-new Mercedes XLS, the day's work having dwindled to dregs, Jason had one last scheduling call. Benison's accusations bothered him about as much as Pamela Anderson's bra size. Kind of like this conversation with Alabama's AD, Sal Dohr.

Southern propriety: that 'ole placebo for true compassion. To men like Sal—true-blue Southern men—interpersonal pillars were erected upon white plinths of patrician sophism. The types that found true propriety in such structures were those who saw unimpeachable integrity in their congressional representatives. The types not fond of critical thought, as such thought inevitably questioned God's existence and that of free will.

Jason careened onto the floating 520 as he hammered home the final tenets of their "compromise": that, next fall, Mr. Dohr's Crimson Tide volleyball team visit his. To Jason, this was the only meaningful element of the transaction, lest he was to honestly give a damn how many years Myriadal included Alabama in their non-conference home schedule (they'd agreed to three). The Rapiers women's volleyball team had conferred themselves during last year's title run, and powerhouses didn't design to a teetotaling AD of moonshine country, Tuscaloosa. The unwittingly conflicted fuck.

"We'll have us a good 'ole fashion fish-fry come autumn."

"Ah," Jason sighed, mocking his own smile in the rearview. "Roll Tide, Sal…You too…Bye. Fucking prick," Jason muttered after ending the call via his dash.

His headlights put a dent in the fog. Oversaturated sodium lights lining the bridge fared no better. This hanging mist had been awful all winter. Cars crawled the floating road. Jason couldn't stomach stalling over open water. He honked once, short but firm, despite himself. He fiddled the radio, flipping past a couple crackled stations until settling on contemporary jazz. He ran a hand through his hair, a habit he retained for day's end, its dregs, when he could muss his persona, and therefore the perfect blond waves he moussed in the mirror each morning.

Traffic broke off the bridge. This stretch of road, which ran straight into the lobby of his apartment building, represented his day's denouement. A road more like an airstrip, immaculate tarmac stitched with copper reflectors, and wide, six lanes curb-to-curb. Pristine complexes flushed the roadsides, modern concrete, uniform cream and white. Jason had selected Myriadal from the NCAA president's list of power vacuums precisely because it was made in Bellevue's image. Surreal, was it? That Behrenreich had grown up just a few miles that way?

Jason chased his parking spot to the garage's top level. Through a short crosshatched fence he saw people and their dogs on one of the building's several terraces. Near the fence, stucco stairs led down to an elevator, which dropped him to the lobby, where he took another elevator up to the 19th floor, scrolling emails. The lobby was all posh redolence and arabesque carpets, elegance papering the walls. Varnished chestnut and mahogany tables abutted plushly embroidered couches. In his apartment awaited his middle-definition TV and his impending decision to call it a night shortly after watching a montage of media nonsense.

"Mr. Derekson."

Jason looked up and around the lobby. At the concierge nook stood three men. His immediate reaction having betrayed his identity, he approached them.

"Gentlemen," Jason said, his voice reaching octaves just short of a question. "How may I help you?"

One of the men met him halfway and offered a hand, which extended from the arm of a trench coat clung too tight to his padded brawn. "Agent Paul Hoffman with the Federal Bureau of Investigation's Fraudulent Crimes division. This is my colleague, Agent Rooney, and our associate Mr. Kaufman with the Federal Communications Commission," he indicated two men in equally drab business garb.

Jason nodded, assessing first Hoffman's intentions, then whether he needed to evade them. Jason gauged the agents unlikely to have come all this way just to lean on him. Yet this Mr. Kaufman's presence posed a problem. While the FBI was not wont to investigate petty bribes, the FCC—inherently and eponymously—probed communications.

"We were wondering if we might have a few moments of your time," said Agent Hoffman.

"This way, gentlemen. I'll mix us some drinks. I make a mean mojito."

Agent Hoffman was pleased, thank you, with plain water. Agent Rooney's gruff wave communicated he was copasetic sans liquids of any kind. And Mr. Kaufman hadn't touched his mojito (though spent a good deal of optical energy on it). Not much of a midnight imbiber, Jason slipped into his seat without a drink to call his own, clearing away a heightening stack of mail. (Otherwise, his place was cleaned by the resident maid each morning after he left for work.)

The apartment—spit-shine marble, gunmetal diamond tile, Rapiers plaques and historical sports photos adorning the cream walls—seemed to neither please nor put off the men, who'd hung their coats on the kitchen's wrought-iron chair backs as Jason mixed the lone cocktail. Maybe the feeling stemmed from his earlier conversation with Dohr, but absent any formality, he rather appreciated the silent transition—straight to sitting, sans all that doorway dithering. Then again, the agents' silence itself grew inscrutable. Mr. Kaufman looked on like a blind man, staring at random angles, shooting bitten cuticles as if Jason couldn't see him either.

"Rooney, you want to begin?" Agent Hoffman said.

"Not particularly."

"Fine," he grumbled. "Mr. Derekson, we're to assume you're aware of the article in the *Times*, or news in general."

"I am. I'll also assume it threw quite the wrench in your investigation."

"It did introduce chaos into the system. And that's what we're here to talk about."

Jason took this information with a swig of water.

Agent Hoffman continued, "By virtue of the investigation we've had FCC technicians scouring every archived second of Behrenreich Interpreting Services' Video Relay Service. Needless to say, we came across some interesting footage," he said, more playful than malicious. "You can wipe that look off your face. You're gonna get to keep that slick little vehicle you've been roaming around in like some idiotic drug-dealer. We're more interested in what transpired after Behrenreich hung up on his end."

"Smooth stuff. I took notes," Agent Rooney added. His ratty face and cuey pate had somehow triumphed homeliness, as though he were a granite bust whose beauty was compositionally inherent.

Jason leaned back, reflecting Agent Hoffman's posture. Just because he saw no reason not to cooperate didn't mean he should. There were things Michelle had said to him, things he knew they'd be interested in, things he'd barter only if the price was proverbial.

"It didn't last. We met once for drinks. She—" Jason canted his head as if working a crick out of his neck. "It was only a couple times."

"And this began over the phone," Agent Rooney asked, pen and pad brought out to play. "The affair."

"I'd hardly call it an affair."

"Either way. It began with the VRS calls. Meetings between you and Marc, interpreted by Michelle," Rooney clarified.

"The only one he trusted," Hoffman annotated.

All of a sudden with this one-two heat? Jason leaned on his forearms, grinned, adjusted his glasses. "Why don't you gentlemen cut to the chase. I'd feel more comfortable helping you out than playing cops and robbers."

The Feds shared eyes. Agent Hoffman nodded, his sun-blushed mug shining under the kitchen light. Agent Rooney pocketed the pen and pad. Stuck in his trance, eyes glued to his sweating mojito, Mr. Kaufman crossed his arms.

"Let's do some top-down processing," Hoffman said. "What has Michelle Thibodeaux said to you about the company?"

"That a lot of the money was going to some guy not on the books."

His shovel had hit something hard.

"She told you this."

"A few drinks in her and that Louisiana drawl dumped enough dirt to cover the Puente landfill."

Rooney snorted dubiously. "Any other canned lines you wanna practice on us?"

"Let's stay on brand here, fellas," Hoffman said.

"She was on her way out," Jason said. "Senioritis type of thing. She went a little slack in terms of discipline, started talking about how she'd gotten attracted to the idea," he said, rubbing fingers against thumb. "So she got creative."

"Oh yeah. *Faites le mur.*"

Apparently Jason had left the door open for querulous quips. He flipped his hands, palms offering all they could in response to such tone and language.

"What did she say about this off-books figure?" Hoffman asked.

"I suggest talking to Marc Behrenreich about that."

"About what?" Hoffman said. "The finer points of leverage?"

"I don't know," Jason said, impatience bleeding nerves. He had to stanch it up. "All I'm saying is, you're talking to the wrong guy if you're looking to know about him."

From nowhere, Mr. Kaufman said, "He need convincing." Jason looked up. Mr. Kaufman flicked a cuticle into his drink, a flash of his index finger, reddened at the quick. Uttering another series of clipped phrases, oddly pidgin, Mr. Kaufman said, "Tell him bout Klimmick. Tell him who he is."

Agent Rooney extracted from his inlaid coat pocket a rolled packet, relinquishing it onto the table's white linen. "These were declassified after Obama's E.O., which mandated all docs be open to the public after 25 years."

Viscous seconds leaked a full minute, time slowing as Jason read a clinical description of borderline paranormal activity. According to the document, in the '60s, deep-state Soviet scientists and doctors were given access to unidentified orphans on whom they performed invasive "enhancement" procedures. Ten-dollar neuroscience-speak surrounded words he barely remembered from his college psych course, such as "amygdala-hippocampal" and "superior temporal cortex." By severing specific sections within these brain regions, surgeons induced—was he reading this right?—*psychopathy*, while blocking its more counterproductive symptoms, namely aggression and impulsive behavior.

"This is…" Jason inhaled and rubbed his face. "I don't know. This is just insane."

Agent Rooney started in, "What we needed you to understand is that this isn't another protected kingpin subsidizing a multimillion-dollar fraud scheme. Stephan Klimnick is a state-sponsored weapon gone rogue."

"Whether the *Times* article played a part doesn't matter," Agent Hoffman said. "What matters is this: Marc Behrenreich holds serious sway over the honorable Judge Tate"—the name and title said with a snide streak—"but we've been playing our own ace close to the chest. During the investigation our tech forensics guys found footprints from deleted VRS calls between Marc and Johnny Raciti, their platform provider's CEO and known associate of the DeCavante crime family. We're confident that any one or several of these calls mention Stephan Klimnick explicitly, the scheme, anything that could help us. Now," Hoffman spread his fingers over the invisible Risk board, "Marc ordered the archives' deletion right after the subpoena. Ms. Thibodeaux must've executed the order being as Marc wasn't in a position to trust anyone else, ironic as it is. At the least, it's safe to assume she interpreted those calls. If we can just talk to her, we might be able to get her to retrace those footprints."

Jason nodded, hand treating his mouth like putty. "Yeah. Yeah, of course," he shook his head, disentangling from mental purgatory. The new world mocked him. Myriadal's two championship volleyball teams—the second, in so many years as AD, against Stanford, won less than two weeks ago—meant nothing. His name on the billions paid out to college athletes, and the tens of billions more earned by their administrators because of it—nil. Then he saw his Jesse Owens still-frame in the TV room, oblong from this angle. Black-and-white, a headlong shot of his runner's pose, prepared to put his dent into Hitler's presumption of a mongrel race.

These agents were crusaders toting old-testament virtues, bent on beating into his brain the oldest dialectic there was: good vs. evil. But Jason kept his wits. They could preach the importance of a grand moral complex, but in reality, once he made his decision, he'd have to live with it. He had mere moments to make that decision. No time for questions regarding where survivalism ended and ethics began. Time only to consider whether he could supply them information as a neutral entity. How did that define his position on atrocity? Impossible to say. Even realpolitik notions had others' interests in mind, and therefore an ethics.

The fire alarm's *cheep* brought Jason back to. Low battery. The three men assembled at his kitchen table awaited his word. Staring between hands lifted from the table's linen, Jason said, "I don't know."

"So you do know something," Agent Rooney said. "I mean Jesus, Paul, the guy left one of his players—a human being—as a sitting duck, and did nothing about it. Most likely he *wanted* something to happen to Benison. I bet he figured a way to use it to his advantage."

"Mr. Derekson," Agent Hoffman said, hand held to his partner, smiling flat and brief. "While I'd love nothing more than to hit you with any number of conspiracy charges you've managed to accrue over the past couple years, we just don't have the time right now. That is, unless I'm afforded the time."

Jason shut his eyes. He recalled Gary's brief tirade after the assault on Jonesy. Gary had called it willful negligence, the sort of shadowy rapacity that got people hurt. In response, Jason said, "You want me to put a police detail on this kid? It'll only make everyone nervous."

"Mr. Derekson, I'll repeat: we need you to dig, or we're going to be here all night, and I've already cleared that with the wife."

"Paris," he blurted.

"Have you been in contact with her?" Agent Hoffman asked.

"No."

As though his answer were trivial, Hoffman said, "Call Ted. Have him contact the Embassy over there, check what ran through their cables. If they ask for a warrant tell them it's being processed."

Rooney flung a hand, "Fuck that. Let's call the Prefecture and get a location."

"You should've texted Ted by now."

"Texting fuckin Ted."

Hoffman lifted from his seat, his frame blotting the stove lights. The other two men followed his lead—Rooney zoned into the phone in hand, Mr. Kaufman looking no worse for wear. Meanwhile a new deal was struck with Jason. Escorting the agents and their associate to the elevator, pledging to keep in contact at his discretion, he knew what he would do the very next day.

Like a bluebell's stem, Westlake Avenue ran from South Lake Union—the heart of Myriadal's campus—until hitting Stewart, downtown's topsoil. Along Westlake was a Whole Foods Market, often referred to as Whole Paycheck by the wittier of well-off Seattleites. But more annoying than the market's prices were the *Real Change* workers stationed just outside.

There were two *Real Change* workers at any given time. Notable to most was the *Real Change* hawker, who, well, hawked *Real Change* newspapers. The *Real Change* hawker was in fact an ever-changing homeless or indigent face that the *Real Change* editorial hired as part of its inherently philanthropic endeavor: to employ homeless or indigent persons. The *Real Change* hawker stood half-a-restraining order's length from the Whole Foods, heavy reserve of *Real Change* papers stacked in a belly-pouch slung over his or her shoulders. One single edition brandished high overhead, they belted jocular *Real Change* jingles, melodies obnoxious or mildly entertaining, depending on one's mood or company, or other such circumstances that influence human judgment.

The *Real Change* hawker was loud. They were boisterous. They made their intentions clear: I'm standing here in this bone-withering chill of a mist, most likely suffering incipient withdrawals from this or that scheduled substance, and using—or trying to use—clever lyrical cadence to sell my wares for but one American dollar. There was no confusion about this.

But then there was the hawker's sidekick. Contrary to the *Real Change* hawker, who was swapped out each week, their sidekick was a mainstay.

From a distance, one might've suspected from Lyle's emaciated figure and frizzled length of gray-gold hair that a slatternly woman hunched there on the corner of Westlake and Denny. A former debutante, perhaps, full of the city's promise, then fallen into disrepute. But come closer—down the cement steps leading from the plaza above, or from either side of Westlake—and it resolved clearly that Lyle Crosby was in fact a man—a man who hadn't cut his hair since his last stint with sobriety.

It could however be said that heroin hadn't compromised his cunning. For while the *Real Change* hawker went on hawking his drizzle-dampened product, Lyle—the unofficial *Real Change* sidekick—slunk up to people about the Whole Foods premises, paperless, drawling but one thing—"Chaaaaange…Chaaaaange… *Chaaaaaaaaange*"—until chancing upon someone who'd hand him but one dollar. He'd then slink back into the crowd, leaving the generous person bereft of the *Real Change* paper they thought they'd paid for, questioning what hope there was for humanity and its perhaps dwindling capacity for integrity. Indeed, Lyle left them real changed.

Yes, Lyle Crosby used sneakier sales tactics. Unlike the hawker, Lyle wasn't a real *Real Change* employee, in the formal sense of the term, "employee." Lyle didn't wear a real *Real Change* uniform. Lyle accrued revenues not so much via as vicarious to the *Real Change* brand, and it appeared that most passersby and Whole Foods shoppers were willing to overlook copyright infringement, income tax evasion, and misappropriation of the *Real Change* brand.

Less finesse, however, was lent to the manner with which Lyle spent these modest earnings.

An all but abandoned parking lot a few blocks northeast of the Whole Foods, up Denny Way, beckoned him each evening. A gravelly smudge just east of the otherwise serenely sloped, skyscraping downtown area. A place to cop his fix.

It harbored dark pasts, this lot. Sketchy memories of July Fourths' unruly fireworks and fistfights, bottle glass tossed off Aspira's highrisen ledges, even a couple rogue stabbings never brought to justice. But most of the time the lot was quiet, the silence of things decayed well past death. Rusted cars' rubberless hubcaps. Faded parking partition lines. Outmoded telephone wires sagging under the weight of vigilant sea hawks. And, of course, the rickety ticket-vending booth by the lot's entrance.

He'd lurk by its northwest edge, mist collecting in his carrot-rot beard, hunched in his thin tattered jacket, shivering out the chills. He'd clench a skeletal fist around his wad of the day's *Semi-Real Change* revenues. He'd wait for his man.

Drunk on Dickel. High on coke. Low on life.
Monday.
Wednesday.
July.
Another day that ended in y.

Had his birthday come to pass? The big two-two, celebrated almost unawares, autonomic flask-to-mouth. Who knew, who cared. Another day begun belated in bed following his graveyard shift. Another day worth seeing through only because of those chemicals he used to trick him out of himself.

Julia gone.

He woke to a text from Cammy about a flask left on the concierge desk. Replacing his phone on the nightstand, he saw two empty bottles in the aftermath of their drunken brawl: the victorious upright, catching afternoon's gleam; the defeated one prostrate, dregs pooled along the side like an impossible bottle missing its ship. He lay sidelong as late summer light burned through the blinds. Here, at peak of a transcendent hangover, rife material rose to the surface like refugees from blasted lands of consciousness.

Mr. Kaufman had offered to put up his freshman tuition. He'd declined, knowing he'd fuck it up, and that if he did, as he had, Mr. Kaufman's son, his old chum Robert, would resent him all the more. Wouldn't have mattered anyway. Astronomical cycles charted Peter's texts, every couple months or so sending his child-hood brother an abrupt Whaddup. To which Robert would reply from his wealth of conscience, Not bad, u? As if cobalt ions could channel untyped thoughts, Robert's texts implied knowledge of his drinking, his isolation, his total desperation. Then the third and last text: Killin the game while still playing it, and other paradoxes of such ilk, which went unanswered.

Through this brusque and bravado, Peter effectively canceled out the very reason he'd hit up Robert in the first place, as if quarantining himself from his medicine.

Meanwhile, a month's radio silence between Peter and his employers transmitted doomful signals. Neogangsters who shook municipal economies, who decided fates far more worthwhile than a used-up Peter Fosch's, would make waste of him—lest Raciti was jettisoned first. Perhaps it was for the best.

Julia gone.

So he drank. So he snorted. It was all he got out of bed for, all that kept him in bed until he did it again. He slept with his piece under the pillow and woke with it somewhere else in his room. Unconsciously bereaving the satchels at his back—bereaving his means—again he moved Ravjeet's Canadian bud and dished skimmed dimebags to Aspira residents. Again 405 devolved into a squatter's den. Kindling between binges on booze and coke, the wild oscillations of his blood drug content warped 405's confines to match his mind's.

A sacrifice.

So there he was. Bumblebee bike jacket, treading 405's flotsam. Plastic cup with the Huskies monogram, whiskey's sharp waft dulled to his nose. Pacing vectors, blowing lines, kindling, unclipping, emptying, reloading, chambering, repeat. Waiting for word from Rameen, waiting for the next move, the two large that kept him afloat until the next move. Treading flotsam, blowing lines, unclipping, repeat. 405 pressing in on him. His roommate, Brad, rattling his knob, opening, shuffling out to class.

Silence.

Ding from phone.

Not Rameen.

Standing at 405's picture window, wondering what she was doing now, he saw the black town car slow along the Iliad's stoop. Notions of the end caught flame in his gut as he descended the stairs to meet them.

He slid into a cold backseat cut off from the front. Opposite him lay a pair of handcuffs. Over an intercom came his instructions:

"The blindfold on the coat hook—put it on. Then the cuffs."

He obeyed. He resigned himself to thinking of things that, within an hour, would become irrelevant. Perhaps they were already irrelevant, depending on one's opinion of things and time, but such abstractions were beyond the scope of his current state of besotted nausea. He rested his head against the tinted window, imagining them in a faraway copse, together—until she vanished. Sobbing, a phantom satchel strapped over his shoulder, he retched himself awake. Bent over between his knees, he wiped his cheeks, swollen and viscous, on his black chinos, helpless to the orangey goop smearing his sneakers. He felt much better. He snorted up some phlegm and said, "Saw two club foots yesterday."

No response over the intercom.

"Get it? Two people with club feet. A club foot each."

Silence.

"Not together or anything. Two totally different places." He chuckled, "What're the odds."

The car revved up the highway for over an hour before slowing, wending, buzzing through a gate. Like a dog wearing a cone Peter rubbed his face against the door, the blindfold slipping to his neck. Down a kempt path spread a gothic estate: a mansion of medieval stonework; mosaic gardens of glossy hedges and pastel hollies; stained glass windows bookended by broad wood shuttering; high spires flickered with gray silhouettes.

Two suited men stood in his opened door, studying the mess at his feet. "You gonna be cool?" said the white one, unlocking his cuffs.

"Cucumber."

They escorted him toward the portico's masonic arch. A waistcoated butler with a broken roman nose answered their knocks, wooden and heavy. Led into a darkening parlor, Peter dropped his head back and took in the squared silo of books and ladders, prosaic footage ascending forty feet until meeting a glass ceiling. His dropped eyes were met with a .44, trained on the bridge of his nose. His vacant stare down the revolver's barrel was just that: a hollow show of existential indifference.

"Ain't like I'm a fuckin cop, man," he drawled as the white guy patted him down. "Could've plugged me 150 miles back."

The black guy holding the gun pointed out his potential lack of recollection vis-à-vis inebriation. The white guy groped him without a word.

"Car service and massage?" Peter said. "Never thought I'd get a happy ending."

For which he received a blow to the gut, doubling him over like a mangled lawn chair.

"That's from Mr. K," the white guy growled.

A fourth voice drifted from cornered shadows, soaring and light and pointed like a rising arrow: "Enough, Casey."

Mr. K, Peter knew, stepped into the drawing room's gilded light and stood over his crumpled body.

"You received the note I left for your last delivery?"

Peter tipped his head once, retching dry gobs like gaseous sand.

"Then why do I feel so...unrequited?" Mr. K said.

"You want to call your boys off?" Peter geared his voice to something gruff and got nothing but another look down the six-shooter's barrel, finned by its aimer, trained on his head.

The bespectacled man knelt near him, breathing close. "You've given me no choice."

The six-shooter clicked. Peter could've gone either way. His mouth opened and flipped the coin: "Didn't hear anything from Raciti after the last one," he said and retched once more. "Think he knows you're gonna move on him."

Mr. K nodded once and went to a shelf of uniform navy tomes, shadows pooling into the parlor's farther reaches. He tilted one, the book prizing like a porthole's latch.

"Come."

Peter stood unsteadily and shambled toward the shelf.

"Closer...Closer."

Inches from the shelf, Peter could smell the aged wood, the old volumes, leather and parchment and centuries all breathing their slow sibilant breath, their wheezing chuckles, mocking his fleeting foolery.

"These books concern the United States' most vaunted secrets and why they keep them…Go on. Take one."

Peter found his arm raising, slow, his hand unfurling, about to brush a book—until Mr. K took vicious grip of his mouth, stuffing his other hand down his chinos, under his wear.

"This is going to be very *sim*ple," he lilted, and Peter bleated as he pulled up hard after entering him. "I'm very ap*prec*iative of your information. It was a kind gesture. I'll take *note* of it, rest assured. Now now. Relax," he whispered, breath neutral as nitrogen. "It'll all be over very *short*ly if we can only find ourselves in a*gree*ment. There's a thing about loyalty, you see. It's a *choice*. Look at these books," Mr. K growled, smashing his face into the volumes enveloping his view, the hard-bound spines crunching his nose's cartilage, the finger pulling hard up his tailbone every few syllables. "If you so much as laid a *fin*ger on these I would be forced to protect my*self*, as proxy to the Agency that wishes to protect *it*self. Does this make *sense*? Do you see how *thin* the ve*neer* of *trust* is? And yet, there's something about *trust* that I value so highly."

Mr. K released him, liquid leaving with his finger. Peter stumbled back and fell prat. The white guy—Casey—chuckled.

"I decided long ago to maintain confidence in Mr. Raciti's loyalty," said Mr. K. "He knows this. Now it's time you made sure to maintain my confidence in yours."

Somewhere amid the peal of pain Peter heard a *click*. He looked up to find one of Mr. K's goons, skin toned continuum opposite, holding a pen by his ear.

"You will deliver this recorder to Mr. Raciti," Mr. K instructed. "You will tell him it was yours."

Lifting his head, his posture one of presentation, Peter looked at the pen until understanding the ruse: that Peter would be the one who'd recorded this conversation. "Why's he gonna believe me?" he said, coughing, rising from the floor.

"Have I underestimated you?"

Peter accepted the silver pen recorder, its rough texture cold and heavy in his hand.

"Very well. Kochman," he said to the black guy, "if you'll get the car?"

A few nights later, Peter stumbled into The Living Room, a bohemian bar on Olive, a ragged book in hand.

"Rye," he ordered. "Neat."

As he peeled open his Henry Miller, the skinny bartender started chuntering at him about something or another.

"This ain't a prop," Peter nodded toward the book, which looked more like a waterlogged chip of mulch.

So the bartender slung him his rye. Within moments of phasing into the prose, Peter heard an unmistakable *flick*, followed by the fug of ripe smoke. He looked up to find the bartender taking luxurious drags behind the boutique little bar. Peter put his book down, a sad tent sagging on the woodgrain. He frowned, nodded, "Well if you're gonna…"

In his bumblebee bike jacket and black chinos, Peter pounded whiskeys and rapped with Scott, the human opioid who tended bar—limbs sucked to bone between jagged joints like emaciated dumbbells, high-nosed whinge-bitching about too-drunk patrons, like college kids' sad attempts at copping pills. "Tagalong faggots," he scoffed. "Think they can just eat 100s and not vomit all over their fucking Keds." Watching Peter tip blow from his snuff bullet, Scott bitched about the bar's owners, who'd granted him charge while they toured India. "They send these fucking envoys to check in, well maybe they should come back and run the fucking bar themselves. This isn't the fucking Roman Empire." Squinting behind compressed glasses, taking rails up his deviated septum, Scott offered war stories and cigarettes, scenic-route admissions that he'd been squeezed out of other bars, unattributed to his any failings of course, least of all his side enterprise. For Peter, Scott simply held witness to his surrender. There was no one else now.

When Scott stopped spewing words, Peter reminisced on the East, where the air was heavier, where the exhaust was thicker, where the trees' gnarls were like wooden templates for squirrels.

Somewhere thereabouts he went fuzzy—around the time other people began filtering in. They wore ethical pleather coats, frilly scarves, shapely glasses. They ordered drinks that Scott muddled, muttering indignations under his breath. They took their slipshod cocktails to the loft area above, where they sat on secondhand couches and divans and spoke as though sparring their merits. They inspired Peter's drinking. After an hour, Scott blared sitar-heavy stuff, drowning them in sound, draining them out the door. Peter's lip hung slack over the hilt of his smirk like a downed communication line. He placed his piece on the bar. He and Scott watched as hipsters who'd come for a casual drink recognized, deduced, then decided how they should proceed. Peter picked it up, gripped it, used it to dictate his speaking points. He turned it limply toward a middle-aged woman with a glimmering auburn bouffant who'd ordered a Negroni without betraying a modicum of heed to his hand's deadly extension. The piece aimed flaccidly at her bust, Peter said, "Don't you agree?" to which she pinched her features and said all haughty, "Please redirect your overcompensations."

Nights off from work he spent there at The Living Room. And before work began. Just after opening on a Tuesday, sunlight bursting into the bar like a prism exposing crypts, Peter tapped the grainy wood lip for another. Five more and two hours later, he was weaving along Stewart, downtown, nearing 3rd, no idea how he'd gotten there. A skin-stippled rage galvanized his velocity, the velocity of his vectors. His shift not for hours yet, he posted up at the bar adjacent Aspira. He raised his glass to Puget Property lease managers just off work, his gun and taser belted in perfect view. They hoisted frothy stouts, toasting to another diurnal tick toward death. He ordered another Jim Beam, neat. He relished his truancy as night carried past 10PM. He looked down at his drink as though he'd made a huge mistake.

"What am I…Barkeep," he barked. "Make this a double."

His notion's slurry had cemented as truth: he was the fall guy. A pawn of Raciti's and Mr. K's cold war for surreptitious power and egoistic primacy. He'd gone undercover as a runner—as a means of working his way into Mr. K's circle. He'd succeeded, though the exculpatory pen recorder, FedExed last month, had gone unrequited. He knew the next move. Mr. K's guys would either contract him to take care of Raciti or simply frame the hit as such. Either way, after the hit, they'd take care of him.

He felt stupid for not recognizing it earlier. Not that it mattered. He woke, drank, went to work, drank, unclipped, emptied, reloaded, chambered, drank, worked, kindled, smashed and bought burner, repeat. He found mail atop his mailbox saying that his mailbox was too full to receive more mail. He received an email detailing his missed tuition payments and absences. The last paragraph threatened to boot him if he didn't rehab his whole deal, was the gist of it. Like school, he'd soon stop going to work altogether.

He maintained a blood drug content liable for complicated amnesias, nesting dolls of unremembering. Booze and coke helped maintain the mirage. Sucking at his hellfire, chambering, nipping at his flask, he recalled those runs through the dunes. He romanticized the weight on his back—the real mythology to his work. He was destined. He slipped into blackouts that blended with consciousness and the cycle began again. During the first week of October, he texted Kochman with new demands: he wanted a seat at the pantheon's table.

That evening, he leaned his bike along Loretta's cobbled incline and stumbled back up the stoop where he and Julia had sat to work things out on that brisk February night. He heaved upstairs and found a modest brown box reclined against 405's door, a perfectly edged *flâneur*. No postage. A note tucked under the string's knot read:

For the highest disciple.

He woke up the next day and couldn't find the box, the note, the research. Someone had taken it—they'd entered his mind and stolen it.

His skin rippled. His bodily palsy and cement stomach receded behind his sensory veil with each additional swig. He swept his laptop and Dickel over to his blasted desk, where he'd once half-assed his essays within a carrel of cash, stacked and banded bills like he'd ran a trap house. That money was gone now. Now, sucking from the bottle, he searched the U of Washington's academic database. His hands trembled, all passion and shorted nerves, as if transcribing nuclear codes from the floppy disk as no apocalypse rumbled above.

From a keyword lottery describing the emblazoned satchels he found a scholarly article on an ancient Myncan plant: that which was packed in the satchels he'd ran. Attached was a scan of old parchment—proof of his wishes. He was his father's son. Ultraviolet floaters wormed in his periphery. He swigged.

No semiotician, he couldn't sort the parchment's letters and symbols—except for one term he found passim, like a prayer's amen: *antinomine*. Famished for more information, he gobbled phrasal scraps on the Myncan tribe's sacred plant, whose myth and majesty metastasized around his brain's imaginative centers. The research, its drive toward a sole knowledge, his grand unifying theory, turned his belief into the plant's active intoxicant.

Drinking. Reading. Repeat.

"This life," a televised inmate said, pausing to consider his words during Episode 2 of *Fast Times at Penitentiary High*. Elbows and back on a picnic bench, blue jumpsuit topped by a red skullcap. "Makes us all walking paradoxes," he proclaimed like the pseudo-philosophical wannabe thug he was. Peter couldn't remember his fucking name.

Say your fucking name.
Sip.
Watch.
Read.
Chamber.

Brad returned from class as Peter lay in bed with his door open, staring at a square of afternoon sky. From a crescent awareness of Brad's presence, Peter knew his roommate would begin packing for a weekend home in Spokane. Brad's efficient shuffle rustled within his attentive register. He listened, roiling ire, flushed crimson from the chin down across his chest.

Even the most mystically-minded historians, horticulturists, and anthropologists agreed that antinomine's effects were purely apocryphal, bandied by one Master Góvis to have consecrated the subequatorial jungles of Central America, specifically the area where the Myncan tribe once thrived. He ignored these smug academics. He wailed on the keys, composing the requiem to his final dogma. He sucked off the Dickel's teat, burrowed deeper into UW's scholarly archives. He found a peer-reviewed meta-analysis that correlated the Myncans' antinomine ritual with "transcendental experience" as compared to placebos sans ritual. As a final rebuttal, the firewater waging war with his bladder, he emailed the article to the first person he could think of.

Drinking. Reading. Unremembering. In the way a winter's real cold comes well after the solstice, Peter's shakes settled only once he'd licked up half the fifth of Dickel.

The lazy, lingering, last-luck light crept faithfully back to its source, which impaled itself on Mount Rainier's white peak. He brought a scan of the photographed parchment into the common area. He was exalted, manic, his knowledge shimmering before him, ready to pass through this portal finally and for good. He sucked down the Dickel save for a finger or five to mix into hellfire, which he flasked and pocketed in his bike jacket for warmth—acting on unremembered impulse to ride up into the sticks. He scudded north in jump-cuts. The pines tasted like gin on his breath. He entered them. An hour later he pulled up and, bestriding his bike, garnered his surroundings. He'd reached a bluff out in unchartered boonies, not too far from the dunes. His hand leapt from the grip like it'd caught the spirit. To his left lay a line of sawed logs, looking like they might wake up from his phone's harsh flashlight. His flashlight revealed the single-file tire tracks behind him.

"Mother*fucker*," he spat.

Hours passed retracing his treads back to the freeway. He dragged up to the Iliad in the next day's noon light, churlish in wake of his abortive rustication, his needing skin prickled and searing, and plugged his bike between two cars. Strange blots occluded the present like a film reel with bad negatives. The Living Room swaddled him in darkness before he could question how he'd gotten there.

"You okay, man?" Scott said. "Look like you just ate some bad pussy."

"Just need some of daddy's juice," he dredged from his burnt-out warehouse of levity.

Now striding past Pike Place, the Seattle Center risen to his right like a misplaced theme park. He glared at the last-shift canvasser that stood waving to him. He squeezed his eyes, shook the sand out of his head—

On the 8 bus now, inclining up Denny Way like an old wooden crank-up 'coaster. His mouth tasted like a gas station, grain oil spotting his saliva, reeking his gums. He searched his jacket for a receipt, bill change, business card. Checked his phone and burner—checked his phone and burner again. He'd missed his shift at Aspira. As the bus leveled out atop the Hill, he saw Robert's response. Rage tugged his left eyelid like a stitching machine.

Down the length of the bus he saw an older man bent over, back brace under backpack, black moss for hair, *snapping* his cane with each loud step. Glaucous chemicals clouded his irises, his intentions, as he took center stage.

"Ladies and gentlemen if I may interrupt you on this fine evening. I am suffering a very rough time right now. I am unable to obtain work as a result of several surgeries on my—"

"No," he growled.

Startled, the man turned. "Excuse me?"

"I see you."

"You see what?"

False faith.

"I see you."

"You got a fuckin problem?"

He rose, staggered, staccato, slapping onto a pole and steadying himself. He lunged forward and feinted a thrown fist. His truncated haymaker smoked out the vagrant's gambit, betraying vitality enough to draw rigid his defenses.

"You'd hit an old man?" the man grimaced, bending over again. "The hell is wrong with you?"

Passengers watched without turning, their eyes straining to get a look at the unlikely altercation. The bus stopped—pneumatic relief, a resting sigh—and the doors opened.

"Get off," he ordered through grit teeth. He shoved the man along, their feet captured in the flashes of his failing power grids.

Outside, the wavering worsened, every third frame blotted, moments defined by an uncontrolled rage, axiomatic, searing his neck and forearms. The beggar was long gone. He clung to street corners like ladder rungs. Buildings bent and moaned. The sidewalk went liquid. He slugged off the rest of the flask.

Over the long weekend he'd shirk his last scheduled shifts. He collected piss in empty peanut butter jars, serried like soldiers under his bed. He shat behind the dumpster in the garage. He poured Dickel into pint glasses, the medicine taken straight. He microwaved rubbery Stouffers.

He went out in the evening. Not a hundred yards from the Iliad, he chased a woman around the Bauhaus café and down Crawford. With stitches in his side, he limped to a halt and clutched the spell.

"Come back!" he bellowed after her.

Friday night's fog thickened. He held fast to the Iliad's dumpster, whose rancid waste regaled of man's wicked process. He was one of them. He was thrown into blindness, nauseated, confused—he retched. Up lurched black magma, rorschaching the shape of his spirit against the dumpster's rusted avocado siding. Bent over, dark strains of saliva hanging off his lips, the mere act of wiping his mouth brought him down.

He woke to a cradle of darkness and black trash bags. His phone read 10:17. The notification dot cornering his email reminded him that he'd forgotten again. Thumbing the email open, who could interpret his sister's months-old correspondence? *Julia.* He nipped his flask. *Julia.* Kaleigh. *Where am I?*

An attempt to stand failed back into the garbage piles. He groped the bags for purchase and, upon standing, wiped the stick on his bike jacket, smearing it on its black parts as if to better blend the mess. Weeks of drink had wrecked his guts. Fricative hissing was all he could muster against the pain, which threw against his cerebellum images of deep pulls off the bottle, clipped pictures of his phantom savagery, his bouts of sciamachy, memories of being mounted, memories condemned to dark caverns where kept was such unseemliness.

He shuffled down the Hill. Cool autumn air parted around him as though privy to his gauzy conscious, not wanting to rouse his waking dream. Fairy lights twinkled along Olive, diodic yellows whose LED pixels buzzed in his periphery. He turned onto Terry, where lustful instinct led him before Aspira's façade. Who would suffer his reprisals. Head just canted, he stared through the glass. Matthew didn't look up. Lucky for him, Peter sensed movement near the lot over yonder. Foot patter around the abandoned ticket booth. He caught sight of a vagrant and his feral carrot beard.

Broaching the lot, he circled the vagrant's wake, following the lank silhouette like a fur trapper. Through a gap between two rusted chassis he peered into darker planes where the silhouette had slunk, rustling in the thin knoll between lot and burnt-out shack. He crept between the cars and saw the vagrant sitting against the shack, rigging his works. He saw him spurt treacherous air bubbles from the syringe, its serum of the poppy.

Her father had fallen prey to such treachery, and now—gone.

He crouched, waiting for the junkie to slump over in serene leave from this ghastly place, this awful everywhere, and before registering his decision to strike, his hands had released the vagrant's wrung head.

Panted, he staggered back up Olive. A flicker of loss crossed his mind.

The charlatan had once asked whether he'd made any close friends here in Seattle.

"Depends what you mean by close," he'd said.

"Like Robert."

"It's a city," he shrugged.

The charlatan had then asked if he thought people in cities were less friendly, less kind, less intimate.

"The Seattle cold front, the Seattle freeze, the Seattle go fuck yourself."

After a moment the charlatan said, "Like your license plate."

"Am I supposed to awe at the significance of this connection? Really, is this what you went to school for?"

"Okay, then let's get back to the city."

"Haven't gotten around to taking a census."

"I'm interested in your thoughts," the charlatan goaded.

Eyes at half-mast, he'd said, "I think cities are an infestation, and we're also the rats."

The next day he got a text from Dylan: What's with this new schmuck doing your shift?

He glared into his phone's glow, swigged from the Dickel. His forehead twitched—*something amiss*—but he maintained conviction. Brows tilting into a chasm of concentration, he replied: I'll take care of it.

The sun was a lemon cookie dipped into Mount Olympia. He needed bad. Forgoing for the third straight day a change of clothes, he hit up the liquor store on Broadway. The clerk levered the Dickel off the shelf and placed it on the counter, rapping his fingers as Peter searched his wad of bills, paused, contemplating the dampness of each wrinkled paper, their sharp chemical odor.

Kindling.

"You alright, sir?"

Peter looked up at the clerk. Sans any verbal response, he handed over a twenty.

Back at the apartment he lugged his laptop into a common area drenched in late fall light. His purpose took the form of searches on UW's database: "antinomine"; "Mynca"; "Myncan ritual"; "antinomine ritual"; "ancient rituals"; "Myncan antinomine ritual." All produced links that strayed from the path. He opened Google and searched the same. Folly. He pressed on: "tribal hallucinogens"; "tribal alchemy"; "chemist forums."

He created an onion browser on Tor.

Navigated to the Silk Road.

Bought bitcoins, with which he bought:

Acetone;

Butanone;

Isopropyl alcohol;

Chloroacetone;

and HDPE buckets.

He had tarpaulin from that time when he wanted to start cutting his own stuff.

He'd resort to a kitchen spoon for stirring.
Kindling.

The stuff came in boxes marked FRAGILE.

Slumped on one of the buckets, he paused in a prism of sunlight, unable to suss whether the solution was separating from the reagents. He should've bought a glass bucket. He urinated in a corner clear of clothes and returned to his work.

Brad found him late in the evening.

The tarp's rustles—Brad's shoes, his waking movements—roused him quick. He labored to his feet. He'd either lost consciousness over the bucket or passed out from Dickel. Or the combination. "Fuck," he said, and leered at the work as if it were an intruder.

"What the hell is this?" Brad demanded.

405 was awash in acerbic odor, burnt rubber Stouffers, piss and shit, the Dickels in his room, another warming on the windowsill. He did not make haste in hiding the equipment.

"Thought we made a deal, man."

He remained calm—he thought. That, or his brain redacted the spat, dirt over dead bodies until the clever crow came tapping at his window—

And now he was standing at Brad's door wearing a hospital mask and gloves, clutching a sharp rag and rapping twice.

"Brad," he said several seconds after his knocks.

"I'll call the cops."

"But don't you need your phone?" he asked, holding it up as if Brad could see through the door. "Brad?"

The rag rendered him woozy, so he slid his back down Brad's door and waited, the wet rag curled like a radioactive snail on the carpet nearby.

"I'll fucking call the cops, Peter."

"Brad," he sighed, opening YouTube, "I have your phone in my hand."

He typed "Rwandan machete footage."

"Peter please."

"Are you sorry?" he said vacantly over the grainy screams emitting from Brad's phone.

"Yes," Brad pled. "Please, I'm sorry. I promise you I'm sorry."

"Okay," he said, standing. "I'm going to toss this then."

He went to the kitchen and pedaled open the trashcan, which exhaled death. A noxious bomb mushrooming a cloud of encrusted Stouffers, half-bitten confections, Dickel empties, a couple pairs of soiled briefs, paper towels wadded in various liquids like piss or smeared with feces. He recoiled, rag still in hand, as Brad ripped out of his room and bounded for the front door, his head start eliminated by the three locks—knob, bolt, and chain—whereupon with one hook of his hand around Brad's stiff neck Peter was able to wrestle him to the ground, jamming the rag into his mouth and nostrils, wringing its juices, his other arm fending off Brad's weakening flails. Whether from the chemical or a lack of air, Brad's limbs went limp, his body slack.

But Brad came back to as Peter was dragging him by the ankles down the hall, toward his room. Catching him by surprise, Brad kicked off his ankle-truss and pushed himself up—only to stumble sideways, trip over his legs, his head *thudding* and *cracking* the sheetrock wall, body crumpling into a twitched lump.

He turned Brad over and looked into his glassy eyes, slapped his drunken hands away. Preempting another escape attempt, he dragged him past his room and into the common area.

"The fuck are you going?" he grinned, panted. He clenched his cheeks, made fish of his mouth, foam on his lips like salivated row. Lowering to his knees, he straddled Brad and smothered him with the rag, other hand unzipping his chinos.

Gaping at the volcanic divot made beneath Brad's sternum, the blade run bloody in his hand, he gave a quick gasp—as if realizing himself for one more moment.

He carried the body like a baby, arms swabbed in blood by the time he delivered Brad onto the tarp. He stood and watched it exsanguinate and begin paling. Watched while his sharp rag took pink wiping the serrated blade. His hand had done what he couldn't have. He flipped his burner: Need help with the body. My place. A quick response: Wait there and do not leave.

He waited the long hour-and-a-half by 405's picture window. His listless gaze chanced upon the black town car as it pulled along the curb, its blinding gleam reflecting the balmy autumn sun.

Indian summer.

He watched the besuited men open the door and wait as Mr. K stepped out in his beige slacks and green windbreaker and wire-rimmed squares.

Drinking.

"Well, this ain't Raciti," Casey said. "Not sure if that's a good thing."

"It's not," Kochman peered.

"Damaged goods," Casey said, surveying 405's squalor, glaring at its creation.

The apartment's rot stung of acid. Mr. K and his men studied the mess with handkerchiefs and jacket sleeves over their mouths.

Robert could be Brad.

He let them talk about him in his room as he polished the fifth by the picture window, where sunlight bloomed ambient dust like gaseous urine. He pulled the tufts of his Aspira work shirt through the arms of his bike jacket and wiped his nose.

"Smells like total fucking disengagement in here," said Casey as they came out from his room.

"Gentlemen, if you'll excuse us," said Mr. K.

"Boss," Casey urged.

"Enough."

The men complied. Mr. K led them to his room, where they stood in patient silence. His toe goaded Brad's sidelong body into afterdying twitch, which startled them. Soon after, Casey or Kochman clicked his front door closed.

"Are you afraid?" Mr. K asked him.

He shook his head.

"Good. Because I'm not going to hurt you. I should, but I won't. Do you know why?"

Peter's unwavering gaze said he didn't know if he knew.

"Because we want the same things," he said, and stepped closer. Closer.

One more—and he lunged, whipping Peter around and thrusting a hand into his chinos. "Do you under*stand*," Mr. K hissed, thrusting inside him and filling Peter's groan with gruff lust, "why we need this?"

"Yes," he moaned as if to any question. But he did understand. He understood the shape of his use and how to take its form.

"Good," whispered Mr. K, pulling out and wiping the finger on his chinos. "Go fetch them."

Mr. K had pulled a chair to the common area's panorama, where he sat legs-crossed, rubbing his fingers. Peter admired his golden-age gaze, quivering dewlaps, huge spectacles. Meanwhile, Casey worked in his room, and Kochman lugged from the town car boxes of baking soda and tubs of bleach, his dark pate glistening, toiling, working the rug into submission as if crazed. It wouldn't wash. He'd need box cutters to tear up the compromised carpet.

"Keep going."

Kochman attacked the floor with the futility of a dog trying to bury a bone indoors, tearing off linty suds like cloud seeds that he swept into a pile. Mr. K's first miracle: the carpet's small balding spot, though paler than the rest, was clean. Not even the lightest pink of proof. Meanwhile, Casey had opened every window and broken down the chemistry set, breaking the legs off one of the common area's two rickety wood kitchen chairs, collecting the materials in black garbage bags, and making gunnysacks with the chair legs to better transport the equipment downstairs and into the garage dumpster.

"That the kid's room?" Kochman pointed down the hall.

He nodded once.

"If we automate a few emails it'll give us a few days."

Peter followed him to Brad's room. He stood over Kochman, watching him draft emails in vague keeping with the diction in his sent box, monotone treacle addressed to his mom and hometown girlfriend, Jenny. Every so often he offered a suggestion or leaned and typed himself. He couldn't feel the keystrokes. His fingers were calloused, or he was numb. Kochman no longer needed him, not as much as he needed a quaff, so Peter returned to the common area, took the bottle off the sill, and swigged, staring out at late afternoon's clear skies. Casey had folded and stuffed the body in an outsized duffel—for the most part. As he grappled with the body's extremities, crunching bone and gristle, popping tendons and ripping sinew, Peter spread an arm toward the cityscape, barely aware of his stilted presentation, wearing a mask of human pall.

"Sublime," Mr. K agreed.

It was dusk when they took to the Iliad's staircase. He lagged like a shy child, Casey slowing to check on his progress between flights. Peter and Mr. K took either backseat, and Casey powered down the partition, through which Kochman poked his dark pate.

"You got his phone?"

Peter fished it from his chinos.

"Time for your buddy to go on a little vacation," Kochman said, much to Casey's delight.

Using Brad's credit card, Kochman reserved two flights to Anchorage—one out of SeaTac, the other Spokane—rented a serviceable sedan, and booked a bed and breakfast, all in accordance with an email to Jenny explaining the plan (first having made sure, under Peter's direction, to disclaim Brad's unusual spot of spontaneity).

"Rain," said Mr. K, craning to look over the pines and at the sky.

After an hour north on the 5, they pulled onto a dirt path bordering a farm that then splayed into several smaller trails marked only by rutted tire tracks from previous activity. "I own this land," Mr. K said, as if Peter were worried about the burial's location.

Casey chose ways edged by tall canebrakes and parked against this fence of stems swaying to sloughing rhythms. Peter made to egress but Mr. K stayed his hand. The wind whipped the canebrakes into ritualistic fervor. The sky was a violent gray. Uncertain how much time passed like this, the besuited men dug the hole and chopped the body, which they bleached in modular PVDF vats.

Mr. K inched his window down and said, "Bring me the hand."

Peter watched with detached longing as they severed the left hand from the severed left arm. Casey pinched its index finger, scrunched face turned from the meaty gears and marrowy gristle.

Kochman poured the foamy pink flotsam into the ditch, to seep sickly into the earth. The splash of Brad's corroded remains separated from his senses, preserved, somehow, from time's ceaseless roll. Moments stood in terrifying sovereignty from one another. The clouds above warred, violet and gunmetal underbellies merging ranks, beginning their air raids, pelleting the roof. He was the pantheon's highest scion. Envying his station, the gods above rained terror upon him.

Her dorm's musk, its reek of neurosis, all but absent cats and curdled milk, filtered life through this gray exposure—not reviving the art of the spinster so much as projecting such patriarchal hues onto her depression.

She spent one Saturday afternoon staring at a receipt from Bathtub Gin, where the speak's tender of bar had slung her a licorice shot spotted by conspicuous oils, effusing a piney scent—after that, she couldn't remember. Felt like a weed hangover. It was almost dusk when she stuffed the receipt in a lumpy clay utensil-holder she'd crafted in art class as a 2nd-grader at Ashbury Grammar.

She went back to bed.

With one week until her sophomore year, Julia made an appointment at Myriadal's health center. That week later she met with Diana Muller, MS. Led along a hall to an annex of offices, sat across her glass desk, Mrs. Muller apologized for the college's small coterie of therapists being booked through to the second trimester.

"These west coast ivies are rough on kids," she lamented.

Julia nodded.

"I'm glad you came anyway," Mrs. Muller said, unleashing her clinical weapons, pen and pad. "Why don't we start with what brought you?" She reposed in wait, her aquamarine pantsuit phased with the teal-tinted window behind her. That pantsuit, the semiprecious rock on her ring, the necklace of uniform turquoise beads—the whole tropical waters getup befitted her bullshit gestalt, what with her cloying poet voice and transparent techniques. Therapists treated precisely what they too suffered from—how else would they understand it? Just like Julia. One day she'd be a dragoon in clinical drag, fulfilling some sense of certainty through its false doling. Perhaps she did need therapy.

"Well…I—uh…" Julia shook her head and made a stunted sound. The thought that she couldn't explain why she'd come warded off the truth that she wouldn't.

Mrs. Muller set her blue Rapiers pen atop her Pfizer-issued referral pad. "I see your major focus is psych," she tilted her head and flipped her hands. "I'm not sure if you feel conflicted about needing help when you're in the beginning stages of training to provide it…"

She shrugged.

"…or if it's something else entirely. Either way, since you are hesitant, and this is a consultation, let's break the fourth wall so to speak."

Mrs. Muller pointed her pen behind her. Julia obliged a glance out the window, the mall's stone fountain, the steps, the students and professors, all of it looking like indigo left in the sun too long.

"Out there in the real world," said Mrs. Muller, "we put up a façade. Those façades come down when we get to know people. And that's great. But familiarity places another limitation upon us: one of expectation, or projected expectation, which can put us back into another box. With the people you know, your range is ignored in favor of the sliver of the you you are with them. In here, that range is widened. You're going to feel like you do now—hesitant, withholding, frustrated, sometimes even angry—and you'll feel it a lot. But for every time spent at one pole of seething and silence, you'll spend equal time on the other pole, expressing things you'd never be able to express to anyone you know. 'Unacceptable' emotions. Desires. Petty thoughts other people dismiss as boring but which carry massive weight in revealing the nature of your consciousness. Sexual fantasies and fears. All your sins and secrets. Without finding a space like this to widen your range, it's difficult to even begin to reorganize your mind and break the confines of your circumstances."

Julia nodded. She was wearing sweatpants for a third consecutive day. Mrs. Muller ripped and slid the referral slip across her oak desk. Taking it up, Julia gaped at an Irish surname all too familiar.

"Something wrong?" Mrs. Muller said.

"Is this—" Julia stopped. "Never mind. Thank you for your time."

Some nights it rendered her manic: the idea of visiting the office of one Finnegan O'Reilly, MSW. Her imagination turned this conflict of interest into a desperate gambit: from Mr. O'Reilly she'd tease out Peter's motives and drives, peeling back her psychic layers by proxy, a pulpy fiction best left to fantasies, or so went the clinical manual. This referral slip cooled in her desk's drawer—a dungeon for dead skullduggeries.

In published form, tonight's visit to Mercer Island would put a seal on the book of Peter.

Between bowls of Brazilian corn kernels and immaculate ceviche bass, she spoke more to Patricia, Johnny's cook, than Johnny. His discontent with the dish was a childish redirection of his frustration with her. He poked at it a few times in his normal way.

"You give up the ghost?"

Her eyes flicked up with his.

"We don't see each other anymore."

Without Peter she was worthless to him, and she relished in this.

"Young love," he chuckled, poking. "Trish! Vino!"

He looked up smiling, swirling his glass and emptying it, swallowing a great desperation that Julia couldn't place.

A strange sense of *jamais vu* accompanied Julia into Comp 37's first-floor lab room, where she located her stenciled nametag. It wasn't unpleasant, this sense of unfamiliarity, despite having spent her freshperson year's second trimester in this lab room. (Her biology practicum had been a series of genuinely enjoyable planter experiments and questionably ethical dissections on amphibious animals. She'd hedged her efforts for an A-.) But jarring, nonetheless. Perhaps fumes were permeating the padlocked cabinets.

"Okay everyone. Let's break the ice by introducing ourselves to our lab partners. I'll set the timer for two minutes, and then we'll switch."

The lab captain, Arjun Sidhu, a TA grad student, paced before the touchscreen chalkboard as the warm chatter frothed up through the fissures. That Mr. Sidhu ("Please, Arjun") wore a white coat said much about him considering the day's only experiment would involve a water-bong—or so said her partner, who then bent and peered at Julia's nametag.

"Julia Paolantonio," she said with cheeky pop and circumstance, pulling at the long plait slung over shoulder. "Peter Fosch's girl."

"What?"

"I dated David Lissener?"

This, she could believe. She was Dave's type: this bartender-by-the-Bay with her woke-up-like-this looks.

"He like, pushes yeah?"

"Uhhhh," Julia's laugh stuttered.

"Don't play coy," her partner simpered, playing the dirty-blonde plait near the red collar of her raglan Silversun Pickups shirt, mustard bodice and cream sleeves. That her peep-toe heels were a wonderfully dull beige didn't indemnify this breach of social conduct. "He runs some weird shit down the dunes. Highly hush-hush."

"I don't know what you're talking about."

"Neither does that lawyer-lady outfit, I'm sure."

"You're blaming me because your mirror sees a ten-year-old?"

"Whoa. I think we need to chill."

"We?"

They were silent for the remaining three minutes of icebreakers, stuck in their cryogenic contention as classmates chirped and twittered, rejoicing in the thaw.

Blustering back, umber skirt stiffening her strides, a muckraking force stalked Julia across the mall. Everybody—every*thing*—was in on it. Just look at the damn sun: that molten ball of cosmic espionage. That flaming periscope stood to expose her now, boil her inside-out until gluts of organic intelligence slimed full their test tubes and vials.

Julia hadn't even gotten this mermaid-shed-of-her-scales' name, and yet *she* sure seemed to know a *lot* about *her.* Swiping now into Compartment 56, Julia all but vowed to gut and tenderize her lab partner into isinglass, and serve the jelly back to those fish-fuckers from whence she came.

Comp 56's lobby was quiet, which suited the glossy cream floor tile, gleaming white coffee tables, frigid-blue blown glass, simple spheres and curving shapes, set on pearlescent stands and end tables. Centering the white satin couches was a sterling silver statue of a stickman, *en garde*, this reimagined Myriadal mascot a gift from some wealthy alumnus or another. At the reception desk, the RA's turbaned head hung concentrated on a worksheet, his antiquarian transistor rattling a Q-Tip verse.

Julia slipped into the mail room for the first time in months. Hand unsteady, she flashed her student ID, heard the click of her mail slot, and found, among junk mail, a stack of envelopes.

She hadn't seen (much less talked to) Dave since that Halloween party last year. How he'd found out about Peter struck her as less uncertain than who else knew about him, which she refused to entertain in her parlor of possibility—just like the envelopes. The world spun on several axes. The door flung unto this Borgesian infinity of mail slots. She glanced behind her, catching a boot-clod boy with fussy dark hair. He seemed a harlequin, an absurd character amid abstract prop art. She gazed up at the motes strafing in sunlight. Hot: nothing in this city, not even this billion-dollar institution, was air-conditioned.

Indian summer.

For the first time since, she was fiending for a spliff.

Uncut tobacco delivered her into a necessary state of oblivion. The vertigo drew her down to the curb in a nauseous eddy. Cigarettes tasted less like the smoky date palm she'd imagined as requisite accessory to '70s Beiruti beer importers, and more like burning lung. She studied the small blue Camel stamped above the dotted butt, looked up slit-eyed from her perch atop Westlake's plaza, the Whole Foods below, Denny Park across the street.

Julia took inventory of the welfare state's dole (the envelopes), its source of subsidy (her granddad), and what she knew (little). Dragging down to the camel's hump, hypnotized by Peter's smoky proclivity, Julia was drawn back into byzantine spirals—attempting to balance life's complex equations through her imagination's most quixotic calculus. Not for the first time this week did she scan the plaza as though someone were performing psionic theft, telepathic terrorism, gleaning her thoughts with sadistic delight. *Killin the game while still playing it, and other paradoxes of such ilk*, she thought at them. Peter used to rattle off these mordant little epigrams with the earnestness of a dog frolicking in mud.

She arrived early for her shift at the Student Union co-op, the vegan meat of Comp 50's three-story sandwich. As a generalized rule, the granola-crunchy bohemian potheads ate here, while everyone else ate in the Commissary upstairs. A rule akin to the swimming pool on the school's roof—a vestige of student myth and lore—upheld by your frattier types, or others requiring illusionary categories. As a practical rule, everyone ate at the co-op. The veggie hummus sandwich slayed your taste buds.

Weighing, packaging, and price-stamping reams of seaweed and bundles of quinoa—Julia's imagination punctured such monotony. She envisioned a bar called Opening Night, festooned with festive yellow bulbs like beads of frozen sunlight dawning upon the Roaring-20's floor plan: intimate tables; Art Deco room roll; ragtime band; stage and swing for burlesque entertainments. Opening Night welcomed all—so long's you didn't ask if it was opening night.

During her break Julia luxuriated along the mall, less enjoying than getting through the cigarette she'd paid for. Ash dusted her blue co-op smock. The sun dipped into the horizon without ripple, clean and dry. With twilight came warm moonlit breezes off the Puget. She saw an email from her lab partner, apologizing for possibly offending her, or whatever. She conceived of her response, one that would carry her beyond reproach. Once finished, this veritable Ariel would cease to exist as she once had. Drawing from her deep well of snark, Julia poured condescending absurdity into her thumbwork. With glee she called up such phrases as... normally advertent transmissions of authenticity, or...must apologize for my behavior, which reflects the current phase of the zodiac.

The Myriadal College faculty had colluded, as they did each summer, proven by this year's record-setting price for good grades: her professors unloaded syllabi whose 10-20 pages of arduous specificity induced peals of panic that took hours to settle into capitalism's *leitmotif:* that low drone of anxiety and onerous acceptance. Her only fluff class was an off-campus seminar meant to equip luddites (such as psych majors) with basic tech skills. Azalai had reserved a conference room halfway up the Andreas Building in South Lake Union. For one credit, the luddites gathered for their weekly assimilation into Azalai's suite of office tools.

Following the first seminar at Azalai, she made the short walk back to campus, then the co-op, for her first annual review. A day of firsts. A selfie to remember. A caption to go with it: Guess who just took a class on Azalai's campus. Hint: she's in the picture. The text package meant to bail the water from their sinking relationship. As usual, her mother responded within minutes: Yay! So proud of you :) Mira and I went shopping today and I splurged on a little black dress. The guy at Nordies gave me 20% off because I wouldn't pay the sticker price! Will send a mirror model upon my return. Glad you're enjoying classes sweetie, ttys xoxo.

Julia's boss—a fifth-year American Studies PhD whose can-do deportment had run dry over the past year and now relied on scheduled stimulants and a bevy of brain-hacking nootropics—worked in a pantry. She entered as Patrice put final touches on the last employee's review. Head bent to work, Patrice's hair was the color and texture of besoms in a sauna. Julia could've touched all four walls from her seat across Patrice's terrace nightstand-cum-desk. The pantry-cum-office needed but an oil lamp and quill to complete the picture of this mad captain's quarters.

"Julia," she looked up, turning her pen over. "Welcome to my office. As you may have heard, I'm a pretty private person. No comma after the pretty," she said and ripped a rimshot, as if simulating the sound of a joke landing without wheels. "Anyway, I don't invite people in here that I don't intend on having back. So, you're here."

"Yay."

"So let's get right to it. Your work is great. You're on time. You finish the tasks you're assigned. You don't complain about what tasks those are or whom you're working with. And you don't steal," she clucked and winked over a trigger-finger. "There's not much here to complain about here."

"Cool."

"Cool. Yeah. Totally. And well. It's just. This is nothing big. We've all just noticed that you're awfully *independent.* And hey. Look. I get it. To each their own. It's just. This is a coöperative, right? We're here for the people. And your colleagues are people, too."

"They are people."

"Right. Exactly. You understand."

According to Julia's relatively accurate estimation of social dynamics, one big genuine grin would suffice to end this interaction. But she didn't possess the strength for affected bullshit, so smiling would've put her at risk for pulling a lip muscle. Some people were better built for bureaucracy, able to press forth in blithe perpetuity despite hating it all, but more likely it was the Adderall.

Patrice continued, "When you're back bagging, it's a totally different chi than when you're up at the register or stocking the shelves, right? We'd really love to see a little more of what's underneath, because everyone here knows you're super smart and kind. On the other hand, maybe you'd like to get more hours in the back. I'm totally flexible. I'm here to cater to strengths. Julia," she said, reaching a hand across the table, "I just want to see you soar here."

Patrice lifted a few more lines from the inspirational tripe sold in beachside boutiques. The differences between Patrice and the horrific face of Ashbury Grammar's anti-meth campaign—which began and ended with a one-week unit in health class that included a video depicting a once-promising young woman's rapid surrender to crystal—were privilege and a prescription slip. Julia had better jokes and nearly kidded herself into thinking that, in sharing them, this situation would improve.

I am but a young goat.

It was all fucked.

"Do you want to soar with us, Julia?"

Julia heard his screams from the end of Westlake Ave. Halfway to the Whole Foods, she saw the crowd across the street, along the Varzia building's auxiliary strip. She sped her stride and joined the ranks of voyeurs circled around a middle-aged man lying decumbent, pounding his fist into the pavement—his foot perpendicular.

Surgery.

Orthoscopic.

Orthogonal.

My life is that foot.

One man's cheery alarm bell is another woman's idea of sonic dread: Julia's wakeup call came in the form of the ambulance's colorful caterwaul. She'd spent the past three weeks viewing the world through a dichromatic prism of gray petulance and black sarcasm. Watching the EMT workers lift the wretched man onto the gurney and into the ambulance, she said a secular blessing for her health, and vowed to improve.

That night she cleaned. Busted out the broom, dust-bin, cleaner fluids, paper towels, mop-and-bucket, trash bags. Started with old socks and panties with holes. Dresses handed down from her mother's mother, fit for a Sicilian fishwife. Then trash. Q-tips, used paper towels, tissue paper used to blot makeup, the receipt from Bathtub Gin, Commissary takeout trays, to-go coffees, go-to cock (a good sturdy carrot wrapped in cling). All divvied into garbage bags tagged for consignment, recycling, or trash chute. She scrubbed her bathroom until woozy. She hoovered her carpet—then the common area's. She swept and mopped the kitchen, did the dishes and sparkled the stovetop, organized the—

So now she organized, starting with the silverware drawer. Old show tickets got tacked to the wall in an expanding rectangle. She made the bed, arranged toiletries, cleared her laptop's recycling bin. She emptied her desk drawers' have-you-nots, the giant black marker she'd used for pleasure for like a month while trying to finish her Algebra III homework (she should've taken the W and signed up for something easier over the summer rather than limp across the finish line with her first B- since geometry her senior year). There was no mouse to speak of. Her father's books, scattered and splayed underfoot, were stacked in a corner she'd cleared while vacuuming, books on books, shelves made of shelves, elemental labor working her soft hands.

Near 1:00 AM she was winding down, listening to Oscar Peterson, markering band names and their symbols onto an ancient pair of white Reeboks classics. She couldn't remember who she was before Peter, where he ended and she began. Memories like blunt-rides, her father's dinnertime commentary, and yes, lots of lone hours spent reading books and mazing online and getting lost in reverie on her bed as she fiddled with gimp from summer camp, a tertiary plaything. Loneliness vs. withness. She capped the black marker and stepped into the shower.

She woke up bloated ugly manic. Though such feels fell under subsuming human experiences, they happened to be on schedule as well. A hard scrub using imported soap, a coarse brown lump coagulated by whole grains, whittled the whiteheads gorging on oils in her nasal nooks and crannies. She rubbed the mirror, charging condensation residue as responsible for the frump staring back at her. Inarticulate lurches of excited doom turned her stomach. She modeled outfits in front of a long mirror near her window, tampering with lamps and overhead lights to compensate for the drear diffusing across her window like the excess skin of a ghost. She strutted the runway of her room, striking poses and campy expressions. Nose upturned she proclaimed, "'Zis dtress iz sheet." Between outfits she studied herself, blubbered her lips, lifted a breast, navigated her hips and thighs. In the face of aesthetic proof, her frown had returned, as had her room, to its natural state of chaos.

In the kitchen, unable to open a package of co-op oats, she went for the kitchen knife—and with one overzealous gash spilled steel cut grains in mock-cornucopia across the tile. Layla slipped out as Julia swept and transferred handfuls from floor to bag, the oats filtering through her fingers, repeating, "Seriously? Really, like, are you fucking serious." Not but five minutes later was she coddling her breakfast bowl, milk-bloated grains foaming from her cackle as Johnny Knoxville got a football punted into his nuts for no apparent reason other than her entertainment.

Dionysus was a man.

Crossing the mall en route to class, Julia hoped no one would notice her bad-body day. Then again, she charged such scrutiny as steeped in objectification—but to bury all notions of beauty under mass graves would've been to do away with aesthetics.

"It is only shallow people who do not judge by appearances."

Her father's examples of moral subversion aside—she really needed to cut this kind of pedantic shit. Other things, other things. Walking was a thing, singular. The sun had triumphed, and so her summer swart. She or Dionysus had deigned to a loose black shirt and blue-jeans, but she'd remembered close-toed shoes: her exquisitely defaced reeboks, the *Zeppelin IV* sigil and a trumpet sketched on either tip.

There appeared the triple-doors. Within its metal frameworks were three Comp 37 residents, inhaling cigarettes as though pre-empting the smoke-free campus bill still pending in student congress, their ratty shirts suited for morning's slouch—debating what "dick cheese" might taste like. Remiss to join the conversation, Julia did add to those estivating under the portico and, with two minutes until zero hour, lit one up like a Hollywood movie's insouciant world savior.

"Are we talking grated shaft skin or like, pubic dandruff?"

"As if the dick only provides shavings?"

"As if someone's out there grating their dick?"

"If some dude had like an aneurism right on the cusp of busting it would make a pretty mean profiterole."

"Jizz is nothing like ricotta though."

"My apologies you'd know. And I think it's ri*coh*tta?"

"Dude, you've *seen* jizz. We've all *seen* jizz."

"Okay buddy, relax there about the jizz and the seeing."

"Just saying, jizz looks more like icing than any cheese I've seen."

"My ex in high school? Nicknamed my dick Polonius."

"That's ironic. Nothing less sage than a stiffy. Pretty much the symbol and essence of all savagery."

"Why can't you just give me this one thing?"

"We're on a tangent here, fellas."

"Duck butter," Julia interjected. The boys, all shag and mane, looked over at her. She dragged to the quick. "It's when you don't wash your cooch for like as long as you can then scrape off the buildup."

"That's frankly disgusting."

"Sounds like a misnomer."

"As if you've spread a woman's finely aged lard across your breakfast toast?" Julia said.

"True," the taller one appeased.

Then a fifth voice joined in, "It's more like a bog-vinegar than any sort of curdled milkfat."

Julia turned and saw her step from the sunbath and into the portico's cool shadows. She wore classic corduroys and a pastel yellow shirt, an outfit practically indistinguishable from last week's. She procured a cig from ear. Julia held out her red Bic and glanced back at the boys, who stood transfixed in the presence of that which was unmistakable.

Through bared teeth, her lab partner continued, "I once kept myself submerged in an unwashed swamp for over twenty seconds before coming up for air. Didn't want to hurt her feelings. She was a shanty girl, hella bad time for me. Took me a year to finally kick the junk," she said, dragged, and looked up. "I'm fucking messing with you guys."

The boys fell over themselves with wheedling relief, and Julia hated them all for it.

"No but really, I've gone fishing for some toxic flounder only to catch the runoff, if you know what I'm saying."

"Totally," one of the boys said, disposing his butt and collecting his backpack.

"Anywho," she pushed through the smoke. "Lab awaits. Shall we, *pahtnah*?"

"Hey, I just wanted to say—"

"Don't worry about it," she said, swiping her Student ID. "I'm giving you extra credit for duck butter."

Julia lit up like a power grid after blackout—the bright lights burning off any last illusions as to why she'd obsessed over her ~~~er's knowledge and affiliations. She didn't mind the ten for having forgotten her lab coat, reciprocated by eep-toe heels (again). The lab captain betrayed no eir forgetfulness, merely marked and moved on with us manner and clipboard.

What the fuck? her partner mouthed.

"I'm not sure he's human," Julia said.

"Right? Like, has he encountered a scenario he can't scientifically deconstruct?"

"Okay, what next."

"50 mils of this piss-looking shit with a gram of this bath salt stuff."

"Put on your goggles," Julia said. "This is my first cook."

So it went. They traded witticisms and candid questions. For a few minutes they talked out a film treatment of the lab captain's life story, titled *The Perturbation.* Labmates looked askance as they cackled over increasingly trivial comments. But then, near the end of lab, her partner brought back the past.

"Wanna know why I transferred from UW?"

"I dunno, do I?" Julia said, winking at the scale.

Their eyes met above the network of fulcrum and beams.

"So what's your name anyway?" she asked, since she hadn't used her Myriadal email, and Julia doubted she could deduce anything useful from TaterHots@gmail.com.

Her lab partner laughed and said, "Beck."

"Rebecca? Becky?"

"Neither. Just Beck."

"Why not," Julia ceded. "So why did you transfer?"

Beck took a breath and said, nodding, "To get away from Dave."

Julia measured to full height, an inch or so shy of Beck's, still holding the tongs over the crystals on the scale. She pushed up her loose goggles, which kept slipping down the bridge of her nose. None of their test tubes' colors corresponded with that which they'd reported on their lab sheet, and her mouth added to these facts:

"Peter and I aren't together anymore."

"I know."

The lab captain announced that worksheets should be placed in the grated bin on his desk. Students stuffed lab coats into backpacks and began shuffling out. "Clean up your stations," the captain added, the threat of docked points lurking beneath his reminder.

"You free?" Beck asked, zippering her bag. "Buy you a drink at the Unicorn?"

The sun echoed off buildings and statues in a stately gleam. Beck's hand grazed endearing surfaces as though bestowing a mysterious grace unto mossy lampposts and slicked Tesla hoods. A lone sea hawk commanded the plaza's airspace, into which the *Real Change* guy belted his jingle. Beck guided her like a dirigible along Pike, crooking east, further up the Hill, where the Unicorn's sign hung like a carnival post.

Beck said, "I saw a dude get hit here by one of those duck-boat tour buses."

"Did he die?"

"Not sure. He was pale."

This past summer, Julia had parachuted two points of molly at a Madeon show to less effect than desired, so dropped another roll with a few randos here at the Unicorn. The double-dose had her hips hula-hooping in the rhythm of perfect pleasure. She spent three full hours grinning like a beatific savant, caressing all amenable surfaces. Mainly she gushed, over and over, "Oh my god, I feel so *guuuhhhd*." The next day she'd nursed her tortured neurotransmitters by binging on bowl after bowl of indica bud and bromidic episodes of *Gilmore Girls*.

That late-June night, the Unicorn had been packed with bro-grammers in flat-brimmed hats and girls painted, powdered, and scantily clad in slips and halters. Now, however, at nigh past noon, the bar hosted offbeat rubes looking for a day-buzz and a quick fuck and, failing that, someone to misuse as a vessel for their fucked-up childhoods. Like most Seattle gay bars, the Unicorn was gay-by-day, taking a turn for the heteronormative at night, when the sexual bipartisans headed to Neighbors.

The lower level was dark, crossed with baroque trusses and balustrades, boutique shop witchery and lace woodwork. The beers came fast and flirty. The dayshift bartender, a clinically skinny bottom, sounded the fire alarm and said they should just get it over with right now, right there on the bar, and Julia retorted with

her theory that flamboyantly gay men projected the sexual energy
they'd never been privileged with freely expressing.

"Me-*ow*," he purred in parody.

"Yeah dude," Beck smirked. "A bit harsh."

"Cry me a river. We're all repressed."

"So what brings you bitches to the danger zone at safe-thirty
standard time?"

"Celebrating our first successful experiment as lab partners,"
Beck toasted.

"Woo-hoo," he cheered, uncapping two more bottles on the
bar's paneled edges.

Their fourth Stellas slugged, Beck dragged her onto the dancefloor. "They're fine," she hollered about their backpacks.

Linked by pinkies and taking up the rear, Julia slithered through
the mostly empty seats and tables. Beck pulled her into the pocket
of a Joy Division song, her corduroys describing perfectly meandering hips. Neon lights stained the dark wood floor. Pressing and
knocking their pelvises, desperate for fleshy purchase—within two
minutes of woozy grinding, her body poured open, her lips locked,
her back arched in the shape of conflicting motives. Reverberating
power chords climaxed with a distant crooning, a hand fluttering
under the hem of her shirt, clinching her waistband, guiding her
back in—rubbing her intimate geographies, gerrymandering her
most partisan longings.

"Wait," Julia rent herself away. Bowing, her head on Beck's chest,
a boxer on last legs, hair draped like a beaded curtain around
her face.

She turned and fled, covering her mouth before it all lurched up.

"Mmmmm," she groaned, squatting by the bowl.

Wiping sticky foam from the corners of her lips, she heard
the brain-buzz of being drunk in sudden quiet. The stall's graffiti
mocked her with raunchy ejaculations, sarcastic emotional surrender, and other such first-world punkery when Beck banged
into the bathroom.

"Can I come in?"

"Just leave me alone."

"In the boy's bathroom?"

"Sure. Whatever."

"Guess I should've cut us off at two. You weigh what, ten pounds dipped in molasses?" she chuckled.

"You're not my father."

"Good, I don't want to be."

"Please don't talk to me like I'm going to be your girlfriend," Julia coughed.

"Oh yeah, right," Beck said. "Forgot you Ashbury girls had chastity spikes lodged in your twats."

"Fuck off, will you?"

"What's your deal?" Beck screwed. "Like are you bipolar or something?"

"I don't know. Maybe?"

Julia dreaded this soap opera, exchanging feelings with dramatic pragmatism, precisely because she'd scripted its setup.

"I'm sorry."

Beck's breath broke above the next Joy Division song.

"I think I'm just mad at my mom."

Beset by rapid-onset sobriety, Julia labored from the grimy tile, sat on the toilet seat, and unlatched the stall door, arms stippled by the bathroom's chill. For some reason this action, more than the day's previous decisions, initiated the launch sequence for mutually assured complication. Beck stepped into the frame, all but a silhouette before the mirror's bare fluorescents.

The bathroom door blew open. Beck glared at the kid in question. Her mean profile compelled a meek apology and forthwith evacuation.

"Boys," she shrugged.

A faucet's drip measured some moments.

Julia acknowledged Beck's hand, its limp femininity, and took it. Julia pulled and Beck bent, planting flush effusions and, still drunk, tumbling down among the toilet's metalwork, their laughter turned to soft moans, worming their fingers into the warm spaces.

"Wait," Julia said, apprehending Beck's hand. "I'm bleeding."

As mob lore went, back in the spring of 1977, DeCavante consi-
gliere, Mario Gibralti, hosted a high-stakes game in Trenton. A
couple university donors were in town looking for some action
and, where two patrician patriarchs saw thrill and novelty,
Gibralti saw an easy score—and lo, a couple Lucchese capos
saw an opportunity to pull one on Gibralti while he hustled
the rich lushes.

Gibralti went down seven jars of gravy—boxes of macaroni,
C-note bundle, hundred hundreds—before sniffing out the fix. He
caught the Lucchese patsy overplaying his signal, knock-checking
the green felt with his index flung out a bit too far.

The youngest of Gibralti's crew—the Jumbo Jet, just a lowly
numbers runner—took the initiative. He gathered some muscle
and hit a nearby cathouse, where they found the Lucchese capo in
question, his slacks crumpled at the foot of a servicing courtesan.

"Mr. Gibralti just wants to see his property returned."

"Okay okay. Just calm down. It's not what—"

"Oh it's not?" he seethed, gripping the Shark's neck. "Get the
loot or wear your brains inside-out."

Thus in one night, Johnny the Jumbo Jet Raciti both made his
bones with the DeCavante crime family and played a starring role
in putting flint to the DeCavantes' feud with the Luccheses, for
whom Julia's maternal grandfather, Dino "the Shark" Paolantonio,
was underboss (acting underboss, technically, while Eddy "the Cut"
Cicero was doing five-to-ten on pandering charges).

Julia had learned of the feud after eavesdropping on her father's
commitment speech. Her parents' origins were like the stories
she'd hear at Johnny's dinner table, otherworldly tales involving
people she didn't know, would never meet—until hearing that
Dave Lissener, her de facto cousin, was in fact her cousin by code
of omerta, which meant Dave would never have said anything to
Beck about Peter and the dunes.

"Not unless—"

"He didn't know," Beck finished her thought, "who Peter was working for."

"Except—"

"He brought Peter for you. So he knows something."

"None of it makes sense, and yet there's something..." Julia said and looked over Tutta Bella's promontory, the plaza below busy with hive-bodies. Their table was cluttered with decanters of house red and half-eaten Margherita pizzas. Twilight twisted its violet brush into the welkin's canvas. She passed Beck the cigarette.

"I told Dave to invite Peter to the party. But the dunes? All that stuff?" Julia shook her head. "No way. He wouldn't even talk to me about it."

"Couldn't Dave have found out some other way?" Beck asked then took a drag. "They did both go to the same school for a minute."

"No," Julia shook her head, gazing at crepuscular colors, commingling between buildings. "That's not it. I know it isn't."

"Sounds like you need to have a conversation with your mom."

Despite her untrustworthy lust, Julia trusted Beck. But trust lent little expedience in relating to Beck why conversation, singular, was a gross understatement.

There was a correlation here, between her fear of difficult choice and her avoidance of it. Then she'd start spiraling out, like a dying planet from a weakening stellar mass.

"So," Beck leaned back, wine in hand, the picture of smug. "When do we tell Dave about us?"

Julia couldn't remember the last time she saw someone beautiful in the mirror—someone she *liked*. So she returned, stylus in hand, to the drawing tablet: her one-credit seminar on Azalai's main campus, a few blocks northwest of Myriadal College. Using the corporation's newly-issued proprietary tablet, she summoned G-chat and saw Beck was online.

She asked Beck lofty questions about love and fate and death—casting philosophical krill as bait for a whale of a conversation.

She leaned forth toward Beck's response-in-the-making, denoted by the blinking ellipsis by her name.

Beck: key word being determined. so like do I believe in deter- minism? i think only depressed ppl ask those qs, is wut i think

Julia: Fuck, you're right…Beck…I think I might be depressed…

Beck: lol

Julia: Guess I better study up so I can fix myself.

Beck: or jus call yr mom.

Beck: i mean i get it. but do you rly think yr mom is like plotting against you?

Beck: it goes against basic bio

Beck: being a mom is a ponzi scheme for giving up yr hopes and dreams so anything shes done no matter how much u disagree w has been for u

Julia: Did I order a guru?

Julia: How much is this ashram going to cost me?

Beck: no but payment is always appreciated

Beck: preferably in the form of oral labor

Julia: the NSA is reading this

Beck: rly though its not a far jump from expectation of pain to addiction to it.

Beck: its a whole theatrical production. props, soundtrack, script, the works.

Beck: same conversations. same pictures.

Beck: the same songs with the same strained morrissey tone, finding this fucked up contentment w it all.

Beck: it becomes a ritual. you get cravings for it.

Through nervy-worded wickets they made plans to make a pizza from scratch. Julia sent a smiley-faced signoff and flattened the tablet atop the grainy roundtable. Mr. Martinez's jaunty lecture on Azalai's scheduling software ran like a babbling brook over smooth stones of fantasies of Beck. She shifted in her seat, stifling squirms.

Following class she tasked herself with a hard run around Lake Union (which meant not stopping at Gasworks to "admire the scenery"). She took a primordially boiling shower, bringing to her skin a sanguine burnish. Twenty minutes of wardrobe deliberation (black slip), five minutes of facial appliance (foundation and mascara), and she arrived at Beck's apartment on Broadway bearing two wooden crates of co-op goodies under one arm and a bag of flour and eggs in the other.

"I come to barter my wares," she said into the speaker.

"Your goods might not cut it," replied a graveled tone. "Perhaps you can provide a corvée tax, you know, the manual labor we discussed?"

"Can we continue this inside? I'm a few minutes' holding all this shit from completing some ancient rite of passage."

Eerily near Dave Lissener's apartment, Beck's faced a small square cornering the intersection of Pine and Nagle, which hosted farmer's markets and a mélange of Hill-characters. The grayed bronze Jimi Hendrix statue wailed just below Beck's trestle windows, shuttered by prints of South American landscapes. In fact, Beck had all but reconstructed an Andean dwelling, replete with zoomorphic ceramics and end-tables, ceremonial tumis and wooden war masks on the cream walls. An alpaca rug lay under cotton-stuffed couches of llama wool. The kitchen, with its post-linoleum tile and generic countertops, would've clashed if not for the frayed beige alpaca string hanging in its entrance. Looking over the breakfast nook and across the Peruvian creations, their polygonal designs and odes to Pachamama, Julia was moved to say, "Your apartment is incredible," while unloading a sack of Jamaica peppers.

"Thanks."

"Are you—You're not…"

"You serious? I'm as honkey as they come," Beck pinched up her arm's pallor. "Every time I move into a new place I pick a country I've been to."

"What's that?" Julia pointed to the steppe of books beneath the trestle windows. Atop the books were potted flowers, lurid and verdant and thriving.

"Good eye. The Incas built terraced plots to test their crops within microclimates created by just a few feet of altitude difference. My tribute to their experiments," she presented, "and to the difference between Boroughs and Hughes."

"They're orchids?"

"Except the one on the end," Beck said as if finishing Julia's thought. "That's the moonflower. Incan priests would use it to numb virgin sacrifices when crops were failing and everyone was hungry. They'd dress the girls up in beautiful lace garments, with gold leaf and jewelry, and carry them to the top of the Andes to die of hypothermia in the snow."

"Jesus," Julia ogled. "Should I be worried about a date-rape situation?"

"I was hoping my new insanely affordable outfit would have more consensual properties."

Julia indulged herself a full-body scan—Beck's pleated white skirt and off-the-shoulder shirt, her distant constellation of freckles fading down her neck to the animal drape of her bust—only to be assailed by the sudden hunger of a hypoglycemic. All idiom unique to her courting style shed like old scales. She pulled Beck by the wrist and thrust her against the running sink. A moment of lust-shock eyes preceded frenzied lips and limbs and any lenticular fitting. Beck understood what boys hadn't: that you're nothing but an erotic vessel, privileged to carry her toward pleasure, whose climax makes a male's seem a sputtering mistake; that, unlike the male, for whom sex is a painful slog toward completion, the woman is fulfilled from within.

Beck understood Julia as if pleasuring herself. Her hands bound gold-leaf pages of erotic fantasy, her licked script all fancy loops, teasing before fervently obliging—

"Holy *shitfuckfuckfuckfuckfuck*."

Her eyes ablaze, Julia blinked out hot snaps of the apartment. She might as well have been in Cuzco. Her entire body was flushed crimson. Her left leg quivered of its own accord. Weakened to ectoplasmic slack, she struggled to her elbows, sensing softness, the brown alpaca rug beneath her. Within her swimming vision, movement. Beck in the kitchen. A familiar domestic *rip*.

"Here," she heard.

Julia's arm raised like gelatin, floppy, trembling, as if gravity might lop it off. Beck took her wrist, and Julia the paper towel. For a moment she just looked at it.

"Oh."

Disembodied giggles bubbled from her mouth as she padded the moist spot on the rug between her.

"Let me help you with that," Beck smiled, caressing her back.

Julia giggled again, gaining, uncontrollable now, falling to the sheared fur as though she'd pushed off china white. Beck rested her cheek on Julia's quad.

"Soooooo. *That's* never happened before."

"I gathered as much." Beck's tone juggled the pomp of her experience and the admiration for Julia's dearth of such. "I guess you'll get me back later," Beck clucked, winked, and smiled.

"What were you even doing? Like, what?"

"Aw," Beck frowned. "Thanks."

It wasn't that Julia had, until now, faked it. Not necessarily. It was that she hadn't known. It was a game-changer. It was beyond superlative, a perfect cocktail that took the edge right off, put her on the nod. And the feeling itself—O, the *feeling*. Not only the feeling, but the feeling's multiplicity. Within a span of seconds the feeling discovered new pockets, at first expansive, then collapsing onto a locus of euphoria.

Soon after the glow wore, she'd begin worrying over her ability to reciprocate. Worse, she'd fear losing this lioness lazing along her leg. The complications of adult attachment would puncture her seraphic aura. But for now, she could only feel that if Death's umbrage comprised her every neurosis, she'd met its match in Eros, whose golden light of a thousand pleasures yet consummated burned off the mere notion of concern. Through to the next morning, Julia would find it difficult, walking under another strong September sun, listening to Stevie Ray Vaughan's "Lenny," to imagine much anything wrong in the world.

Born in Salt Lake City, Beck had lived widely. Her hobbies were cigarettes, coffee, beer, cis-boys, and lithe girls. She liked poetry but didn't read it much.

Indicating the steppe of books, Julia said, "So you read fiction then?"

Beck shrugged, "They're more for scaffolding."

She'd kept a journal as a kid. That first lock-and-key diary had since begotten sixteen notebooks of gradually increased girth. Which brought her back to the book-terraces. Within the steppe was an old trunk, a sarcophagus for her Incan tribute, lined with all her journals. She claimed most of the entries were riddled with mawkish tantrums. "If there's nothing truer, it's when I wrote, 'The world is like a cigarette.' I have no idea what it means, but it's how I felt."

She'd moved to Eugene at sixteen, the last stop on her stepdad's military tour. He called her by her given name, Mary-Katherine (Beck was short for Brubeck, her mother's maiden name). He set all the rules, made all the plans, spent all the money. He rigged the relationship against her mother, who'd never have been able to satisfy him. "She only married him to get health insurance before a big surgery, to remove spinal fluid." Once, when furious with him after another announcement to relocate, Beck tore through his things while he was dozing in front of the TV, half-drunk, half-hungover. She knew what she'd been looking for—and she found it. In his Army canvas, under his neatly folded uniform, there were the chaps, a garter, condoms. She left the canvas open, contents revealed. He had to have seen it. But still he stayed, set all the rules, made all the plans. "Guess you can't become a colonel without maintaining discipline," she said, then sat up. "You know, I really don't like talking about this."

Julia watched Beck lock herself in the bathroom, heard her run the water. Despite the explicit transitionary signal, Julia couldn't move, and before she could assume an upright pose, Beck barged out of the bathroom.

"The weird thing was, when I found all his fag gear? I couldn't bring it up to him. I'd known for so long and fantasized about being able to shove it right in his fucking hog face," her laugh rasped, was wizened, something to be revered. Julia made room and she sat crosslegged on the couch, indexes drumming something syncopated against her thigh. "But then I realized how sad he was. That he'd been punishing me for what he viewed as his own defect. So I stopped hating him. Stopped sabotaging whatever situation he'd drag us into. Stopped begging my mom to let him go onto the next place without us."

"Guess it's not just the flamboyant ones then," was all Julia could muster.

Beck's breathy laugh was both humored and annoyed, and Julia regretted her poor taste, a vestige of dealing in Peter's emotional incompetency. Entangled in bed with Beck, Julia felt that good relationships were like emotional telesis, progressing the species one generation of joy at a time. Except she couldn't reciprocate.

Her life was smaller than Beck's, less deserving, less aware of itself and the world. Rather than profess this aloud, her sense of inadequacy manifested in contentious certainties, which she rationalized, beneath the threshold of conscious thought, by assuming Beck would forever begrudge Julia's flippant response to her stepdad's secret proclivity—a convoluted hall of cognitive mirrors.

"So let me get this straight: all of this shit"—Beck's sweeping arm citing the entirety of American comforts by virtue of that which made up her bedroom—"is not only unnecessary, but is also the bounty of the glorified geopolitical piracy which sustains our evil empire?"

"Why not?" Julia shrugged and frowned. "Which part of history makes that hard to believe?"

"Man, your dad must've done a number on you."

"The Reagan administration funded jihads to counter the Soviets in Afghanistan. *Now*, those *same* Wahhabist jihads are being denounced, now that the American-made Frankenstein has inevitably turned on its creators. All the *while*," Julia laughed mean, "we still solicit them for their oil reserves. Hypocrisy!"

"You're telling me you'd be just fine living somewhere like Ruhengeri," Beck challenged, "where no one even knows what a FAFSA looks like, let alone any government subsidy."

"I don't know where that is."

"Exactly."

"How does my ignorance equal unwillingness?"

"As one who had trouble at the bar tonight because she'd forgotten—"

"I *thought* I'd forgotten."

"—who *thought* they'd forgotten to tweeze their other eyebrow, I harbor grave doubts as to your ability to mentally withstand an all-out genocide—much less times of peace, since the buildings are still made of mud and crumble after a couple years," Beck said, her blunt terms delivered with unsettling calm. "Theirs is a culture of brutal survivalists. Meanwhile, we've been enjoying the Renaissance's zeitgeist of critical thought for over 400 years. The gap is wider than the ocean separating there from here. These are the realities. So not knowing a city by name, the title of its very existence, represents the difference between experiencing what it's like there and not. I lived there for a year. My stepdad was dispatched as an embassy guard a few years after the genocide. I rode my bike in the rain so the little boys hanging out under awnings shouted, 'Mzungu! You crazy, mzungu!' Meaning I'm a crazy white girl."

Julia stared at the ceiling.

"You look mad," Beck smiled.

"I'm pretty sure I'd be just as insecure about my eyebrows in Africa."

Cars and their music scudded along Broadway.

"And my dad didn't *do* a *number* on me."

Propping up on her elbows, Beck's hair fell at a painfully becoming angle, pooling upon her pillow in a wealth of blonde gleam. "Julia, it was just a figure of speech."

"I'm just saying, only I get to talk shit about him. And I'm nothing like he is."

Within the ensuing quiet lingered her use of present tense, almost palpable, a smell of decay, a thing kept past due. Her head hurt. She caught her reflection in the window, supine, swaddled in Beck's big green comforter. Far from sobbing, her sudden shudder felt as if she were exorcising an antigen—a thing that needed to come out. She wanted to burrow deeper into the bed, but Beck held fast, wrapping her in warm flesh.

"I trusted him," she chattered. "And now I don't know who to trust."

"I know, I know," Beck whispered, rubbing circles into her trembling back. "But you can trust me," she said and held Julia at length, looking all over her face, a saccade so different from Peter's. "I promise."

But so had her father.

As a future professional, Julia asked why she avoided internal confrontation. She entered the "contemplation stage" of opening up to her mother, of doing therapy, alternating commitments in avoidance of internal confrontation. Conversations that devolved into vapidity were another failure. She turned obsessions into compulsive tics, sucking spit through the small gap between her front two teeth until the connecting sliver of gum got flappy. Beck caught her doing it once, said she looked like a fish swallowing seaweed.

"Ugh," Julia grumbled. "I can't stop."

"Can you hold my bag? I gotta pee."

Cradling Beck's purse, Julia stood in the hallway leading to the water fountains and restrooms. Owing to her mom's approaching birthday and love of overpriced electronics, Beck had scheduled today's visit to Seattle's quite literal silo of consumerism: the downtown mall.

Drafty noises simmered beneath her thoughts. Lately, she'd tried the Fuckit technique—mentally repeating "Fuck it" until the thoughts stopped or slowed. A poor palliative, it felt like Shaz telling her to just chill as she'd uncorked that fifth of cask-aged bourbon swiped from her dad's liquor cabinet, swigging as she captained the hooptie. By the time they found the Bose store, she'd started sucking again.

"Mom'd cream her jeans over that," said Beck.

"Over what?"

Beck pointed to the woodgrain speakers in the display window.

"It makes no sense why she needs to enhance the quality of pseudo-country, but as they say about the heart and its desires."

Leaving her to admire the display, Julia entered the electronic emporium and located the first clerk she could find.

"How much are those floorstanding speakers in the window?"

The young man, an ill-looking lank in thick glasses, delivered the number without irony. Julia glanced at Beck, who was perusing noise-canceling headphones near the cash register, shaking her head without irony.

"Here," she said, offering her card.

Hands behind his back, the stolid clerk looked down the unseemly fuzz of his upper lip.

"That's my card," Julia said. "I want to use it to buy those speakers."

"Um, well, do you want to purchase a warranty option? There's the three-year for—"

"Just give me the best warranty," she hastened, checking on Beck, whose corduroys flapped between a set of shelves carrying cables and adapters.

"Credit?"

Julia shook her head. "Debit."

Otherwise unable to glean anything amiss, the clerk took the card over to the register and explained the situation to the cashier. They looked at her, she waved, and the clerk waved her over.

Beck met her at the register. "Whatcha getting?"

She saw in her lover's hands electronic knickknacks and kitsch— an outmoded standard for bass-enhanced earbuds; an HDMI adapter for a Mac—the stuff of poor folk attempting to shop above their station. Beck's apartment spoke to her ingenuity. Julia considered saying the word aloud. Instead, she continued round the long route.

"What's your mom's address?"

"Why?" Beck's brows furrowed in perfect confusion.

"Because we're sending her her present."

Returning from the back, the cashier said, "Okay, so that's going to come out to $3,489.56 with the ten-year warranty."

"What the fuck?"

The cashier looked up, flummoxed.

"Surprise," Julia smiled, eyes flittering between parties.

"So where're we sending this today," said the cashier.

"Julia, you can't do this."

"Sure I can," she shrugged.

"Would you like more time?"

"Yes." "No."

The cashier slid to the other register and took another customer.

"We'll say it's from you," Julia said.

"Holy shit, Julia. Do you have any idea how this makes me feel?"

Julia's silence was fatal.

True, the impetus sprung from personal need. But she could've done worse than buying a big birthday present. Justification flashed through Julia, and in this moment of madness, she said the wrong thing: "Beck, you look mad."

Beck gaped at her. Rather than retract her petty vengeance, Julia doubled down and crossed her arms. Blustering out of the Bose store, wretched sirens commanded that Beck replace the earphones and HDMI cable. Julia stood there and watched, alone, on the third level of this silo of consumerism, as the love of her young life smashed the products back into place and, once more, stomped out of the store.

Julia spent the walk to campus spiraling away from the only truths that mattered. Shivering against the first day of fall-like weather, gunmetal clouds racing windward, she confabulated a conversation in which she demanded forgiveness despite her lack of fault in the first place. Almost back at Comp 56, she sketched another wide loop around the issue, drafting a text that begged for help and understanding, but avoided the consequences of her actions altogether. Back in her dorm, aware that her untenable need for guarantees had simply been superimposed onto that of Beck's good graces, Julia texted her.

I'm sorry.

Not everything is about you.

At least she'd responded. At least she'd gravitated back to resolution within the twenty-minute return walk.

She fell asleep knees-to-neck, hugged into a baby ball.

Her iPhone read 12:31. No messages. She mashed her face, stretched, padded to the window, parted the pale blue curtains. A campus in transition, compartments like whales exhaling guppies. Seasonably gray again, the window of daylight halfway shuttered.

Fuck it. Fuck it all. Fuck today's only class, which she'd already overslept, and fuck its take-home essay on 2x2 factorial experimental design that she could just turn in on Whiteboard, Myriadal's inhouse assignment database.

She rocked back and pulled up Bay Heights sweatpants, sifted the rubble for a bra, rerouted and turtled into an Ashbury Grammar hoodie. She struck along the left slash of the mall's stretched-X sidewalk whose nexus, a traffic circle encased in park benches and kept hedges, was a fount for student uprisings. Today, a yenta of Jewish yuppies had set up a bake sale. Beside each macaroon, a set of white lace shawls. For each loaf of challah, a Zionist pamphlet. Every tupperware sloshed with matzoh ball soup paired with a poster of Torah quotes whose Talmudic glyphs were to be read in reverse as though the words were switched up by Mid-Eastern magnets. Along with such victual packages they sold, a la mode, yarmulkes and dreidels and other Yiddish trinkets. Underneath their shawls they wore H&M, yapping about boy bands they'd followed as children. Jesuit students raising capital for Judaism— totally gaming the system.

The dining hall's din pressed on the Commissary's clamor, the war of noise testing her brittle spirit. White-checked tile glared under harsh lights and serving-area heating lamps. Hungry students swarmed like wasps under the direction of a monarchal intelligence—Myriadal College. It was all a racket. Waiting in line for a slop of butternut squash soup, Julia realized she'd forgotten a citation for the take-home paper.

Some girl at the front was paralyzed by the choice between salt and pepper. Yahweh forbid she take both. They'd all be dead by the time she chose, the squash turned to rot, the earth burnt over. And why not. The bimbo was enjoying the attention, posturing in her skin-tight volleyball jersey and form-fitting faded-blue mom-jeans. Since when had mom-jeans come into vogue? About when barefoot running shoes had? This was your basic bitch, your common come-dumpster, your—her phone buzzed!

Julia's eyes soured at sight of Shaz's text. Shuffling left (finally), her tinny tray rattling along the service conveyor, she reread the disembodied apology:

I'm so sorry.

A strange sense of knowing—like watching a truck on train tracks, aware that road-rail vehicles existed, but never expecting to see one rusting along all lonely.

She hurried through checkout lines, where middle-aged Latina women dressed like porters rung up kids who then slunk into the dining hall, and hastened toward the set of TVs hung from the ceiling near the condiments hut. With the bandstand empty, not one wire snaking from the house amps, snippets of pundit-babble bubbled over the dining hall's din. MSNBC's anchors cut to shots from a doorless chopper presiding over a local island's shore. Figures in bright orange ponchos, shrouded in mist, lugged a canvas gurney across the pebbled beach. Underneath MSNBC's chyron, which read "Bainbridge Island," rolled a breaking news ticker: DECAVANTE UNDERBOSS FOUND SHOT ASHORE BAINBRIDGE OUTSIDE SEATTLE…Then there it was. Among those he'd been survived by: Julia Paolantonio. Granddaughter. Sophomore at Myriadal College. How had they gotten ahold of her senior photo?

Leaving her tray at the condiments hut, Julia approached the TV, walking blind to all below the belt, her head fallen back, chestnut ribbons unfurled, accepting this grave rapture.

The next day, Julia met her at Westlake's Link Light Rail stop.

She watched her stumble off the train, an avalanche of luggage and fluster. She watched her scan the bustle, flushed and huffed from the effort. Watched her eyes find hers.

"Ohhh boy. You said the train was easy."

The station's tunneled echoes washed over their filial embrace.

"I like your coat," Julia said, pulling away.

She wore a checked wool coat with fancy strings fastened to long buttons like pinwheel spokes. Her hair up in a cone, teasing at coif before falling into an intricate tail, swung heavy, a tribal regality.

"I like that hoodie—that I bought you in the seventh grade."

"Coffee?" Julia grinned, a parody of bared teeth.

"Read my mind," she said, tapping her vein.

They grabbed Americanos from a stall on the corner of Westlake Station, where red-vested canvassers crowded around their leader for a pre-work pep-rally. Her mother's cab dance, a desperate flail, a miraculous coffee balance, somehow summoned one unto their stretch of road. Bags toppled into the trunk and backseat, wherever they might lodge, her mother directed the cabbie toward the Olive 8 and, soon enough, the big blue building dollied into sight. They unloaded her bags onto a lanky bellhop who escorted them into an opulent 44th-floor penthouse—Sound-facing panorama, mint on pillow on king-size bed, welcome basket stuffed with delectable goodies and sumptuous accessories. A blue-and-cream theme running through carpet, linens, and bathrobe. Her mother was at the window when Julia clicked the door home on the tipped bellhop. The skyline's chrome glow cast her in silhouette. Julia set her coffee on a nightstand of petrified wood, admiring for an unconscious moment its slate-gray finish.

"Remember the time when you told me the whole world was full of shit?"

"That wasn't great mothering."

"It was a fight," Julia said, turning from the nightstand to her mother. "That happens between mothers and daughters."

"A while after your father...passed, his father called."

The way she cracked her knuckles when concentrating.

Those blue-moon mornings, when she'd announce that Julia didn't look too well, and perhaps she better stay home from school and eat tomato basil soup and grilled cheese and watch Fellini films with her as heavy rain sounded off its searing thrum. Or those rainy nights when her mother made the Paolantonio special: an *aperitivo* of cheese and tomatoes, a main dish of eggs in purgatory.

They'd watch yolks dropped in vodka cream sauce develop their vulcanized whites. She'd let Julia sip Chianti while edifying her in the virtues of a dry house red and the restaurants she'd gone to growing up, where the owners greeted her family personally and asked if they had a quorum to sit.

Julia sobbed into her mother's perfect coat. It was surrender, this weeping, surrender to the fiction of fault. Time revealed the truth as simply happening. What did that leave for hope? For correction? For purpose and imperatives? These questions, though perhaps more direct, couldn't be addressed immediately. Only always.

"What is this?" Julia said, mocking the moment, wiping tears. "I don't know if I can have this conversation right now."

Lucia pressed her lips and nodded, stroking her back. "Let's say we get our shit together and go get more coffee."

Victrola's pale-wood tables were packed save one, so Lucia queued and Julia snagged. She sat like a child waiting to be scolded. The impossible hounded her. *Like trying to walk two hounds carryin a stack of books—impossible.* Peter's half-mockery of his father held more wisdom than her mental high-beam routine.

A cappuccino apiece. Shorn light coming through the glass façade. Samba music, backed by conversations of varying volume yet uniformly buttoned-up. With one sip Julia ruined an art form. As the mug hit table, she said:

"Shaz was the first one to text me."

"Hm." Her mother's peer betrayed another thought, or question. Something like, "Tell me about Peter."

And Julia would inhale, look away, say, "…Tormented."

"Not since your first word have you used only one to describe something."

"He was already losing his hair when I met him. He reeked of booze and cigarettes and general decay of like, the human spirit. But he was sordidly handsome and funny and *complicated.*

Complicated being a euphemism for fucked up. My feelings for him then versus the prospect of self-actualizing with him—the friction forced me to convince myself that the temporary is a greater truth than the permanent. But deep down I knew that was just a bullshit excuse to fence off the pain coming at us."

Of course, none of this could be said. Not like that. Instead, the questions and curiosities lingered in Lucia's eyes, and she said, "So psychology, huh?"

"You said it yourself," Julia sipped and smacked her lips. "I'm more like Dad. Sometimes I wonder what he was thinking."

Her mother nodded as if at another thing, the things she was thinking. "I wonder if they serve Turkish coffee here," she said, and started undoing the strings around her checked coat's buttons. She frowned at a piebald Scottish Terrier cantering by the glass façade. She looked around the coffee shop and resigned to the roasting machinery, enclosed by wide windows for viewing, where a vintner had set up a table for tastings.

"Mom."

"What?"

"Why can't you talk about Dad?"

"It's done," she shrugged, still looking off. "You either accept it or you don't."

"I don't see it that way."

"You want me to start a charity in his name?"

She excused herself, and Julia watched her try the bathroom, come back and ask for the key, tapping her foot before the barista handed her the distorted coat hanger.

The barista spurred the grinder. Laughter battered the roasting room's windows, tasters *clinking* stemless wine glasses. Julia's hands began to work at what hadn't been put together, knowing her mother was long for the bathroom, always had been.

Thinking was dumb, an illusion, a dream for the dreamers. Socialism and fascism were adjacent points on opposite ends of the ideological circle. No ethics would synthesize a worthy supplement for that which sated human desire. It was all an addiction, this thinking. It was hanging out on the corner in chills mumbling an insane arithmetic she'd never parse, the crank postulates of a former laureate driven mad by limitlessness and crystal meth. It was mainlining higher questions, hooked on hypotheses, suffering withdrawals from hard cut theorems that were never pure enough. It was taking another hit as the world carried on at human level, her hovering above it, high on uselessness and solipsism.

But the bank account, its starkly economic facts and figures— it was the alluvial earth of human contact, its most tender and tactile means.

Julia had gone to Beck's the night before. Sixer of Stella in hand, she explained through the buzzer's gravelly speaker that her mother was flying up the next day and, if nothing else, she needed her as a friend. Sure, she'd used her situation to curry forgiveness. But it was true, wasn't it? That people didn't change, just their circumstances. Tangled in the sheets, Beck admitted in low tones that she understood why Julia was remiss to open this discussion with her mother. If she was prepared to drop three grand on a woman she'd never met, sums alone couldn't describe the qualitative problem at hand.

As her mother sat, Julia slid her phone across the pale table. "Twenty-four thousand five hundred and forty-dix dollars and twenty-two cents," she stated. Her mother bit at her gums, which— of all moments to make such a connection—reminded Julia of her recent sucking compulsion. "I need to know how this happened."

"What do you propose we should've done?"

"We struggle?" Julia shrugged. "I take school loans and get a job. You keep hosting until finding a better one. Maybe go back to school and finish that business degree."

Lucia chopped a harsh chuckle. "You haven't struggled a day in your life. And given the opportunity, you didn't seem to take to it."

Bilious refutation scorched her throat. Julia had struggled. She had fucking struggled. For example, she was currently struggling over whether to communicate examples of her struggle, whether to demand recognition for said struggle, despite the truth of her mother's charge.

She'd never struggled like that. And she had indeed denied the chance. Just like her parents had stayed on the take, only one degree removed from her great granddad's Union money. The whole thing was quite Catholic: no one was absolved until they died. Julia felt eyes flickering from neighboring tables, spies for the great orchestrators on high, awaiting her response.

"Fuck this."

She scuffed her chair back and strode out, ignoring the eyes. Outside, she sucked in some taffy breeze, carrying scents of the Sound's saltwater across the Market.

"You want to know why I sent you up to Johnny's?" Holding the door for a couple that ducked past their private conversation, her mother realized her own question as rhetorical and stepped closer. Her high pine perfume mingled with the savory-sweet breeze. "You're right, Julia. You deserve to know, and I haven't given you that."

Julia did entrechats, motion for thought. "Being there, doing his bidding—"

"That was never my intention," her mother said strictly.

"It's just…I saw things. And it was *fucked*, *up*, you know?"

Lucia grasped her shoulders as if making room for Jesus. "Come back inside. We'll talk, and have something sweet to sip on."

Jonathan Raciti Jr. ran away upstate in his early twenties. Up there in northern backcountry, meth was cheap and easy. He fenced what he stole and squatted where he could. A wash of tweak and psychosis, memories better left for those waking dead spirits that floated like the shadows of ghosts in his unslept periphery, whispering and hissing at the grip around his kitchen knife. He did this for a couple years, maybe three, until one night a task force cleaned house—his house—and picked him up. He always said he wouldn't have made it another winter. The state's cleanup squad could've hit another trap and he might've died there. Instead, he charmed the judge and stuck with AA.

Lucia met him on his 24th birthday. He was waiting tables at a college joint near Cornell's campus, saving for night classes at the community college. They left west without warning the families, which chased them in the form of letters containing sentimental seductions and, eventually, barely-veiled threats. Many years later—long after Julia, now a junior at Bay Heights High, had learned about her father's past—a car slowed alongside Lucia as she was walking to the bank. It looked like a rental, a nondescript sedan. A man wearing a flat-cap rolled down the window.

"You Lucia Paolantonio?"

Summoning her inner thespian, Lucia cocked her head, furrowed her brow, squinted, and with her most irritated inflection said, "No?" She couldn't tell if the man believed her before rolling up his window and driving off. Regardless, to appease those who followed, Lucia went to the bank before going home to call Jonathan, who said he'd cancel his last lecture.

Lucia had left the family with an eye over her shoulder. Information came along whatever slackened landlines ran from her house to that of Ginny and Herschel Lissener's. Growing up, the Lisseners had been like older siblings. They took her to movies and toy stores and arcades, spoiling her like the child they'd yet to conceive. The Luccheses were never going to open the books for a Jew, so, following Herschel's retirement, they'd quietly moved out to the Bay Area. Julia and their son Dave grew up as family friends—that most obligatory of relational statuses.

Naturally, following Lucia's incident en route to the bank, the Lisseners were the only ones she and her husband could call. She told Ginny the story, trying her best to interpret the subtler nuances of the man's arrival, his manner, his inquiry.

Ginny bickered with Herschel before her voice crackled unclear over speakerphone: "There's a contract out."

Wary that Julia might come home any minute, Jonathan picked up the phone, covered the receiver, and began relaying Ginny's words to Lucia.

"Herschel's gotten wind that…" Jonathan said, relating Ginny's words to Lucia. "…Johnny—my father's kick-ups are thinning…

Come again?" he said to Ginny. "…Millions—Johnny's making millions from an FCC rip-off…Something to do with Deaf relay services. It's all funded by some Russian expat…Stephan who? Klimnick? Stephan Klimnick…They agreed—who agreed? He and the Lucchese bosses agreed that…they would…hit Johnny…" Jonathan's voice trailed off. A listless gloss lacquered his eyes, like an intelligent fish caught out of water. "Ginny? Listen, Ginny? I gotta go," he said vacantly, and put down the phone.

Silence expanded in wake of the call. Lucia embraced this husk of her husband. "I'm sure those guys at the bank were just doing their due diligence."

But her leaden hug went unrequited, as did her words of consolation, meant to diminish the significance of the conversation: that her father had put out a hit on Jonathan's. Releasing him, she heard Jonathan say that he was going to tell him. He was going to tell his father, with whom he hadn't spoken in almost 20 years, that her father had put a hit out on him.

Lucia couldn't understand. They kept in contact with Ginny and Herschel expressly to *avoid* their families' designs. Moreover, what did Jonathan owe a father whose litany of sins was too long to fathom? Her questions surged against the bulwark of his latest conviction. He muttered abstract justifications, orders of ethical operations that ruled an alternate reality in which his wife and daughter were somehow unaffected by his decisions. She'd never known such exasperation. She threatened to leave—a threat that dug trenches, armed their convictions, marking this no-man's land neither of them could cross without certain death of their principles.

A few nights later, Jonathan assured her they would figure this out. He reached for her hand, slipped his chilly fingers through hers—but she recoiled, rolling to face their curtained bay window. That her husband could even entertain the idea of injecting them back into precisely that which they'd fled—such fury blinded her to what would come next.

They say you pick up right where you left off. After almost twenty years, a marriage, and a child, he told him: he told his father about the hit out on him. The next day he went back out there—sleeping in the streets, stealing, scheming. A few months later—right on schedule—Johnny called.

"Lucia," he said, his words smothered in slime. "You heard from Jon?"

Lucia said nothing, playing his impatience—playing what little patience she had left.

"I know you've got a couple little birdies with intel. That Jew and his wife."

"You sent that fucking guy?" she spat.

"Sweetie," Johnny cloyed, "there's no use in getting your panties in a bunch. I'm here to help. You know how they say trade benefits all. I'm thinking, you and me, we work out a deal."

Leading her through the precinct's crush, Detective Shanna Alvarez admitted to Julia that, were it possible to have been debriefed on the true nature of homicide work prior to the academy, she might never have enrolled in the first place. It was brutal work. It may have begun with a gruesome crime scene, but it only got worse from there.

Collecting clues didn't only assign things to bodies. It told stories of attachment. It held forth proof of their will to live. It then left these attachments and proofs to widow in a cold evidence room, a psych ward for the sentimentally inanimate.

Then there were those by whom victims had been survived. Interviewing the killed's kith and kin was inherently heartless work. Worse than overlooking, it solicited their fragility. It badgered the bereaved in the hopes of uncovering a network of nefarious narratives, leads pointed at motives, motives enacted on passions, spiraling in toward a bloodlust that could be understood with utter finality. And that was the worst part.

A clinical analysis of the night in question shoved Detective Alvarez into the killer's boots. For large blocks of time she assumed their righteous justifications, their tragic logic, and their final act of apoplexy or cold decision. She did this until identifying the killer, until she could empathize with him, understanding him perhaps more than he understood himself—and then went out and ended his life too.

Julia left the precinct trailing a shadow biding its time. High noon's judgment would phase her into its reckoning.

But for now it was cloudy. Stepping out into a leeward mist, the Sound's winter sweat, Julia punched through the belly-pouch of her brown Ashbury hoodie, gulped the cool wet air, and struck for Beck's apartment on Broadway.

Was this proof of dimension, this unhad memory of Brad? Was she not horrified of death qua death, regardless of not having witnessed its work lying on a mortuary's metal gurney? These were reminders of the world she lived in. One in which she could be all alone as her lover caressed her shoulder. To blame the booze would've been to both confirm and contradict the grievances she held against her father. Perhaps this was the pataphysical lesson to be learned from it all—a place where imagination could serve rather than enslave.

This is a compartment party, and this is how they arrive. In timid twos and thrumming threes. Dapper duos and bonhomie bunches. All trying to spell their trepidatious tell via the kitchen's tureen of goopy red shit. This is what they bump on the left coast: Harlem's finest, spaghetti western chords over scratched syncopation: *My gold teeth my French Braids / Gettin those since tenth grade / Wealth is in the mind not the pocket / 'That's the case then I been paid...* Then arrive those not here to stay but there so you've heard, *I'm what you made god / Not many I trust / I'ma go my own way god / Take my fate to wherever you want...* Last are those who remain, the committed, those deranged, trading wealth for future pain, just to feel, for some moments, sane, *I...need...smoke...ooh-oh-whoa-whoa.*

And this is what they say...

"...Nah man that kid's a grundle-muncher..."

"...gonna keep Bogartin, man? I'm tryna smoke on me..."

"...Um, ew. I wouldn't eat there if I was starving to death. No let's go to Lucky..."

"...Fuck IPAs. If I want to drink piss I can just find the nearest ladies room thank you..."

"...kinda funny how part of a world war was in a place called the Pacific..."

"...Can you stop spitting on me when you talk?..."

"...Get me my drunk bib, I am getting *fucked* up..."

"...*Grundle* muncher?..."

"...Ah tell you what though. That there girl's just about a million on the Scoville scale..."

"...really the hangover that shows you what's important in life." "Which is?" "Drinking..."

"...see this here? This wet ring marks where my drink used to be. Who. The fuck. Took. My drink..."

"...just saying, you're throwing the best years of your life away, for the *only* girl you've had sex with? Have you ever said that out loud to yourself..."

"...Dude. Lookit. No dude look'me. Look-look-look...The *fuck* you looking at?..."

"...Dude's *on* one right now. Fourth generation *slosh*bot..."

"...Grab me a Ran-yay?" "Pinkies up, *batch*..."

"...nuh-nuh-no I pulled out and she like *geysered*..."

"...have to say: looking forward to that Michigan State game."

"Yeee," Benison says, slackjaw, accepting daps.

The kid grins off, leaving Benison at a glass coffee table. Strobe-lights rotate a dancefloor flooded with partygoers like a reveling catchment. Behind Benison, Rapiers of all race and year rampage through booze and bibulous conversation. Joints float along neon auras like insectoid space craft, blue and yellow pills of purple effect, white tabs of low pH, funky caps and their less potent stems, spansules of molly and whatever it was cut with—such psychotropics jump bodies like greedy parasites, entering and running their course before the night will its end.

But for Benison, Peter has promised something far better—far more *necessary* than anything these kids are popping. The strange security kid smuggled into this raucous rave's back nook a leather satchel from which he now removes a small dark mass. This virid ground plant releases a dark aroma, ominous and rich.

"Whoa," Benison admires his hand, reflecting in the lurid lava and strobe light.

"You feel it?" Peter tugs at the cuffs of his black security shirt, which flare from the arms of his bumblebee bike jacket like a black rose.

"I feel...something," he says, body lolling around as though deprived of a skeleton.

"Good."

"Rockin the home team blacks?" Benison dips his head toward Peter's shirt and salutes. "I heard they fired you."

"I quit. Make sure you finish the rest of that."

Benison's gaze drops, besotted. Peter taps tobacco out across rolling paper. He spools it deftly and scratches at his stubble, looking loused in the wild light. After lighting the cig, he pinches up a sphagnum of the ground plant. Benison watches it squirm, brightening and dying to darkness. "Just one spoonful, and"—Peter's fist flowers—"*quyllur*, as the ancients called it"—tapping his head—"a star is born."

"I *knew* you pushed," Benison urges, raising his Solo, waves of liquor lapping over its rim.

His pupils are popped to psychotic diameters. Bass ripples beneath his feet. Body-shaped shadows sway to its rhythms. With a gulp of jungle juice he forces down the rest of the virid flora stippled by whiter chunks of rank fungi. "Whoa," he stops laughing and erects himself. Again he examines his hand. "Everything is like, green, and purple, and other colors too!"

"The process is starting."

"Not sure if I feel so good."

A large shadow looms behind, draped in a retro nylon jersey with stitched block lettering and navy jeans. A single diamond refracts bluely from his earlobe, descending close to Benison's ear.

"Boo!"

"AHHHHHHOOHH*fuck* dude you scared the *shit* out of me."

"Ahhhhhh," Jonesy dabs and dances.

Benison appears the dissociated patient, clutching his head and rocking.

"The fuck?" Jonesy says, grimacing at his roommate's weird brand of humor. "Pete, right?"

"How's that?" Peter bends an ear.

"Security dude?"

Peter gestures that he can't understand him for the noise. Jonesy flicks Benison's lolling head, sets his crutches against the coffee table, and joins them, pulling up an idle stool.

"We were having a conversation."

"Uh?"

"Benison and I were speaking privately."

Jonesy directs his confusion toward Benison, who continues swaying. He kneads his roommate's shoulder, shakes him. "Ey, man. You okay?"

"Your words are ruining it," Peter sips from a silver flask.

"Yo my boy is fucked up." Jonesy lifts Benison's chin, revealing a sallow excuse for a face, cross-faded with a z-coordinate.

"It's beginning to work."

"The fuck you give him?" Jonesy barks over his shoulder as he struggles to support Benison's failing architecture.

"Grace," Peter replies, his gaze fused to Benison's.

Jonesy glances at the satchel, center table, which spills mounds of dark green plant pocked with fat off-white chunks.

Partygoers erupt on the dance floor, cheering a new club cut, heavy bass and reverb vocals. Cultish intoxicants chant to the banger's hook, their arms waving overhead. Jonesy, hobbled by a sprained right ankle, steadies Benison against the swelling tide, crushing into all corners of the compartment's common room. He rises, begins lifting Benison from his seat, but is yanked back, his fall a fast-flickering series of frames cast sharp blue. He's strewn along the floor, caught beneath the riptide. It's beyond loud. Peter's heel traps his chest. He surveys the immediate area as Jonesy struggles underfoot. Satisfied that the flies are facing the light, he unsheaths and shoves his taser into Jonesy's hip. It *clicks* like a feral cricket, unnoticed amid the expanding revel. He crouches and covers him, vibrating Jonesy with enough voltage to render him unconscious. "That's what it feels like," he says as Jonesy judders and seizes. "Now you know."

Panted, he erects. Wipes sweat from his brow. Dehydration glosses him in timeless wax. The roar is confusing. A girl nearly trips over Jonesy and asks if he's okay. Peter can't hear her. "What happened to him?" she asks, then genuflects to Jonesy. Peter steps back once. Benison's seat is empty, the bathroom's doorframe gilded. The taser slips from his cold wet fingers.

"Hey Cathy? Jonesy is like, passed out."

"Basssse…liiine," Coach drew out, his echoes swallowed by the Balloon's cooling vents, ever overhead. The squad jogged to the other end of the court, Delmar huffing up last. Coach's bounce pass hit his ass flush before he could turn around. Low-eyed and breath-deprived, Del collected the ball and dribbled high toward the foul line.

The tennis team was away at Stanford, the Balloon absent their grunts and *pocks*. As Del took to his free throw routine—three shimmying dribbles and a backspin toss into a low springing crouch—Coach established a narrative:

"Seven twenty-three left in the first half. Down five. AJ's playing like dog-shit cause his girl dumped him last night—his main squeeze. Said he wasn't man enough after dark. He's torn up over it even though he knows in the long run, they weren't spiritually in sync. A fan right behind the backboard just spilled nacho cheese all over his shirt."

Del's lips rippled—but he was staunch in his crouch. He bounced, released, followed through.

Ck.

Just net.

Next to shoot, Benison stepped off baseline and collected the ball. He tended to jog when on court, exhausting the value and meaning of hustle. Today, he ambled out to the foul line, ball clamped against his hip. Cool air thrumming above, he set in his stance, pigeon-toes angled slightly left. Five hard dribbles and a breath.

"Oh-thirty-seven left in the first half. Tied…" Benison paused, baiting Coach, not wanting to get babied. "…Some bluestocking in the back row's leaning over her first edition of *Catcher in the Rye*. She lowers the classic, adjusts her glasses for a better view…"

Lately, Benison's pre-shot breath, rather than rolling him loose and smooth, ready to shoot, had made him seize up, as if serving only to remind him that he was embarking on something with stakes. Not today. He wasn't high or even hazed anymore, but in that state of came-down calm. Coming off his routine's fifth dribble, his arms cocked set, exhalation triggered his release, and he shot. The shot was short. He felt it. He leaned in a little, reaching for front rim, dead center, a larkish bounce off the backboard, hitting center square, back around the rim, and rattling home.

Ten free throws and two suicides later, Coach dismissed practice and called Benison to a side basket, where awaited Jonesy and his two new friends: first aid's tallest crutches.

"Fellas," Coach said, arms crossed over his Rapiers polo. "I'm not gonna yell at you. Kids are going to kid, it's New Years, you've got your cone hats on, I get it. But y'all should know better than to put yourselves in precarious situations like that, okay?"

"Yes sir."

"So we've got the detective coming to meet y'all at your residence at around ten tomorrow. AM," he said, looking between them. "Just tell her everything you know and we shouldn't have a problem."

"Yes sir."

Since childhood, Benison had been saving the best for last. As a college-bound lad enjoying his last home-cooked meals, he'd slung imaginary cordons around his mom-made manicotti. First, he worked his romaine-and-tomato salad drizzled with balsamic and EVOO. Then he bit into the garlic bruschetta topped with sleek slices of savory carpaccio (Angelica's doings). By the time he got to the manicotti, he was full. He'd trowel up the creamy wash of raisin and hazelnut, his stomach struggling to complete this order of gastronomic operations.

But he'd made a new year's resolution. Regardless of basketball's physical demands, each morning he'd get up and do a warmup run. Just a meandering jog, meant to clear the muscles, move the blood, kick instinct into gear. His body was designed to work in kinetic concert, at peace only when in motion.

He pulled on blue shorts, high socks, and running sneakers. He turtled into a thermal cotton shirt and zipped on his Rapiers raincoat. He jogged in place by the wide panoramic windows, watched stratus play with sunlight, catching and smothering it like a cat's paws. Jonesy's alarm rung through his door. Shortly after, he toed from his room.

Two minutes later he was jogging past Abrogate. Through its gothic iron slats were concentric beds of lilies, alternating like a blue and white target. Fresh mist sparkled the sidewalks, speckled the asphalt. The wind licked his uncovered skin. He picked up the pace as he crossed toward the lake.

His easy strides allowed him to gaze at the houseboats hooked to short piers, the purple clouds saturating early sunlight. At Gasworks, he crossed the fairway grass and slalomed the steep slopes, which morning bikers and joggers had crested to snap photos of the morning skyline. Yawing back toward the pathway, a quagmire of sodden grass and muddy slop lay before him. He turned and jogged backwards, watching his squelching footfalls print the asphalt until he passed Gasworks.

He returned spooled in sweat, slowing to an ungainly lumber as he crossed onto Terry. His fingers were a caliper on his torso, more assuring than measuring his mesomorphic cut—he was his father's son. He met a passerby's gaze and pressed his stomach, grimacing at a feigned cramp.

A police car had parked outside Aspira's entrance. Just behind it, an unmarked car. Through Aspira's aqua façade he saw the swimming figures, two uniformed cops, speaking with the spikey-haired concierge. Benison swiped his fob and pushed inside.

"...and he worked here for how long?"

The concierge searched the lobby for answers. Then his sanded voice replied, "I dunno, like, maybe a year or two?"

"And then he just stopped showing up?"

The cops' presence reminded him of yesterday's hangover: his stomach stuffed with insoluble fibers he didn't remember ingesting. Jonesy had nursed him with Cokes—as many as he could manage—to help break down the indigestible material. By last night, Benison had recovered enough to oblige a follow-up call from the King County Precinct.

"Benison," he heard his name now. A robust woman in a gray blouse, her black hair back in a big bun, rose from the couch. "Detective Alvarez," she flicked her badge.

Benison shook her hand over the arm of a peach armchair. "Jonesy should be down soon."

"...I'll leave you with this," Coach said. He pointed at the riotous crowd above KeyArena's home lockers, revealing the dark spot under his arm. "The Spartans are eight-and-two. We're ten-and-oh. They're coming into *our* house, and yet despite this"—panning his players—"they're favored by three. Despite this, they're third in the nation, and we're pressing down on the top five. That's not right."

Bitter mutterings.

"That's not just."

More bitter mutterings.

"Let's go show the *pundits* why they should save their opinions for politics. Everybody in!"

Twenty-three-hundred pounds of human bone and blood and sinew collapsed on Coach Gary Williams.

"Rapiers on three ready one two three."

"RAPIERS."

As was custom, Dave Kelly rounded the guys for his modest rendition of the Lord's Prayer. Benison took AJ's and Bouman's hands and closed his eyes. Afterward, the team huddled close, arm in arm, together now:

"*Up the hill and into the wind / the odds be tilt which way we'll win.*"

"BEEEEEEEEITCH," Gabe Griffin screeched.

Dangerous levels of adrenaline coursed through these corded forms. At one point Dominguez had hold of Gabe Griffin's head, imprecating, spittle flying from his lips, Gabe Griffin sitting there all straight-faced as if there wasn't anything he could do to stop the smacks across his cheek. Delmar skipped about the room, nodding his head—"*Vamanos ayiyiyiyi*"—and whipping asses with a coiled towel. AJ and Greenie Steve executed an impressively choreographed handshake. Bouman sat facing his locker, hunched, bobbing his head, the small curled hairs crawling up his shoulders standing at attention like an alarmed animal's. Benison, tightening his laces, asked if Jonesy felt alright.

"I'm good," Jonesy winced as he wrapped his ankle.

"Yeah?"

"This fuckin leg, man."

Coach returned with Brock Wyles whispering in his ear.

"Let's hit the tunnel, fellas."

Benison trailed the mob from the locker room. Eyes fixed on their warmup wear, supple and acquiescent, flashing in the low light, he caught up with the squad at tunnel's mouth, gazing at a stadium packed with people and light. Aside from the visiting section's green sliver of Spartans fans, students donned in the blue and white t-shirts left on each seat shouted at lung's tops. Benison caught a sign that read: IT'S GONNA END LIKE 300 DID. Below which was a grainy photo of Gerard Butler, flexed arms spread wide, embracing with bared teeth a flood of Persian arrows. Shifting on either foot, head down, mind buzzing blank, he heard his name cut into the Rapiers' intro music.

"Benison!"

He turned back towards the darkness, from which Coach Wyles appeared, downcast, his dark pate like a battering ram. Stopping before him, Coach Wyles fingered the Rapiers pin on his blazer, two curved swords crossed under an R. His skin smelled like sour ethyl. His eyes, all pep and hype, seemed to say, "Here's how I see it. You live out there on the floor. It's your home. You shit and eat and study in your dorm, but your heart stays here, on this floor, within those lines. You return each day, you pick it up, you put it into every minute of every practice of every game. You leave it, you shit and eat and sleep and stroke your dick, and you come back and pick up again. You don't get fatigued. Fatigue comes to find you, you look it in the eye and you say, 'What're you gonna do about it you tired fuck?' This isn't a game. This hasn't been a game since you started playing it. It's your religion. You come here to pay penance, atone for your sins, to feel okay about yourself. It's the only place in the world that makes sense. Everything else is chaos. You get up every damn day and try and figure it out, you fuck with the madness, but it doesn't work for you, never has. Not then, not now. But here, it does. You don't know why, but it does. On the court you're tapped into a supreme force—and you owe that force for extending you a line, when it could've just flipped you off for someone else. Your life is nothing without it. Pussy, money, success—these are but temptations, distractions from your God, which is the basketball floor, which blessed you with a piece of its grace. Obey it. Pray to it. Toil before it like the monks of old. You give it your heart, you let it bleed out on the floor, and then you come back and pick it up. There's nothing to think about. You leave it and come back. You see the game in your dreams, waking up and doing it again, and again, and again."

Benison beheld his eyes, which held continent those very words—all Coach Wyles said aloud was, "Jonesy's hurt."

And Benison nodded.

"We like how you looked in practice the other day."

And he nodded again.

"You alright? No PTSD?" Coach Wyles ducked under their line of sight as if to get a better visual on his mental state.

And he shook his head.

"Good. Because you're starting tonight."

He strolled toward Abrogate, in no rush to roll up a righteous doob, one of the tight cones that, free of extracurricular contour, marked stark improvement. His postgame visit with Jason Derekson was a knockout.

Benison dashed back from a real borefest of a team meeting, hastened to sink deep into the couch, hit a fat bowl, and play an egregious quantity of online FIFA matches. He threaded the lunch bustle. He leaned up Denny Way. He executed a quick and unaffected exchange with Cammy, the second-shift concierge—only to get waylaid in his own apartment.

Upon entering 3309 and starting to untie his walking kicks (Ted Baker low tops), he'd somehow complicated the knot into one of those brain-busters whose impregnability proved only slightly less frustrating than how such impregnability had come to be. Especially since, before leaving for the meeting this morning, he'd simply done the standard double-knot—and not this Knoxian half-hitch sheep-shank shit that he could've executed neither quickly nor unaffectedly.

Exasperation mounted. The further he worked his fettuccine strings, the worse their skein. His height made bending over this long a veritable spinal hazard. He loosed curses laced with wild cackles. He stood upright and snorted and shrugged, repeating, "Like, what? Like seriously—what?"

It was ridiculous, this embranglement. Absurd, that time did not stop for this knot: that space did not fracture in the face of this knot; that the knot didn't yield to human frustration.

The squad's lease on triumph ticked down with the locker room's grated clock: any remaining satisfaction related to last night's win would expire upon Coach's arrival. Which gave them another two minutes until 2:00PM, and Coach was never late for team meetings.

Like usual: the Big Three took up the front row of foldout chairs, rapping about this and that before the white erase board's mess of X's and O's; at their adjacent lockers, Boo lectured Greenie Steve on spirituality as an agnostic; Dave Kelly worked on Jones, the frayed ends of whose corn rows Benison used as an objective middle distance for rumination; others lounged at their lockers or, in Dominguez's case, balanced butt-atop-seat-back, for which Coach would award five suicides. ("Less painful than explaining a fractured back from falling off a fucking chair.")

Unlike usual: time struck two, so Coach was now late; Benison was listed at the two for tomorrow's game against UCLA; and Delmar and Griffin and AJ were rapping more in the literal sense.

"...*I take a shot of Hennessey now I'm strong enough to face the madness / nigga bad full of weed laced with hash—*"

"*Nickle bag* full of weed," said the Rapiers' resident 2Pac scholar, Delmar. "Illiterate motherfucker."

"Yo chill, D," grinned Gabe Griffin.

"Ruining a legend's work," AJ said, shaking his head.

"Revising."

They looked at Benison as if he'd undermined their deepest convictions about the world.

"Damn skippy," grimaced Gabe Griffin.

"You gone off the strength of white noise over here?" AJ *tsked.*

"Yo Benchin'im, tell em bout that notebook you got," said Del, fist to snicker.

"He holdin lead," AJ started after him. "He kill it with a number two."

"I dabble," Benison said, paring his nails.

Gabe Griffin sprung for the stereo perched on the edge of his locker's cubby, an antique, all woodgrain and bugmesh. A radio for the girl in stiff blue jeans and a gingham headscarf—a Riveter's radio. Del and AJ jeered as he switched discs and turned the volume, tearing the treble hooks and splintering the nodes—a familiar shuffle, stringy chords and scratchy beat.

"Hundred bucks says I go the full track."

"Let's bear witness," said Del.

"Yup," giggled Gabe Griffin, who swished through his wallet's wad and threw down a bill. "Collateral."

"Yo let's *get this money—*"

"Yo chill."

Dominguez eased down his chair back.

"Behrenreich."

Benison stood, glanced at a few silent faces, and followed Coach out into the hall. Overhead, fluorescent glass like an icy glaze, pale and merciless.

"You can't sit with us today."

Words to break the bulwark of his wellbeing, enemies in plain view across the moat. He felt internal movement, not unlike that of his bowels. His first thought was his father.

"At five today, Coach Wyles is going to hold a press conference announcing your indefinite suspension."

"Coach Wyles." He understood but wasn't sure of showing it.

"Jason Derekson has—" Coach rubbed his hoary anger, inhaled some hallway to cool off. "They're gonna use any way to get you. The important thing is you say nothing. No comment. Lemme hear you say it."

"No comment."

"A genius, he is," he smiled, and patted his shoulder.

Blowing smoke, waiting for Jonesy, Benison remembered going to work with his father—before Angelica, the porch addition, the fraught silences. When his father drove a Toyota. Gas stations on hot days, the backseat packed with errand bags. Or early winter's wet snow, blue and steely and clean. Garlic in oil after practice, after dark. His father's feet, their hard stink of honest work. His mother's musk, ripely cosmetic. Coupons clipped over the counter. Field #7 at Cove Creek, where he launched a moonshot off a kid with a mustache. Fucking around the neighborhood with Ricky, peering over an electrical box. *Open the door you desperate fucking housewife.* The birds chirping. The crickets cricketing. The grass lush green.

"Dude she's not coming out," Ricky said.

"So I should go do something about it yeah?"

"That's what I'm saying."

"Dick," Benison muttered, and slunk across the street.

The porch creaked upon entering its shadows. He slipped through cane furniture, fishnet swing-sets, and potted plants. He bent to the precious cup of piss leaning against the front door—which flung open before he could reach it.

The straw-haired housewife looked at him, then at the piss streaming into her house. For a moment he was sorry. For a moment he saw what life does to one, or what it can do.

"Gotcha."

And he was off.

The smell of beer mingling with perfume—the smell of Halloween, of willful promiscuity and carte blanch fuckupage. Then the morning after, the smell of nothing. Slumped at the kitchen table, staring out at Lake Washington, the pines, their manmade pond down near the water line, upon which swam little ducklings, to and fro.

"Where's their mother?" Benison asked, more of the cosmos than his Deaf mother, busy in the sewing room.

There on the edge of the flagstone, under a pine, he saw the duck mother cut helpless vectors at the pond's raised edge. The ducklings couldn't get out—not without a *deus ex machina*.

Amid the garage's material crisis Benison found a sizable board, somewhat pliant. He gathered the wood sheath under his arm and lumbered around the house, down the knoll, and onto the flagstone surrounded by slatted black metal, the sun beating his arms bare in a shorn tank. The mother ignored him, her desperation concentrated on rapid zags around the pond. But it wasn't long before Benison had devised the ramp. The ducklings took to it by instinct. Little webbed watermarks along the flagstone were rapidly fading evidence of his good deed.

Not until the paddling slipped through the gate's metal slats did he notice one more duckling struggling to mount the ramp. Upon closer inspection, Benison saw its leg bent in ways likened to a nasty football injury. As Benison took the duckling in his hands, his mother appeared beside him and signed to *be careful*, and he expressed that she should *fucking relax* in a way she could fully understand but never prove. Its leg twitched in his cupped palms. Its lack of expression less relieved than exacerbated his imagination. Minutes later they were examining the duckling's mobility on the dining room table. The thought that he wasn't even allowed to put a hot mug on this table didn't elude him.

He envisioned keeping the little duckling. Coming home after school to care for it. Putting its needs before the sporting contracts he'd signed with the blood of his sacrificed teenhood. Before him unraveled a life of duty and honor. The sentiment stuck—until they arrived at the animal shelter. Until the shelter's director took the duckling in her own palms. Until he returned to the car and looked out the window.

A week before the duckling incident, Enid had brought her dog to the vet, who examined Cashew's failing husk of organs and said to see how she did over the next week. "Let love be your judge," the vet told Enid, who told Benison over the phone later that night, the TV filling her pauses. She couldn't hear his breathing, its only evidence the rapid rising and falling of fur as Cashew laid on his side on the cold tile by the front door, as though simply waiting to die.

"I'm taking him back tonight," she sniffed. "He can't go on like this."

After the call, Benison locked up in his room, turned off the lights, groped through darkness. Finding the right song felt wrong, like trying to dictate the meaning of death. He hit shuffle and heard the opening hypnosis of "Dosed," understanding now that the Chili Peppers hadn't just become a bunch of pussies in their later years. Lying in perfect darkness, he grappled with forever, with never again. He'd never again see Cashew fetch that stupid dumbbell squeaktoy, his piebald coat glimmering wet, mauling whoever was in his dive zone. He'd never again point to him and say, "He's eating a piece of shit." Stories may have proved his existence, but he existed now in a baroque receptacle.

After dropping off the duckling, he told his mother. *Cashew died,* his hands flopping over in pathetic symbol of her passing.

I'm sorry, she frowned.

He slid down his seat, legs up on the dashboard, making a bowl of himself. She flailed at him to take his feet down.

"Ben'sn," she warbled high.

I'm trying to tell you that I'm unhappy, he signed.

No one is happy. That's life.

She started the car. They pulled away from the small shelter, along a dirt-clod drive merging into a road lined with high stalks he couldn't name. He kept his eyes on the window and his feet on the dash.

Blowing smoke upon his bed, waiting for Jonesy to return. Another hour had passed and, falling asleep, freewheeling through wormholes of consciousness, his dreams came fast and fitful, laid bare beyond the veil of love and fear…

…Practice. Coach's whistle rings. Blue. Sneakers squeak. Huffs and grunts, face-guarding, sliding feet, pointing out switches, calling out screens that he goes under, again and again and again…

…Practice every day—before and after and during. Knowing he must show up to the Balloon wearing nonchalance. Knowing he must try to play this way, the way he tries to seem. Knowing these efforts to play with calm precision are doubled by having to appear calm and precise. He can't finish his cereal in the morning. Thinking is difficult, yet the drive to the Balloon is a blur of overwrought thought. In the locker room he vomits in the plastic garbage bin near the showers, sieved through his hand, digestive fluids in his nostrils, his throat. He stares bleary-eyed at the orange gook dripping clumps down the plastic crags. Standing there over the desecrated bin, he remembers his preteen phase of constantly threatening suicide. It'd make his friends laugh but also gain a sliver of their sympathy: "Fuckin' *kill* myself dude," he'd say to an obtuse commercial, or after tripping over an uneven sidewalk square. But now he really does hate his life. He has to go out there on the hardcourt and act like he belongs. He has to brick bunnies off the backboard, telegraph ten-foot passes, fumble over simple

crossover dribbles—he has to play like shit and still act like he doesn't usually play like shit, because he doesn't, but now he does…
…The feedback loop speeds…
…Benison the shortstop. He swipes bags like a kid late for school. Clears bases like a plinth bomb. All those diving stops. All those game-winning hits. All those rides home, silent, and finally his father says, "Clean up and get ready for dinner." Because today, Benison botched two easy choppers hit right to him and earned himself a golden sombrero. After the last strikeout, treading back to the dugout, he cracked his bat against a backstop pole and moaned Bullshit. Benison waits until he's in his room to growl at himself that he Fucking sucks, pressing his face into his pillow as he screams himself hoarse. Dinner is tense. Benison's eyes have red puff. His cleats are caked with compacted dirt and it gets on the Spanish tile. For the remaining games until he quits, his dad will pull up to the parking lots perched above the dirt diamonds below, and the delayed dings and popped mitts will prime Benison. It becomes too much. Over so little.
…The feedback loop begins tightening into a disk…
…His father is seated next to him in the summer's sticky grass between fields. *No,* he snaps his fingers, *Wait till we get home for dinner to eat something proper… Please?…Benison, I said no.* Dusky pinks hang a heavenly haze behind the trees. The slanting sun casts the day's last game a gilded light. A few feet away, Mr. Hand sits next to his resilient little catcher, Greg. Mr. Hand's head is also bald as a show of solidarity. Greg plays through nausea and fevers and is playing well while he's at it. Mr. Hand offers Benison the extra ice cream sandwich he got from the canteen between fields 5 and 7, and Benison accepts. Then he turns and signs, *Mr. Hand is a good dad at least.* Mr. Hand smiles at their language. Benison doesn't heed his father's wordless reproach, all in his tightened jaw and imploded eyes. Benison's too famished following a four-game day to attend particulars, only the cookie-cream sandwich's salty-sweetness—the glory of going eight-for-ten with nine RBI synergizing its taste—a glory lost amid the verbal walloping he gets once in the car, shrinking into the seat's nook as his father

bellows how he'll never make him look like that in front of other people again…Benison the shortstop. He wardens the infield with a gun that ranges any no man's land. Spits like a pro, a hyphen of saliva through the slit of his fronts. His bat's got a sweet tooth. All those game-winning hits…

…The loop creates centripetal force, drawing the most distant edges of his dream into sight…

…Benison's fart ends the contest. And yet, as with all victories, this one incurs losses—not only that weightless rip of sulfur, but also, behind his butt's croak follows a brown spray that Pollocks his white briefs. His face says it all, the dilating of every possible circle, from pupils to pores. His stretched, gaping visage over a body stuck in skier's pose, it betrays that this win has come at a cost all too great for a fifteen-year-old, incurring on what his grandmother would've pronounced, *l'eeyo*. He runs grinning into the bathroom, the heavy door's slam cuing a concert of mean hilarity back in the bedroom. The heat of eminence glows pink across his forearms, leaving his body. Uncle Humble's scalpel hollows his gut—but Humble Humble must be off his game today, forgot his spectacles at home; Benison sits on the toilet deciding that this has happened for all the right reasons. Because he's a winner. He does what it takes. He will return to the vacation home's bedroom wearing the holier-than-thou hubris that says Yeah, I'll shit my pants for a W. So he sits on the toilet, briefs browning in the cracked window's sun. He grunts. Groans. Judders his reddened face, evacuating the rest…

…Behrenreich Interpreting Services' '03 holiday party is at their Bellevue home. Adults pour in to stand around and do nothing but hold absurd wine glasses while signing to each other with their other hand. Benison and Owen Harcledrode raid his parents' bed-turned-coat-room. Full throttle theft. Scouring leather- and mink-jacket alike, none of their apparent worth seeming to correspond to the riches within. Prada purses, handbags that seem as if woven in the deserts of Arabia. Washingtons, Lincolns, Benjamins. Later on, Benison revisits the night and coils under his covers, how sleep evades the souls of sin. Of course, the next day there are complaints. People's things have gone missing. His father assures the robbed that he'll look into it. His parents sit him down at the kitchen table. "No," Benison says when they ask if he stole from the coats. "I didn't," he urges. His mother leaves for her manicure. He keeps his head down. *Are you lying?* a stiff hand across the chin. "No." Moisture gathers in his eyes, the heat of lies to his skin. "Even if I was, you do the same thing anyway so who cares." The paneled oak floor in the dining room turns blurry. Then he hears, "I suggest you think carefully about what you tell them." He watches his father go into his study. These words rip Benison's universe open. He dumps the stash—the bling, the Benjamins—down a gutter, a block from his house. Every last bill, not one treasure kept. Later on, Benison, emboldened by jettisoned evidence, affects bewilderment at the missing cash and valuables. The policemen waddle back to their cars, satisfied that the case is a mystery too great to interfere with their crimeless docket…

…Benison stumbles on the way down his porch, bursting through their constitutional pillars. The night is constellated through clean Seattle sky. He's just turned sixteen. He takes to his driveway and up to the street, where his Audi's tires are tickled by luscious grass bending over the curb…*It's time you sat down and had a proper drink with your old man… You once asked me what it takes to be great…* He wants to see Enid, and now he's been set next to her by the omnipresent he doesn't believe in, on the hood of her pickup, parked twenty feet from Alki's shore. They're lying back and gazing up at the sparkling holes poked into black canopy. She wipes sand that makes her heel look like the bottom of an English muffin… *You're seeing that girl again tonight…*Benison's saying things without knowing from whence he contrives them. He says, "Dude's just selfish's shit," cue a pull on his Ran-yay… *You hang around fawning over that girl…*He feels a brush at his pinky, lambent and brief… *If you don't, she's not going to respect you…*His pinky locks with hers. He turns to her. She's freckled and desperately pretty. Millimeters subtract from the distance between their lips, then whole inches. Bodies twisted together, delicate at first, then not, ignoring an empty bottle that's sliding off the hood, its plastic patter against the pavement signaling earnest their embrace. He has Enid's gold roots threaded through his fingers when she suggests they find a place more private; Alki Beach, during summer, crawls with imbibing youths... *There's greatness in you Benison. But you're scared to use it...* "Like where?" Benison's breath is sweet and sour with Rainier's residue. He's remiss to leave the car, this moment he's in. Enid looks out to the beach, appearing cool and oblivious to what's happening... *One more for both of us. Neat this time. No. Neat...* He's led by hand across the beach to a spot behind a tree washed ashore. They giggle, dodging the sharp sea glass scattered about the white sand. "Ah! Fucking *white* people," Benison yelps, holding his toe and hopping on one foot... *It's time you become a man...* Enid tells him his brand of irony is weird, then takes the collar of his t-shirt, pulls it towards her... *I want you to show her she needs you...* They fall together onto the powdery sand. It's cool by the water. She hisses lascivious things through his fingers slatted over her mouth. Benison removes his hand as she does... *I'm teaching you force of mind...* She props on her elbows, looking at Benison, he's on his knees, athletic waistband supporting a pulped tremor, useless before it's even been used, his eyes shocked as they meet hers, as if he's just noticed that she's there. He pulls his shorts back up and plods over to the water...

...The loop accelerates, its disk whirring with incredible celerity, summoning everything toward its center...

...A scent within the blond wood armoire in his room, like super-consolidated earth. This thicksweet musk is tied to this childhood. It's tied to make-believe x's crossing sidewalk blocks that he must avoid with his feet. To yearnings to write with a pen in grammar school. To feeling bookish under the weight of books. To florally perfumed preteens in bellbottom jeans. It's a smell tied to a languid evening. It's back to the middle of 2003, so Benison's bed's still bunked up in a corner, both top and bottom covered by Mariners sheets and blankets. Clothes are everywhere despite a decent row between he and his mother earlier that morning. Benison is telling Adam Schaffer about his 1952 Topps Mickey Mantle card, the one of Mantle's face all long and lignified like a hero's, like he's in the on-deck circle, looking back to the front row where his latest flavor of the week sits with a flask of peach schnapps stuffed into the ruffles of her closed parasol, and just for her he's gonna aim for the flags whipping in the wind along the white curve of Yankee Stadium's outer limits. Benison pulls out the Beckett, a magazine that valuates baseball memorabilia. He opens it to the '50's section, a decade that printed Fleer and Topps sets worth more than most modern American homes. He twists his gooseneck lamp over the page. Adam's eyes widen at the black print above Benison's small finger. The '52 Topps Mantle is priced at $17,342. Adam asks to see it, the Mantle. But Benison won't show him. It's in his pocket but he won't show him. Because the card is clay. It looks like the real '52 Mantle except it's clay. It's clay and it's a reprise of the vintage worth $17,342. Benison tells him that the '52 Mantle's at his dad's office, but he can get it for him, if Adam leaves his signed Ken Griffey Jr. rookie card. He tells Adam that he'll do it because Griffey is his favorite player. At the age of eleven, Adam still believes in Santa Claus, while Benison's early exposure to R-rated cinema and tenuous ties to Reform Judaism have kept him cynical on the matter of a red-robed jolly-man sleigh-flying around the earth in one night to sprinkle gifts onto all the good little children. Their parents keep getting the two together even though their only shared interest is baseball cards, and though Benison doesn't yet understand nor care how valuable his ability to communicate with Adam is to Adam, their excruciating differences *are* apparent: Adam visibly winces whenever Benison gesticulates a bad word; Adam can't walk, let alone have a catch; Adam doesn't care much for baseball, just the cards; and Adam is just another human with whom Benison must operate in silence. Adam bends over the creaky arm of his wheelchair to sort through the rare and expensive cards that he's set into small plaques. *Careful,* Benison signs, two k's connected at the fists and revolving. Just as Adam replaces the Griffey from its white-veined plaque into a transparent plastic sleeve, the lights flash; Adam's mother is here to pick him up. Benison's chest thumps, willing Adam's weak hands to complete the transfer before adult voices or changing hearts can stop it. But it is done, and they leave the room, Adam bowling toward the foyer. Mrs. Schaffer is tall and austere and warm all at once, and she's a year older than Adam's dad, which Benison finds odd, because dads are older than moms. In broken ASL she reminds Adam about his inhaler. She signs poorly but valiantly with his mother. Suddenly Benison runs to his room. He has the same Griffey rookie card in his '89 Ultra set, unsigned. His plan was to use his Griffey as template for grafting a forgery, then call off the trade, giving back the Benison-signed Griffey before going to his dad's office to pick up a card that's not there, the Mantle's in his pocket, and it's clay. Instead, there's Benison now, sliding Adam's white-shot plaque off his nightstand. He replaces the Griffey into the plaque's display window as he returns to the foyer. "Here," he says, keeping his eyes away from the flash of Adam's wrist, an emaciated sticklight waving pity to the runway. Because Benison doesn't want to kill; he wants love. But he wants to win it on the battlefield...The dream has collapsed to this core...Benison's just turned fifteen. Flipping between BET and MTV Jams, his body's a slumping staircase on the couch. Usually he's accompanied by friends who find it novel to hang out in a house with parents that can't understand what they're saying, and Benison shows off for them, cursing at high volumes, or saying things like, I just don't understand how I came from that, and all his cronies sniggering at how Mrs. Behrenreich continues to read her celebrity rags at the kitchen table as if her son has not just backhandedly insulted her existence. He embraces his friends' laughter only to the extent that it's tolerated, and only he can deride her; deep down, he does it to resolve the small embarrass-ment he feels for being different—the same difference he, deep down, also needs. But on this day Benison watches music videos alone. His mother idles by, window-shopping her curiosity. He can sense her looking from the TV to him. His hunger's been semi-sufficed by a sleeve of Chips Ahoy!. In her high snapping monotone that only he can understand she asks if he wishes he was black. Whipping his dirty-blond locks, he sign-speaks that why the fuck'd anyone in America *wish* to be black what does that even mean what're you *racist* or something? His mother flicks a placating *okay* at him. Benison throws his arms up and scoffs. They look at the TV again, where snarled rhymes are captioned at the bottom of the screen in a rhythm his mother can't understand but knows they're lyrics because they're italicized and bookended with quarter-notes. Above the closed captioning, where all the visual action is, meretricious women twerk while members of the rapper's crew pour liquor on them. Cameras flash as these gangstas in gold chains and oversized jerseys alternately strut red carpets or stroll along turquoise tropical waters. Benison's wearing a red Marc Ecko jersey and an oversized pair of black jeans, both of which he bought at the mall's Demo store, which he's been kicked out of for popping a balloon and causing a shooting scare. He wants his mom to go away so he can relish in peace this depiction of swagged exultation. Yet after a time, his mother's presence raises questions in him—questions related to things deeper than how uncomfortable it is for him to have her stand there and watch with him, questions more directly related to *that* she's continuing to stand there and watch with him. There are two things he loves, hip hop and basketball. Neither are passions if they aren't first expedients to fulfill his lust for glory, glory that might win him love—indeed, it is a loop. He could do anything that brings him glory—chess, cricket, debating. This lust isn't a black one, but an American one, and *you and Dad are just too scared to own up to it,* and this is exactly what he gestures for his mother in anticipation of her reproach of Nelly and the Lunatics. She seems scared of him. He looks back to the TV before sympathy strikes. He knows they will talk now. But his mother must take the initiative...Because it's been a year and a half of justified irreverence. A year and a half since his balsa-wood bridge project failed in physics class. A year and a half since a mustachioed man pulled up to the pickup line's proctor, provided his father's name, and urged Benison inside his Jeep. A year and a half since riding around with the mustachioed man, who passed the turn for his neighborhood, took the floating 520, and circled the city, and up the 5, and down, minutes not multiplying but bleeding out into an hour, then two, Benison's sole reasonable query—"Where are we going?"—met with telling silence. It's between that silence and when the Jeep stops half a mile from his house that Benison will begin depositing the incident into deep secret banks. Turning to him in the backseat, silencer's muzzle poked into purview, the mustachioed man says, "You go straight home and talk to no one, and no one gets hurt. You got me?" Benison nods. "Get the hell out of here." Benison fumbles with the door, then walks, then runs, bursting into the house, tremulous, blanched, urine spotting his jeans, searching the empty rooms then curling up in his bed, figuring mortal fear, the binary between the man's hurting him or not, phantom shots searing along his back, waiting for someone to come home and make it alright. No one does. He falls asleep. Hours later a yellow light knifes through the darkness. Benison doesn't move as it expands. His father's shadow stretches across the room and up the farthest wall. "Benison," he says. The door's curved handle *thwacks*, his father stroking his hair. Benison can hear his mother sniffling somewhere out there. He's waiting for the words. He hears, "Do you need anything?" There is a rupture within him, an immaculate madness…There is a year and a half of utterly justified irreverence. He hangs out near the Starbucks on 4th, downtown, sucking on cigarettes and drinking out of paper bags and loitering with plaid-clad kids wearing neon-yellow hats who talk about the things they're thinking in a way too fast to manage. His eyes hibernate for the winter behind green-tipped ringlets. Some Fridays, he doesn't come home from school until Monday afternoon, when finally he trundles direct to his room to sleep it off. Some weekends he hibernates, only crossing to the kitchen for food. He doesn't speak to his father. He will transmit necessary information— "Contractor called"—or—"Syllabus, sign here"—but they aren't interactions, just mechanisms. Each day he considers going to the police to describe what happened that day. But the secret, it's carious, it's insidious– it is infinitely pleasurable to keep, to speculate on what to do with it, how to spend it. So he keeps it. A Seattle summer of clarified skies and Mariners games, of fireworks over Lake Union and acrobatic jets booming sonically overhead—that summer never happens, and high school starts like sulfurous lights above a patient's post-op bed. He doesn't know too many kids because he got redistricted. The first day drags, between sterile classrooms, across high-traffic halls, flittering his eyes for a friend. The final bell rings and he lurks in the main hall, stopping alongside a set of doors. In the gym, a gaggle of kids are on their butts changing into high socks and strapping Jordans to their feet. He watches them stand up and hop, run in place. He watches them talk, their low eyes that avoid contact. He watches them strut and skip, jump up and grab the net and climb hanging on the rim. He hears them dribble, and their drawling, vowel-laden, half-sentence synecdoche. No one says anything when he walks in wearing jeans and a bold blue button-up. After the first game he says he's gotta go. "Yo," a kid named Ricky flicks his head at him. "The varsity guys play Mondays and Wednesdays. Get some shorts and shit," and trots back onto the hardcourt. Benison's played rec ball for a couple years, but something's different now. The madness drives him. He plays with intent. He gains respect. He starts listening to feud rap. He keeps to reticence but relishes in their cool reverence. It mollifies him, at least until he gets home, where things are different as in still the same. Where he teases at his father's temper. He knows he does, and he enjoys it, because it's justified and his father is impotent to it. He learns to watch TV in the living room at night, letting the spiteful silence that spreads from him escape no one. He changes the channels, but really he imagines tomorrow's pickup game after school. He puts his feet on the coffee table, baiting his father, who sits in the kitchen scrolling through his phone, pushed to the edges of his son's inviolable radius. "Your feet," he says from the kitchen table. "Benison," his father firmer now. This is not the first time he flicks off his father, who shoves his chair back. Its low grinding screech, a Deaf sound, one of thousands that Benison has grown up with, these little noises that hearing people unconsciously hide, like breathing, like his father, who stands now glowering in the kitchen. "Get your feet off the table." Benison lifts his right foot, examining it curiously. Satisfied that it is a shoe and not a foot he means to rest on the glass table, he frowns and lets it fall with a small rattle. The moment thrills him. It scares him. It's everything to him. It's over. He's alone, the front door slammed shut, the Z4 Beemer whining up the drive…It's been a year and a half of justified irreverence. He knows that his mother will begin to cry and then they will talk. He knows she will then apologize for what happened, a year and a half late. She will say they wanted to talk to him, to explain, but how could they have? He knows that they've been doing shit they're not supposed to do and making a lot of money doing it. It's not only what happened a year and a half ago. It's the Z4 on lease. It's the new screened patio below the porch set with white wicker and brocade. It's his mother's diamond currently glinting in his face, the Goalrilla basketball hoop they put in for him despite their slanted drive. It's his father's behavior, his reckless-ness, the new Mexican maid Benison caught him fooling around with in the new patio over the summer, the nights he goes missing and the sudden absence of arguments between him and his mother. It's the money. It's the muscle behind the money. It's old ties that've come back to haunt—it's men who don't know when to stop yet who decide to say when. It's be-gatted, ski-masked men nabbing his father in their driveway, bagging an ether-smothered sack over his head, shoving him in a van, and thirty indecipherable minutes later trussing him to a filing cabinet in a burnt-out warehouse and holding him at gunpoint, taking the pains to communicate to the wildly high and hard-of-hearing man who's robbed of his lip-readers that his son is on a little car ride with a friend of theirs and his bitch, and he has a minute to decide whether his boy should live or not. That's how Raciti's goons suggest Marc recon-sider his plans to abandon his partnership with VisiTech Platforms. This is when they say when, which is never. This is what his parents thought they could shield Benison from with their silence, which he requited for one and a half years. *I'm sorry*, his mother signs, fist circling her breast. *Your father's business…He doesn't mean to hurt anyone.* She does not cry as he thought she would. The drab winter light is dimming. His father steps into the room, funereal in his black custom shirt and slacks. Benison has never seen him sit with his elbows on his knees, which he does, and signs, *I couldn't—I wouldn't tell you.* His mother mistakenly changes a channel before turning the volume down, adjusting her cochlear and grimacing. The weatherwoman points to a map of the Pacific Northwest slathered in swaths of whites and blues and violets, these gradients of accumulation broaching the coast against all climatology. School will be cancelled tomorrow, along with Bellevue High's second game against their rival, Mount Hebron. His mother seems full of joy. Or is it relief. *We want things to be different,* her index fingers parting like windshield wipers. *You were young. You're still young. We just want you to be happy. To give you everything you need, everything you want. We promise,* she draws a fisted thumb up her bosom. *We just want our son back.* It's all extremely eerie for Benison, his father crouched, staring past the floor, abased by years of sin that've been reduced to the adumbrations of his mother, who sits erect, proud even, one foot touching the floor and the other under her butt. She is surrounded by what she dreamed of—a million-dollar ranch, the domestic drama of her Italian heritage, Steve Madden adorning her dainty feet. But, sitting between them, Benison doesn't care about his mother's shoes. He's losing himself in another man's mystery…

…Something is pushing him into his father's mind…

"*…So what, I just forgive you now?…*"

…Wondering if it's his mystery…

"*…now that I finally know why you're pieces of shit?…*"

…Ice pebbles begin pinging off the sliding glass…

"*…Benison, I make no excuses. I never have. It may not seem like it, but we didn't choose this, and we're doing our best to get out…*"

…Benison looks through the sliding glass, where pearlescent beads coat the world. Big wet flakes mix in. The sleet and snow are akin to his father's way with words, a whiteout of reasonable doubt, a pall of plausible deniability. Go ahead and cook the books. Fuck the maid—fine. Have your son get nabbed and mum's the word on why. Do what you want, really. Let them try to move the snow and ice before you move the bodies. Let them lift the pall only to find the ghosts of his sins, haunting only those who believe the spirit exists.

In this dream, Benison won't wait for him to get caught. Won't snitch on him either. Because in his dreams, he can exact revenge. He can threaten to snitch and watch him sweat. He can send him emails from burner accounts, claiming possession of damning evidence, promising a document dump more shockingly macabre than the bodies at Treblinka. Hell, maybe he'll just kill him in his sleep—or torture him, flay him head-to-toe, douse his hands and feet in propane, light them, and watch him burn inward, smoldering slow.

It's the same trap he falls into time and again. It's what fuels the loop: the deeply buried certainty that his father knows or has something that he doesn't. Something he misses dearly. Something absolutely necessary. But now, he sees the sleight through the smoke. In this dream, he sees the illusion, and with awareness comes choice.

Acknowledgements:

Katie: We met on a dance floor and stood there talking about books, and I still feel like that's what we're doing today—something that other people aren't, something that is uniquely and organically ours, distinct from the rest of the world. Love at first sight is a loaded phrase, but I'd be lying if I said we didn't meld minds that night—or that I wasn't nervous before the next time we met, and the time after that, until one besotted night I worked up the courage to tell you how I felt. You read my book five times and supported me with your whole big heart. No one else knows just quite how hard I worked on this, and no one else put up with more to help me do it. Without you I would be but a tenuous hope. Without you, this life wouldn't be possible.

Mom & Dad: Dad, you spoke to me like an intelligent human being since I can remember and gave me the freedom to explore my talents, shaping indelible belief in myself. Mom, you put up with my worst and worried just enough to keep me from doing something irrevocable. You told me to get my MFA back when I was living in Seattle, writing on a stool pulled up to the corner of my bed, and asked to read everything I wrote, even before it was ready. Both of you provided and then tolerated my existence, which has been turbulent to say the least, yet never doubted me for one moment. You made my life possible, and you're the best parents anyone could've asked for.

Jake (the mentor): One moment I was settled into Aspira's lobby desk, reading Vonnegut, prepared for another graveyard shift ahead. The next, we were talking books and Baltimore. A couple elevator rides later and the Literary Catechism was in my lap, loaned with great warning concerning any threats to your reputation should I have failed to properly decode the work. More than the dozens of books I've read at your direction, your peremptory faith to this craft was the key that unlocked my will to master it.

Sergio & Susanna: At the risk of furthering my profile as a stalker of the De La Pavas—you are the real, tangible manifestation of everything we hope to be. No one works harder and for better cause. Sergio, I was turned on to your first book when Jake began reading it online, back when it was an underground hit. Your writing is why I keep writing. Susanna, I don't know if there's anyone more useful to the human species. Your story kept me buoyant on days when it seemed like it would never happen. As if that weren't enough, you were kind enough to help us get Animal Riot Press off the ground. You've made the world an explicitly better place and I'm infinitely grateful that I got to know you.

David (the thesis advisor): My acceptance to Sarah Lawrence's MFA program instilled hope. Our emails leading up to our first meeting instilled a reason to keep going. You are the reason I developed any semblance of confidence in my writing. You are the reason I had reason to develop any semblance of confidence in my writing. "This shit is on fire"—that's what you wrote at the end of the second chapter of this novel. Before then, I'd only believed the first three words of that phrase. And it only meant anything because it came from The Author.

Sarah Lawrence College: You siphoned my bank account but gave me the most important currency there is: time and energy. Special thanks to Nelly Reifler, Brian Morton, and Garth Hallberg—your perspectives on the craft helped shunt me onto a track I could call my own. Nelly, you allowed our conferences to meander into general existentialia, which helped open my mind more than you know. Brian, you were always available to talk—about anything—and I couldn't think of a better program director. Garth, your posthuman intelligence and brutal honesty reaffirmed my dogged commitment to the craft while reminding me that mastery lingers always on the horizon. The entire SLC staff is unparalleled, and I appreciate every single professor I had the pleasure of studying under.

Devin (25 Stillwell): Without you, this book wouldn't exist in published form, but without your friendship, the form of this book would exist in a lesser dimension. I still remember talking to you for the first time after your reading in Slonim, some piece about a bear, written with Cormacian diction, and therefore I suggested you check out *Blood Meridian*. That marked the high point of your trust in me, I think, but we still managed to become best friends and even-tual roommates after life at Sarah Lawrence. I also remember doing edits on an excerpt before a reading, struggling to work out a complex phrase to convey a moment's fraught silence. You listened carefully to my quandary, thought a moment, and told me to write, "There is a lot of silence."

Jared (25 Stillwell): No matter what we talked about, it seemed like it was existential grist for the literary mill. You were the first person I met at Sarah Lawrence and to this day remain to be the most devoted writer I know. Much like Hitch and Amis, your drive motivates me to be better every day—that, and your pathologically sterile living quarters.

Seth (25 Stillwell): You read my novel when it still sucked, yet seemed convinced that it didn't. Lo, that draft got pretty serious interest and an eventual bite from the Writers House. You also read the following draft and guaranteed that it would get published. We can tally these up to the infinite matrix of things I get wrong. Your support and admiration for my work ethic pulled me through many of the tougher periods, and I can't thank you enough for that.

George (25 Stillwell): I don't know where to begin. Simply knowing someone as enlightened and talented as you is its own gift. Your wit, compassion, and indulgence were necessary mirrors for self-same tendencies. Tacitly, we lived in yearning for the Roaring '20s. As if that weren't enough, you took the time to work on the last stages of my book, which wouldn't be where it is without you.

Cheyenne: Though I wish we'd known you at Sarah Lawrence, I couldn't be happier that you've found your way into our family. The things you caught—whether slips and solecisms or factual errors—turned a charlatan's mad ravings into a book of relative credibility.

Shawn Ferreyra: At the time of this writing, we've still only met once in person. Some people just have good chemistry. You showed me around the New York Library, which only an ascetic like me wouldn't have seen, before sitting down to start working on mock-up covers. I pulled an idea out of my ass and you turned it into the brilliant illustration that covers this book.

Olivia: I'm only working on these acknowledgements because you told me what front and back matter are. You've dealt with all my luddite questions with impossible graciousness. You also connected us with SFK Press, with whom Animal Riot Press has established a great friendship and working relationship. You're an integral piece to the puzzle and we can't wait to keep working with you in the future.

Ben (EC Crew): I used your name. That says a lot. This novel wouldn't exist without you. The depth of your compassion and honesty, your loyalty, and your faith in intellectualism and the dialectical process are values that thrive in me because of you. Without you my first chapter would still suck. Without your friendship, I wouldn't be the person I am today—not even close. I can't wait for you to read the final version, just so you can see how much weight I gave your words and how much they meant to me.

Jon (EC Crew): No one has done so much for me through one text message. A former Writers House client resigned once again to wallowing in submissions limbo, I was seriously considering the self-publishing route when I got Jon's text about starting Animal Riot Press (which I immediately showed Katie). As far as I'm concerned, that text was the single greatest text ever sent—a perfect culmination of our friendship, which also blossomed of the strength of a single text when you invited me to move out to Seattle with you, back when I was just a lowly undergrad finishing my last semester at Maryland. The brain, the rainmaker, the central intelligence of this literary surveillance operation, the demiurge of this myth-making machine—what you're capable of pales only to who you are: a true champion of social and economic change; an anti-dogmatist; a philanthropic capitalist; and just an all-around Good Human Being.

The EC Crew: Ben, Dave, Scotty, Marquise, Zach, Rubs, J, JK, Sammons, and Sully. Some of you I've known since before preschool, but it feels that way for all of you. How far we go back, the depth of our knowledge of one another, the lengths we're willing to go to lift each other up—you are the embodiment of who I am. You are the example that I set for myself. Your talents and love and loyalty humble me every single day. You act like it's a $1 million book deal when I get some piece published that 35 people will read. You are my day ones. It goes without saying, you're the brothers I never had. You're an essential reason I choose to keep going.

Everyone else: So many people have influenced my life and work. To everyone left unnamed here, know that you're not forgotten, but Katie said I have to stop somewhere. Every one of you has changed my course, whether directly or indirectly, and whether for good or bad, I'm grateful for being able to carry these experiences into my writing.

M.K. Rainey

Brian Birnbaum grew up thirty minutes west of Camden Yards in Baltimore, where at four years old he cried because the Yankees were losing. An MFA graduate of Sarah Lawrence College, his work has been published or is forthcoming in *The Smart Set*, *The Collagist*, *Atticus Review*, *SLAM Magazine*, *Lit Hub*, *Political Animal*, and more. *Emerald City* is his first novel. Brian is a child of Deaf adults (CODA) and works in development for the family sign language interpreting business. He lives in Harlem with the writer M.K. Rainey and their dog.

Like what you read?

If you enjoyed *Emerald City* by Brian Birnbaum, please consider leaving an honest review of the work on Goodreads, Amazon, Litsy, or whatever social media platform you prefer. It's our priority at Animal Riot Press to publish books that matter to our readers, and our authors appreciate and value your feedback. A simple review can go a long way in helping small presses continue the work of uplifting writers in our communities.

About Animal Riot Press

Our mission is to publish books that matter in ways that matter.

But doesn't every publishing house want or claim to acquire books that matter? Sure, but we aren't just paying lip-service to a vague notion of literary integrity. We acquire books for the express purpose of investing in them. We do not abandon our authors after publishing, opting instead to cultivate and grow the lifespan of a book and its author's career. Inherent to this process is a more sustainable method of distilling our list down to what really matters to us.

Publishing books that matter: Books that matter take risks, find joy in the process, and above all else exhibit quality. We release books we are proud of, which are: books that tackle difficult issues and manifest real ways of thinking and feeling; books that are critical and thoughtful, while also playful and engaging; and, most importantly, books that remember who they're written for — the reader. We publish books that deepen the literary arts while remaining accessible to wider audiences.

Ways that matter: If what makes a book matter is reflected in its process—one defined by risk and pleasure—then publishing should be no different. Our goal is to deliver books that inspire us, to the widest audience possible. We've spent five years building a network of connections in the literary community. Put simply, we know readers. But we also have broad experience in marketing and distribution, which means we know how to reach readers. Every book creates its own challenges and opportunities, so our methods are adaptive and collaborative. Our transparent publishing model aims to serve each of our writers in a way that creates a uniquely joyful experience and provides the best possible outcome for every book that displays the Animal Riot Press imprint.

Find out more about us at animalriotpress.com.

CPSIA information can be obtained
at www.ICGtesting.com
Printed in the USA
BVHW040806260820
587337BV00008B/61